BODILY CHANGES IN
PAIN, HUNGER, FEAR AND RAGE

BODILY CHANGES IN PAIN, HUNGER, FEAR AND RAGE

AN ACCOUNT OF RECENT RESEARCHES INTO THE FUNCTION OF EMOTIONAL EXCITEMENT

BY

WALTER B. CANNON, M.D., S.D., LL.D.

GEORGE HIGGINSON PROFESSOR OF PHYSIOLOGY IN
HARVARD UNIVERSITY

SECOND EDITION

CHARLES T. BRANFORD COMPANY
BOSTON
1953

PRINTED IN THE UNITED STATES OF AMERICA

TO MY COLLABORATORS IN THESE RESEARCHES

DANIEL DE LA PAZ	SIDNEY W. BLISS
ROY G. HOSKINS	JAMES R. LINTON
ALFRED T. SHOHL	ROBERT R. LINTON
WADE S. WRIGHT	SYDNEY W. BRITTON
ARTHUR L. WASHBURN	EMILIO BULATAO
HENRY LYMAN	JOHN T. LEWIS
LEONARD B. NICE	ARNOLD GROENEVELD
CHARLES M. GRUBER	ARIE QUERIDO
HOWARD OSGOOD	ELIZABETH M. BRIGHT
HORACE GRAY	PHILIP BARD
WALTER L. MENDENHALL	JOSE J. IZQUIERDO
FRANK A. HARTMAN	VALY MENKIN
G. PHILIP GRABFIELD	HARLAN F. NEWTON
DAVID RAPPORT	RAYMUND L. ZWEMER
ROSENDO CARRASCO-FORMI-GUERA	FRANKLIN A. DE M. CAMPOS
FRED R. GRIFFITH	HARRY LUNDIN
MONROE A. MC IVER	THOMAS T. WALKER

WITH PLEASANT MEMORIES OF OUR WORK TOGETHER

PREFACE TO THE FIRST EDITION

FEAR, rage, and pain, and the pangs of hunger are all primitive experiences which human beings share with the lower animals. These experiences are properly classed as among the most powerful that determine the action of men and beasts. A knowledge of the conditions which attend these experiences, therefore, is of general and fundamental importance in the interpretation of behavior.

During the past four years there has been conducted, in the Harvard Physiological Laboratory, a series of investigations concerned with the bodily changes which occur in conjunction with pain, hunger, and the major emotions. A group of remarkable alterations in the bodily economy have been discovered, all of which can reasonably be regarded as responses that are nicely adapted to the individual's welfare and preservation. Because these physiological adaptations are interesting both in themselves and in their interpretation, not only to physiologists and psychologists, but to others as well, it has seemed worth while to gather together in convenient form the original accounts of the experiments, which have been published in various American medical and physiological journals. I have, however, attempted to arrange the results and discussions in

vii

an orderly and consecutive manner, and I have tried also to eliminate or incidentally to explain the technical terms, so that the exposition will be easily understood by any intelligent reader even though not trained in the medical sciences.

My first interest in the conditions attending pain, hunger, and strong emotional states was stimulated during the course of a previous series of researches on the motor activities of the alimentary canal. A summary of these researches appeared in 1911, under the title, "The Mechanical Factors of Digestion." The studies recorded in the present volume may be regarded as a natural sequence of observations on the influence of emotional states on the digestive process, which were reported in that volume.

W. B. C.

PREFACE TO THE SECOND EDITION

SINCE 1915, when the first edition of this book was published, researches concerned with the problems of which it treats have been continued at the Harvard Physiological Laboratory and have been conducted also in other laboratories in various parts of the world—in Japan, Russia, England, Algiers, and Argentina. A large accumulation of new evidence has thus been gathered, bearing on the general thesis that the bodily changes which attend great excitement are directed towards efficiency in physical struggle. This material has been included in the present volume. In addition, as a natural ally of fear, rage, and hunger as powerful motives for action, thirst has received detailed consideration. Experiments delimiting the part of the brain essential for emotional expression have led to a fresh theoretical treatment of the origins of emotional displays and emotional experience. Thus, besides the accounts of more recent discoveries which have been infused into the revised chapters retained from the previous edition, the present edition has five more chapters on special topics: one on emotional increase of blood corpuscles, one on emotional derangement of bodily functions, one on thirst, and two on theories of emotion—a critical review of the James-Lange theory and the presentation of an alternative theory which was suggested by our researches.

W. B. C.

CONTENTS

CONTENTS

CHAPTER VIII

THE SPECIFIC RÔLE OF ADRENIN IN COUNTER-ACTING THE EFFECTS OF FATIGUE

CHAPTER IX

THE HASTENING OF COAGULATION OF BLOOD BY ADRENIN

CHAPTER X

THE HASTENING OF COAGULATION OF BLOOD IN PAIN AND GREAT EMOTION

CHAPTER XI

EMOTIONAL INCREASE OF RED BLOOD CORPUSCLES

CONTENTS

CHAPTER XII

THE UTILITY OF THE BODILY CHANGES IN PAIN AND GREAT EMOTION

CHAPTER XIII

THE ENERGIZING INFLUENCE OF EMOTIONAL EXCITEMENT

CHAPTER XIV

EMOTIONAL DERANGEMENT OF BODILY FUNCTIONS

CHAPTER XV

THE NATURE OF HUNGER

CHAPTER XVI

THE PHYSIOLOGICAL BASIS OF THIRST

CHAPTER XVII

THE INTERRELATIONS OF EMOTIONS

CHAPTER XVIII

A CRITICAL EXAMINATION OF THE JAMES-LANGE THEORY OF EMOTIONS

CONTENTS

CHAPTER XIX

EMOTION AS A FUNCTION OF THE OPTIC THALAMUS

CHAPTER XX

ALTERNATIVE SATISFACTIONS FOR THE FIGHTING EMOTIONS

BODILY CHANGES IN
PAIN, HUNGER, FEAR AND RAGE

BODILY CHANGES IN
PAIN, HUNGER, FEAR AND RAGE

CHAPTER I

THE EFFECT OF THE EMOTIONS ON DIGESTION

THE doctrine of human development from a sub-human ancestry has done much to unravel the complex nature of man. As a means of interpretation this doctrine has been directed chiefly toward the solving of puzzles in the peculiarities of anatomical structure. Thus arrangements in the human body, which are without obvious utility, receive rational explanation as being vestiges of parts useful in or characteristic of remote ancestors—parts retained in man because of age-long racial inheritance. This mode of interpretation has proved applicable also in accounting for functional peculiarities. Expressive actions and gestures —the facial appearance in anger, for example—observed in children and in widely distinct races, are found to be innate, and are best explained as the retention in human beings of responses which are similar in character in lower animals.

From this point of view biology has contributed much to clarify our ideas regarding the motives of human behavior. The social philosophies which prevailed during the past century either assumed that

1

conduct was determined by a calculated search for
pleasure and avoidance of pain or they ascribed it to
a vague and undefined faculty named the conscience
or the moral sense. Comparative study of the behavior of men and of lower animals under various circumstances, however, especially with the purpose of
learning the source of prevailing impulses, is revealing
the inadequacy of the theories of the older psychologists. More and more it is appearing that in men of
all races and in most of the higher animals, the springs
of action are to be found in the influence of certain
emotions which express themselves in characteristic
instinctive acts.

The rôle which these fundamental responses in the
higher organisms play in the bodily economy has received little attention. As a realm for investigation
the bodily changes in emotional excitement have been
left by the physiologists to the philosophers and psychologists and to the students of natural history. These
students, however, have usually had too slight experience in the detailed examination of bodily functions to permit them to follow the clues which
superficial observation might present. In consequence
our knowledge of emotional states has been meager.

There are, of course, many surface manifestations
of excitement. The contraction of blood vessels with
resulting pallor, the pouring out of "cold sweat," the
stopping of saliva-flow so that the "tongue cleaves to
the roof of the mouth," the dilation of the pupils, the
rising of the hairs, the rapid beating of the heart, the

hurried respiration, the trembling and twitching of the muscles, especially those about the lips—all these bodily changes are well recognized accompaniments of pain and great emotional disturbance, such as horror, anger and deep disgust. But these disturbances of the even routine of life, which have been commonly noted, are mainly superficial and therefore readily observable. Even the increased rapidity of the heart beat is noted at the surface in the pulsing of the arteries. There are, however, other organs, hidden deep in the body, which do not reveal so obviously as the structures near or in the skin the disturbances of action which attend states of intense feeling. Special methods must be used to determine whether these deep-lying organs also are included in the complex of an emotional * agitation.

Among the organs that are affected to an important degree by feelings are those concerned with digestion. And the relations of feelings to the activities of the alimentary canal are of particular interest, because recent investigations have shown that not only are the first stages of the digestive process normally started by the pleasurable taste and smell and sight of food, but also that pain and great emotional excitement can seriously interfere with the starting of the process or its continuation after it has been started. Thus there

---

* In the use of the term "emotion" the meaning here is not restricted to violent affective states, but includes "feelings" and other affective experiences. At times, also, in order to avoid awkward expressions, the term is used in the popular manner, as if the "feeling" caused the bodily change.

may be a conflict of feelings and of their bodily accompaniments—a conflict the interesting bearings of which
we shall consider later.

The feelings or affective states favorable to the digestive functions have been studied fruitfully by
Pavlov,[1] of Leningrad, through highly ingenious experiments on dogs. By the use of careful surgical
methods he was able to make a side pouch of a part
of the stomach, the cavity of which was wholly separate from the main cavity in which the food was
received. This pouch was supplied in a normal manner with nerves and blood vessels, and as it opened to
the surface of the body the amount and character of
the gastric juice secreted by it under various conditions
could be accurately determined. Secretion by that
part of the stomach wall which was included in the
pouch was representative of the secretory activities
of the entire stomach. The arrangement was particularly advantageous in providing the gastric juice un-
mixed with food. In some of the animals thus operated
upon an opening was also made into the esophagus in
the neck so that when the food was swallowed it did
not pass to the stomach but dropped out on the way.
All the pleasures of eating were thus experienced, and
there was no necessity of stopping because of a sense
of fullness. (This process was called "sham feeding."

The well-being of these animals was carefully attended to, they lived the normal life of dogs, and in the course of months and years became the pets of the laboratory.

By means of sham feeding Pavlov showed that the chewing and swallowing of food which the dogs relished resulted, after a delay of about five minutes, in a flow of natural gastric juice from the side pouch of the stomach—a flow which persisted as long as the dog chewed and swallowed the food, and continued for some time after eating ceased. Evidently the presence of food in the stomach is not a prime condition for gastric secretion. And since the flow occurred only when the dogs had an appetite, and the material presented to them was agreeable, the conclusion was drawn that this was a true psychic secretion.

The mere sight or smell of a favorite food may start the pouring out of gastric juice, as was noted many years ago by Bidder and Schmidt [2] in a hungry dog which had a fistulous opening through the body wall into the stomach. This observation, reported in 1852, was confirmed later by Schiff and also still later by Pavlov. That the mouth "waters" with a flow of saliva when palatable food is seen or smelled has long been such common knowledge that the expression, "It makes my mouth water," is at once recognized as the highest testimony to the attractiveness of an appetizing dish. That the stomach also "waters" in preparation for digesting the food which is to be taken is clearly proved by the above cited observations on the dog.

The importance of the initial psychic secretion of saliva for further digestion is indicated when, in estimating the function of taste for the pleasures of appetite, we realize that materials can be tasted only when dissolved in the mouth. Even sugar is tasteless on a dry tongue. The saliva which "waters" the mouth assures the dissolving of dry but soluble food and thereby brings it into relation with the organs of taste.

The importance of the initial psychic secretion of gastric juice is made clear by the fact that continuance of the flow of this juice during digestion is provided by the action of its acid or its digestive products on the mucous membrane of the pyloric end of the stomach, and that secretion of the pancreatic juice and bile is called forth by the action of this same acid on the mucous membrane of the duodenum. The proper starting of the digestive process, therefore, is conditioned by the satisfactions of the palate, and the consequent flow of the first digestive fluids.

The facts brought out experimentally in studies on lower animals are doubtless true also of man. Not very infrequently, because of the accidental swallowing of corrosive substances, the esophagus is so injured that, when it heals, the sides grow together and the tube is closed. Under these circumstances an opening has to be made into the stomach through the side of the body and then the individual chews his food in the usual manner, but ejects it from his mouth into a tube which is passed through the opening or fistula. The food thus goes from mouth to stomach through a tube outside instead of inside the chest. As long ago as 1878, Richet,[3] who had occasion to study a girl whose esophagus was closed and who was fed through a gastric fistula, reported that whenever the girl chewed or tasted a highly sapid substance, such as sugar or lemon juice, while the stomach was empty, there flowed from the fistula a considerable quantity of gastric juice. A number of later observers [4] have had similar cases in human beings, especially in children, and have reported in detail results which correspond remarkably with those obtained in the laboratory. Hornborg [4] found that when the little boy whom he studied chewed agreeable food a more or less active secretion of gastric juice invariably started, whereas the chewing of an indifferent substance, as gutta-percha, was followed by no secretion. All these observations clearly demonstrate that the normal flow of the first digestive fluids, the saliva and the gastric juice, is favored by the pleasurable feelings which accompany the taste and smell of food during mastication, or which are roused in anticipation of eating when choice morsels are seen or smelled.

These facts are of fundamental importance in the serving of food, especially when, through illness, the appetite is fickle. The degree of daintiness with which nourishment is served, the little attentions to esthetic details—the arrangement of the dishes, the small portions of food, the flower beside the plate—all may help to render food pleasing to the eye and savory to the nostrils and may be the deciding factors in determining whether the restoration of strength is to begin or not.

EMOTIONS UNFAVORABLE TO NORMAL SECRETION OF THE DIGESTIVE JUICES

The conditions favorable to proper digestion are wholly abolished when unpleasant feelings such as vexation and worry and anxiety, or great emotions such as anger and fear, are allowed to prevail. This fact, so far as the salivary secretion is concerned, has long been known. The dry mouth of the anxious person called upon to speak in public is a common instance; and the "ordeal of rice," as employed in India, was a practical utilization of the knowledge that excitement is capable of inhibiting the salivary flow. When several persons were suspected of crime, the consecrated rice was given to them all to chew, and after a short time it was spit out upon the leaf of the sacred fig tree. If any one ejected it dry, that was taken as proof that fear of being discovered had stopped the secretion, and consequently he was adjudged guilty.[5]

What has long been recognized as true of the secretion of saliva has been proved true also of the secretion of gastric juice. For example, Hornborg was unable to confirm in his little patient with a gastric fistula the observation by Pavlov that when hunger is present the mere seeing of food results in a flow of gastric juice,

Hornborg explained the difference between his and Pavlov's results by the different ways in which the boy and the dogs faced the situation. When food was shown, but withheld, the hungry dogs were all eagerness to secure it, and the juice very soon was flowing. The boy, on the contrary, became vexed when he could not eat at once, and began to cry; then no secretion appeared. Bogen also has reported the instance of a child with closed esophagus and gastric fistula, who sometimes fell into such a passion in consequence of vain hoping for food that the giving of the food, after the child was calmed, was not followed by any flow of the secretion.

The inhibitory influence of excitement has also been seen in lower animals under laboratory conditions. Le Conte [6] declares that in studying gastric secretion it is necessary to avoid all circumstances likely to provoke emotional reactions. In the fear which dogs manifest when first brought into strange surroundings he found that activity of the gastric glands may be completely suppressed. The suppression occurred even if the dog had eaten freely and was then disturbed—as, for example, by being tied to a table. When the animals became accustomed to the experimental procedure, it no longer had an inhibitory effect. The studies of Bickel and Sasaki [7] confirm and define more precisely this inhibitory effect of strong emotion on gastric secretion. They observed the inhibition in a dog with an esophageal fistula, and with a side pouch of the stomach, which, as in Pavlov's experiments, opened only to the exterior. In this dog Bickel and Sasaki noted, as Pavlov had, that sham feeding was attended by a copious flow of gastric juice, a true psychic secretion, resulting from the pleasurable taste of the food. In a typical instance the sham feeding lasted five minutes, and the secretion continued for twenty minutes, during which time 66.7 cubic centimeters of pure gastric juice were produced.

On another day a cat was brought into the presence of the dog, whereupon the dog flew into a great fury. The cat was soon removed, and the dog pacified. Now the dog was again given the sham feeding for five minutes. Although the animal was evidently hungry, for he ate eagerly, there was no secretion worthy of mention. During a period of twenty minutes, corresponding to the previous observation, only 9 cubic centimeters of acid fluid were produced, and this was rich in mucus. It is evident that in the dog, as in the boy observed by Bogen, strong emotions can so profoundly disarrange the mechanisms of secretion that the pleasurable excitation which accompanies the taking of food cannot cause the normal flow.

On another occasion Bickel and Sasaki started gastric secretion in the dog by sham feeding, and when the flow of gastric juice had reached a certain height, the dog was infuriated for five minutes by the presence of the cat. During the next fifteen minutes there appeared only a few drops of a very mucous secretion. Evidently in this instance a physiological process, started as an accompaniment of a psychic state quietly pleasurable in character, was almost entirely stopped after another psychic state violent in character.

It is noteworthy that in both the favorable and the unfavorable results of emotional excitement illustrated in Bickel and Sasaki's dog the effects persisted long after the removal of the exciting condition. This fact, in its favorable aspect, Bickel [8] was able to confirm in a girl with esophageal and gastric fistulas; the gastric secretion long outlasted the period of eating, although no food entered the stomach. The influences unfavorable to digestion, however, are stronger than those which promote it. And evidently, if the digestive process, because of emotional disturbance, is for some time inhibited, the swallowing of food which must lie stagnant in the stomach is a most irrational procedure. If a child has experienced an outburst of passion, it is well not to urge the taking of nourishment soon afterwards. Macbeth's advice that "good digestion wait on appetite and health on both." is now well-founded physiology.

Other digestive glands than the salivary and the gastric may be checked in emotional excitement. Recently Oechsler [9] has reported that in such psychic disturbances as were shown by Bickel and Sasaki to be accompanied by a checking of the secretion of gastric juice, the secretion of pancreatic juice may be stopped, and the flow of bile definitely diminished. All the means of bringing about chemical changes in the food may be thus temporarily abolished.

EMOTIONS FAVORABLE AND UNFAVORABLE TO THE CON-
TRACTIONS OF THE STOMACH AND INTESTINES

The secretions of the digestive glands and the chemical changes wrought by them are of little worth unless
the food is carried onward through the alimentary canal
into fresh regions of digestion. This function is performed by peristalsis—onward-moving rings of constriction produced by contraction of the muscle encircling the digestive tube. In studying these mechanical aspects of digestion I was led to infer [10] that just
as there is a psychic secretion, so likewise there is probably a "psychic tone" or "psychic contraction" of the
gastro-intestinal muscles as a result of taking food.
For if the vagus nerves, which increase the tonic state
of the muscles in the wall of the stomach, are cut immediately *before* an animal takes food, the usual gastric contractions, as seen by the Röntgen rays, do not
occur; but if these nerves are cut *after* food has been
eaten with relish, the contractions which have started
continue without cessation. The nerves in both conditions were severed under anesthesia, so that no
element of pain entered into the experiments. In
the absence of hunger, which in itself provides a contracted stomach,[11] the pleasurable taking of food may,
therefore, be a primary condition for the appearance
of natural contractions of the gastro-intestinal
canal. This suggestion that there may be a
psychic contraction of gastro-intestinal muscles is
supported by evidence that the sight of desirable food

stimulates movements of both the stomach [12] and the intestines.[13]

Again just as the secretory activities of the stomach are unfavorably influenced by strong emotions, so also are the movements of the stomach; and, indeed, the movements of almost the entire alimentary canal are wholly stopped during great excitement. In my earliest observations on the movements of the stomach [14] I had difficulty because in some animals the rings or waves of contraction were perfectly evident, while in others there was no sign of activity. Several weeks passed before I discovered that this difference was associated with a difference of sex. In order to be observed with Röntgen rays the animals were restrained in a holder. Although the holder was comfortable, the male cats, particularly the young males, were restive and excited on being fastened to it, and under these circumstances gastric peristaltic waves were absent; the female cats, especially if elderly, usually submitted with calmness to the restraint, and in them the waves had their normal occurrence. Once a female with kittens turned from her state of quiet contentment to one of apparent restless anxiety. The movements of the stomach immediately stopped, the gastric wall became wholly relaxed, and only after the animal had been petted and began to purr did the moving waves start again on their course. By covering the cat's mouth and nose with the fingers until a slight distress of breathing is produced, the stomach contractions can be stopped at will. In the cat, therefore, any sign of rage or fear, such as was seen in dogs by Le Conte and by Bickel and Sasaki, is accompanied by a total abolition of the movements of the stomach. Even indications of slight anxiety may be attended by complete absence of the churning waves. In a vigorous young male cat I have watched the stomach for more than an hour by means of the Röntgen rays, and during that time not the slightest beginning of peristaltic activity appeared; yet the only visible indication of excitement in the animal was a continued quick twitching of the tail to and fro. What is true of the cat I have found true also of the rabbit, dog and guinea pig [15]—very mild emotional disturbances are attended by abolition of peristalsis. The observations on the rabbit have been confirmed by Auer,[16] who found that the handling of the animal incidental to fastening it gently to a holder stopped gastric peristalsis for a variable length of time. And if the animal was startled for any reason, or struggled excitedly, peristalsis was again abolished. The observations on the dog also have been confirmed; Lommel [17] found that small dogs in strange surroundings might have no contractions of the stomach for two or three hours. And whenever the animals showed any indications of being uncomfortable or distressed, the contractions were inhibited and the discharge of contents from the stomach checked.

Like the peristaltic waves of the stomach, the peristalsis and the kneading movements (segmentation) of the small intestine, and the reversed peristalsis of

the large intestine all cease whenever the observed animal shows signs of emotional excitement.

There is no doubt that just as the secretory activity
of the stomach is affected in a similar fashion in man
and in lower animals, so likewise gastric and intestinal
peristaltic waves are stopped in man as they are
stopped in lower animals, by worry and anxiety and
the stronger affective states. The conditions of mental
discord may thus give rise to a sense of gastric inertia.
For example, a patient described by Müller [18] testified
that anxiety was always accompanied by a feeling of
weight, as if the food remained in the stomach. Every
addition of food caused an increase of the trouble.
Strong emotional states in this instance led almost always to gastric distress, which persisted, according to
the grade and the duration of the psychic disturbance,
between a half hour and several days. The patient was
not hysterical or neurasthenic, but was a very sensitive woman deeply affected by moods.

The feeling of heaviness in the stomach, mentioned
in the foregoing case, is not uncommonly complained
of by nervous persons, and may be due to stagnation of
the contents. That such stagnation occurs is shown
by the following instance. A refined and sensitive
woman, who had had digestive difficulties, came with
her husband to Boston to be examined. They went to
a hotel for the night. The next morning the woman
appeared at the consultant's office an hour after having eaten a test meal. An examination of the gastric
contents revealed no free acid, no digestion of the test

breakfast, and the presence of a considerable amount of the supper of the previous evening. The explanation of this stagnation of the food in the stomach came from the family doctor, who reported that the husband had made the visit to the city an occasion for becoming uncontrollably drunk, and that he had by his escapades given his wife a night of turbulent anxiety. The second morning, after the woman had had a good rest, the gastric contents were again examined; the proper acidity was found, and the test breakfast was being normally digested and discharged.

These cases are merely illustrative and doubtless can be many times duplicated in the experience of any physician concerned largely with digestive disorders. Indeed, the opinion has been expressed that very many cases of gastric indigestion that come for treatment are functional in character and of nervous origin. It is the emotional element that seems most characteristic of these cases. To so great an extent is this true that Rosenbach has suggested that as a term to characterize the cause of the disturbances, "emotional" dyspepsia is better than "nervous" dyspepsia.[19]

THE DISTURBING EFFECT OF PAIN ON DIGESTION

The advocates of the theory of organic evolution early pointed out the similarity between the bodily disturbances in pain and in the major emotions. The alterations of function of internal organs they could not know about. The general statement, however, that pain evokes the same changes that are evoked by emotion, is true also of these deep-lying structures. Wertheimer [20] proved many years since that stimulation of a sensory nerve in an anesthetized animal—such stimulation as in a conscious animal would induce pain—quickly abolished the contractions of the stomach. And Netschaiev, working in Pavlov's [21] laboratory, showed that excitation of the sensory fibers in the sciatic nerve for two or three minutes resulted in an inhibition of the secretion of gastric juice that lasted for several hours. Similar effects from painful experience have been not uncommonly noted in human beings. Mantegazza,[22] in his account of the physiology of pain, has cited a number of such examples, and from them he has concluded that pain interferes with digestion by lessening appetite and by producing various forms of dyspepsia, with arrest of gastric digestion, and with vomiting and diarrhea. The expression, "sickening pain" is testimony to the power of strong sensory stimulation to upset the digestive processes profoundly. Vomiting is as likely to follow violent pain as it is to follow strong emotion. A "sick headache" may be, indeed, a sequence of events in which the pain from the headache is primary, and the nausea and other evidences of digestive disorder are secondary.

As the foregoing account has shown, emotional conditions or "feelings" may be accompanied by quite opposite effects in the alimentary canal, some highly favorable to good digestion, some highly disturbing. It is an interesting fact that the feelings having these

18   BODILY CHANGES

antagonistic actions are typically expressed through
nerve supplies which are correspondingly opposed in
their influence on the digestive organs. The antagonism between these nerve supplies is of fundamental
importance in understanding not only the operation
of conditions favorable or unfavorable to digestion but
also in obtaining insight into the conflicts of emotional
states. Since a consideration of the arrangement and
mode of action of these nerves will establish a firm
basis for later analysis and conclusions, they will next
be considered.

REFERENCES

1. PAVLOV, *The Work of the Digestive Glands* (London, 1902).
2. BIDDER and SCHMIDT, *Die Verdauungssäfte und der Stoffwechsel* (Leipzig, 1852), p. 35.
3. RICHET, *Journal de l'Anatomie et de la Physiologie,* xiv
   (1878), p. 170.
4. See HORNBORG, *Skandinavisches Archiv für Physiologie,* xv
   (1904), p. 248. CADE and LATARJET, *Journal de Physiologie et Pathologie Génerale,* vii (1905), p. 221. BOGEN,
   Archiv für die gesammte Physiologie, cxvii (1907), p. 156.
   LAVENSON, *Archives of Internal Medicine,* iv (1909),
   p. 271.
5. LEA, *Superstition and Force* (Philadelphia, 1892), p. 344.
6. LE CONTE, *La Cellule,* xvii (1900), p. 291.
7. BICKEL and SASAKI, *Deutsche medizinische Wochenschrift,*
   xxxi (1905), p. 1829.
8. BICKEL, *Berliner klinische Wochenschrift,* xliii (1906), p.
   845.
9. OECHSLER, *Internationelle Beiträge zur Pathologie und
   Therapie der Ernährungstörungen,* v (1914), p. 1.
10. CANNON, *The Mechanical Factors of Digestion* (London and
    New York, 1911), p. 200.
11. CANNON and WASHBURN, *American Journal of Physiology,*
    xxix (1912), p. 441.

12. COHNHEIM and DREYFUS, *Zeitschrift für physiologische Chemie,* lviii (1908), p. 57.
13. KATSCH, *Zeitschrift für experimentelle Pathologie und Therapie,* xii (1913), p. 290.
14. CANNON, *American Journal of Physiology,* i (1898), p. 38.
15. CANNON, *ibid.,* vii (1902), p. xxii.
16. AUER, *ibid.,* xviii (1907), p. 356.
17. LOMMEL, *Münchener medizinische Wochenschrift,* i (1903), p. 1634.
18. MÜLLER, *Deutsches Archiv für klinische Medicin,* lxxxix (1907), p. 434.
19. ROSENBACH, *Berliner klinische Wochenschrift,* xxxiv (1897), p. 71.
20. WERTHEIMER, *Archives de Physiologie,* xxiv (1892), p. 379.
21. PAVLOV, *op. cit.,* p. 56.
22. MANTEGAZZA, *Fisiologia del Dolore* (Florence, 1880), p. 123.

CHAPTER II

THE GENERAL ORGANIZATION OF THE VISCERAL NERVES CONCERNED IN EMOTIONS

THE structures of the alimentary canal which are brought into activity during the satisfactions of appetite or are checked in their activity during pain and emotional excitement are either the secreting digestive glands or the smooth muscle which surrounds the canal. Both the gland cells and the smooth-muscle cells differ from other cells which are subject to nervous influence —those of striate, or skeletal, muscle—in not being directly under voluntary control and in being slower in their response. The muscle connected with the skeleton responds to stimulation within two or three thousandths of a second; the delay with gland cells and with smooth muscle is more likely to be measured in seconds than in small fractions of a second.

THE OUTLYING NEURONES

The skeletal muscles receive their nerve supply direct from the central nervous system, i. e., the nerve fibers distributed to these muscles are the filamentous prolongations of the nerve cells, or neurones, whose cell bodies lie within the brain or spinal cord. The glands (except the adrenals) and the smooth muscles of the viscera, on the contrary, are, so far as is now known, never innervated directly from the central nervous system. The nerve fibers reaching out from the brain or spinal cord never come into immediate relation with the gland or smooth-muscle cells; there are always interposed between the cerebrospinal nerves and the viscera extra neurones whose bodies and processes lie wholly outside the central nervous system. They are represented in dotted lines in Fig. 1. I [1] have suggested that possibly these outlying neurones act as "transformers," modifying the impulses received from the central source (impulses suited to call forth the quick responses of *skeletal* muscle), and adapting these impulses to the peculiar, more slowly acting tissues, the secreting cells and visceral muscle, to which they are distributed.*

---

* This suggestion was investigated in 1924 by Querido (*American Journal of Physiology,* lxx, 1924, pp. 29-57), who studied the response of the smooth muscle of the nictitating membrane of the cat's eye to stimuli applied to the nerve trunks above and below the superior cervical ganglion. He found that whereas, when the electrodes were applied above the ganglion (i. e., on postganglionic fibers), high and low rates of stimulation caused inhibition or submaximal contraction, the same stimuli applied below the ganglion caused a maximal response. The conclusion was drawn, therefore, that impulses of widely varying frequencies, started central to the ganglion, induce there impulses which pass to the end-organ at optimum frequency. Querido found also that in postganglionic stimulation the latent period was inversely related to the strength of stimulus—as the stimuli became stronger the latent period became shorter until with maximal stimuli it was constant. On the other hand, preganglionic stimulation, whether maximal or submaximal, was attended by a constant latent period. The conclusion was drawn, therefore, that impulses started central to the ganglion become maximal when they pass beyond the ganglion. Thus the outlying neurones make the frequency of the impulses appropriate

The outlying neurones typically have their cell bodies grouped in ganglia (G's, Fig. 1) which in the trunk region lie along either side of the spinal cord and in the head region and in the pelvic part of the abdominal cavity are disposed near the organs which the neurones supply. In some instances these neurones lie wholly within the structure which they innervate (see e. g., the heart and the stomach, Fig. 1). In other instances the fibers passing out from the ganglia—the so-called "postganglionic fibers"—may traverse long distances before reaching their destination. The innervation of blood vessels in the foot by neurones whose cell bodies are in the lower trunk region is an example of this extensive distribution of the fibers.

THE THREE DIVISIONS OF THE OUTLYING NEURONES

As suggested above, the outlying neurones are connected with the brain and spinal cord by neurones whose cell bodies lie within the central nervous organs. These connecting neurones, represented by continuous lines in Fig. 1, do not pass out in an uninterrupted series all along the cerebrospinal axis. Where the nerves pass out from the spinal cord to the fore and hind limbs, fibers are not given off to the ganglia. Thus these connecting or "preganglionic" fibers are separated into three divisions. In front of the nerve roots for the fore limbs is the head or *cranial* division;

---

for the more slowly acting peripheral structures and transform the submaximal impulses into maximal.

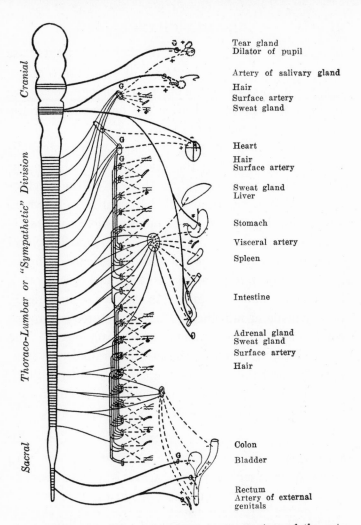

Tear gland
Dilator of pupil

Artery of salivary **gland**

Hair
Surface artery
Sweat gland

Heart

Hair
Surface artery

Sweat gland
Liver

Stomach

Visceral **artery**

Spleen

Intestine

Adrenal gland
Sweat gland
Surface **artery**

Hair

Colon

Bladder

Rectum
Artery **of external**
genitals

Fig. 1.—Diagram of the more important distributions of the autonomic nervous system. The brain and spinal cord are represented at the left. The nerves to skeletal muscles are not
represented. The preganglionic fibers of the autonomic system
are in solid lines, the postganglionic in dash-lines. The nerves
of the cranial and sacral divisions are distinguished from those
of the thoraco-lumbar or "sympathetic" division by broader
lines. A + mark indicates an augmenting effect on the activity
of the organ; a — mark, a depressive or inhibitory effect.
For further description see text.

between the nerve roots for the fore limbs and those for the hind limbs is the *trunk* division (or *thoraco-lumbar* division, or, in the older terminology, the "sympathetic system"); and after the nerve roots for the hind limbs the *sacral* division.

This system of outlying neurones, with postganglionic fibers innervating the viscera, and with preganglionic fibers reaching out to them from the cerebrospinal system, has been called by Langley, to whom we are indebted for most of our knowledge of its organization, the *autonomic nervous system*.[2] This term indicates that the structures which the system supplies are not subject to voluntary control, but operate to a large degree independently. As we have seen, a highly potent mode of influencing these structures is through conditions of pain and emotional excitement. The parts of the autonomic system—the cranial, the sympathetic, and the sacral—have a number of peculiarities which are of prime importance in accounting for the bodily manifestations of such affective states.

THE EXTENSIVE DISTRIBUTION OF NEURONES OF THE "SYMPATHETIC" DIVISION AND THEIR ARRANGEMENT FOR DIFFUSE ACTION

The fibers of the sympathetic division differ from those of the other two divisions in being distributed through the body very widely. They go to the eyes, causing dilation of the pupils. They go to the heart and, when stimulated, they cause it to beat rapidly.

They carry impulses to arteries and arterioles of the skin, the abdominal viscera, and other parts, keeping the smooth muscles of the vessel walls in a state of slight contraction or tone, and thus serving to maintain an arterial pressure sufficiently high to meet sudden demands in any special region; or, in times of special discharge of impulses, increasing the tone and thus raising the arterial pressure. They are distributed extensively to the smooth muscle attached to the hairs; and when they cause this muscle to contract, the hairs are erected. They go to sweat glands, and evoke the outpouring of sweat. These fibers pass also to the entire length of the gastro-intestinal canal. And the inhibition of digestive activity which, as we have learned, occurs in pain and emotional states, is due to impulses which are conducted outward by the *splanchnic nerves* —the preganglionic fibers that reach to the great ganglia in the upper abdomen (see Fig. 1)—and thence are spread by postganglionic fibers all along the gut.[3] They innervate likewise the genito-urinary tracts, causing contraction of the smooth muscle of the internal genital organs, and usually relaxation of the bladder. Finally they affect the liver, releasing the storage of material there in a manner which may be of great service to the body in time of need. The *extensiveness* of the distribution of the fibers of the sympathetic division is one of its most prominent characteristics.

Another typical feature of the sympathetic division is an arrangement of neurones for diffuse discharge of the nerve impulses. As shown diagrammatically in

Fig. 1, the preganglionic fibers from the central nervous system may extend through several of the sympathetic ganglia and give off in each of them connections to cell bodies of the outlying neurones. Although the neurones which transmit sensory impulses from the skin into the spinal cord have similar relations to nerve cells lying at different levels of the cord, the operation in the two cases is quite different. In the spinal cord the sensory impulse produces directed and closely limited effects, as, for example, when reflexes are being evoked in a "spinal" animal (i. e., an animal with the spinal cord isolated from the rest of the central nervous system), the left hind limb is nicely lifted, in response to a harmful stimulus applied to the left foot, without widespread marked involvement of the rest of the body in the response.[4] In the action of the sympathetic division, on the contrary, the connection of single preganglionic fibers with numerous outlying neurones seems to be not at all arranged for specific effects in this or that particular region. There are, to be sure, in different circumstances variations in the degree of activity of different parts; for example, it is probable that dilation of the pupil in the cat occurs more readily than erection of the hairs. It may be in this instance, however, that specially direct pathways to the eye are present for common use in non-emotional states (in dim light, e. g.), and that only slight general disturbance in the central nervous system, therefore, would be necessary to send impulses by these well-worn courses. Thus for local reasons (dust, e. g.) tears might flow from excitation of the tear glands by sympathetic impulses, although other parts innervated by this same division might be but little disturbed. We have no means of voluntarily wearing these pathways, however, and both from anatomical and physiological evidence the neurone relations in the sympathetic division of the autonomic system seem devised for *widespread diffusion* of nervous impulses.

THE ARRANGEMENT OF NEURONES OF THE CRANIAL AND SACRAL DIVISIONS FOR SPECIFIC ACTION

The cranial and sacral autonomic divisions differ from the sympathetic in having only *restricted* distribution (see Fig. 1). The third cranial nerves deliver impulses from the brain to ganglia in which lie the cell bodies of neurones innervating only this smooth muscle in the front of the eyes. The vagus nerves are distributed to the lungs, heart, stomach, and small intestine. As shown diagrammatically in Fig. 1, the outlying neurones in the last three of these organs lie within the organs themselves. By this arrangement, although the preganglionic fibers of the vagi are extended in various directions to structures of quite diverse functions, singleness and separateness of connection of the peripheral organs with the central nervous system is assured. The same specific relation between efferent fibers and the viscera is seen in the sacral autonomic. In this division the preganglionic fibers pass out from the spinal cord to ganglia lying in close proximity to the distal colon, the bladder, and the external genitals. And the postganglionic fibers deliver the nerve impulses only to the nearby organs. Besides these innervations the cranial and sacral divisions supply individual arteries with "dilator nerves" —nerves causing relaxation of the particular vessel. Quite typically, therefore, the efferent fibers of the two terminal divisions of the autonomic differ from those of the mid-division in having few of the diffuse connections characteristic of the mid-division, and in innervating distinctively the organs to which they are distributed. The cranial and sacral preganglionic fibers resemble thus the nerves to skeletal muscles, and their arrangement provides similar possibilities of specific and separate action in any part, without action in other parts.

By means of the general diffuse action of the sympathetic, and the opposite particular action of the parts of the cranial and sacral autonomic supply, every variety of change is provided for. All the viscera can be affected simultaneously in one way or the other through increased or decreased tone of the sympathetic division. And any special organ can be separately affected one way or the other through increased or decreased tone in the special nerve of the opposed cranial or sacral division that is supplied directly to the organ. The sympathetic is like the soft and loud pedals, modulating all the notes together; the cranial and sacral autonomic are like the separate keys.

The cranial autonomic, represented by the vagus nerves, is the part of the visceral nervous system concerned in the psychic secretion of the gastric juice. Pavlov has shown that when these nerves are severed psychic secretion is abolished. The cranial nerves to the salivary glands are similarly the agents for psychic secretion in these organs, and are known to cause also dilation of the arteries supplying the glands, so that during activity the glands receive a more abundant flow of blood. As previously stated (see p. 12), the evidence for a psychic tonus of the gastro-intestinal musculature rests on a failure of the normal contractions if the vagi are severed before food is taken, in contrast to the continuance of the contractions if the nerves are severed just afterwards. The vagi artificially excited are well known as stimulators of increased tone in the smooth muscle of the alimentary canal. Aside from these positive effects on the muscles of the digestive tract and its accessory glands, cranial autonomic fibers cause contraction of the pupil of the eye, and slowing of the heart rate.

A glance at these various functions of the cranial division reveals at once that they serve for bodily conservation. By narrowing the pupil of the eye they shield the retina from excessive light. By slowing the heart rate, they give the cardiac muscle longer periods for rest and recuperation. And by providing for the flow of saliva and gastric juice and by supplying the muscular tone necessary for contraction of the alimentary canal, they prove fundamentally essential to the processes of proper digestion and absorption by which energy-yielding material is taken into the body and stored. To the cranial division of the visceral nerves, therefore, belongs the quiet service of building up reserves and fortifying the body against times of need or stress.

THE SACRAL DIVISION A GROUP OF MECHANISMS FOR EMPTYING

Sacral autonomic fibers cause contraction of the rectum and distal colon and also contraction of the bladder. In both instances the effects result reflexly from stretching of the tonically contracted viscera by their accumulating contents. No affective states precede this normal action of the sacral division and even those which accompany or follow are only mildly positive; a feeling of relief rather than of elation usually attends the completion of the act of defecation or micturition—though there is testimony in favor of elation.

The sacral autonomic fibers also include, however, the nervi erigentes which bring about engorgement of erectile tissue in the external genitals. According to Langley and Anderson [5] the sacral nerves have no effect on the *internal* generative organs. The vasa deferentia and the seminal vesicles whose rhythmic contractions mark the acme of sexual excitement in the male, and the uterus whose contractions in the female are probably analogous, are supplied only by lumbar branches —part of the sympathetic division. These branches also act in opposition to the nervi erigentes and cause constriction of the blood vessels of the external genitals. The sexual orgasm involves a high degree of emotional excitement; but it can rightly be considered as essentially a reflex mechanism; and, again in this instance, distention of tubules, vesicles, and blood vessels can be found at the beginning of the incident, and relief from this distention at the end.

Although distention is the commonest occasion for bringing the sacral division into activity it is not the only occasion. Great emotion, such as is accompanied by nervous discharges via the sympathetic division, may also be accompanied by discharges via the sacral fibers. The involuntary voiding of the bladder and lower gut at times of violent mental stress is well known. Veterans of wars testify that just before the beginning of a battle many of the men have to retire temporarily from the firing line. And the power of sights and smells and libidinous thoughts to disturb the regions controlled by the nervi erigentes proves that this part of the autonomic system also has its peculiar affective states. The fact that one part of the sacral division, e. g., the distribution to the bladder, may be in abeyance, while another part, e. g., the distribution to the rectum, is active, illustrates again the directive discharge of impulses which has been previously described as characteristic of the cranial and sacral portions of the autonomic system.

Like the cranial division, the sacral is engaged in internal service to the body, in the performance of acts leading immediately to greater comfort.

THE SYMPATHETIC DIVISION ANTAGONISTIC TO BOTH THE CRANIAL AND THE SACRAL

As indicated above, many viscera are innervated both by the cranial or sacral part and by the sympathetic. *When the mid-part (sympathetic) meets either end-part (cranial or sacral) in any viscus their effects are characteristically antagonistic.* Thus the cranial supply to the eye contracts the pupil, the sympathetic dilates it; the cranial slows the heart, the sympathetic accelerates it; the sacral contracts the lower part of the large intestine, the sympathetic relaxes it; the sacral relaxes the exit from the bladder, the sympathetic contracts it. These opposed effects are indicated in Fig. 1 by + for contraction, acceleration or increased tone; and by — for inhibition, relaxation, or decreased tone.*

Sherrington has demonstrated that the setting of skeletal muscles in opposed groups about a joint or system of joints—as in flexors and extensors—is associated with an internal organization of the central nerv-

---

* The vagus nerve, when artificially stimulated, has a primary, brief inhibitory effect on the stomach and small intestine; its main function, however, as already stated, is to produce increased tone and contraction in these organs. This double action of the vagus is marked thus, ± in Fig. 1.

ous system that provides for relaxation of one group of the opposed muscles when the other group is made to contract. This "reciprocal innervation of antagonistic muscles," as Sherrington has called it,[6] is thus a device for orderly action in the body. As the above description has shown, there are peripheral oppositions in the viscera corresponding to the oppositions between flexor and extensor muscles. In all probability these opposed innervations of the viscera have counterparts in the organization of neurones in the central nervous system. Sherrington has noticed, and I can confirm the observation, that even though the sympathetic supply to the eye is severed and is therefore incapable of causing dilation of the pupil, nevertheless the pupil dilates in a paroxysm of anger—due, no doubt (because the response is too rapid to be mediated by the blood stream), to central inhibition of the cranial nerve supply to the constrictor muscles—i. e., an inhibition of the muscles which naturally oppose the dilator action of the sympathetic. Pain, the major emotions—fear and rage—and also intense excitement, are manifested in the activities of the sympathetic division. When in these states impulses rush out over the neurones of this division they produce all the changes typical of sympathetic excitation, such as dilating the pupils, inhibiting digestion, causing pallor, accelerating the heart, and various other well known effects. The impulses of the sympathetic neurones, as indicated by their dominance over the digestive process, are capable of readily overwhelming the conditions established by neurones of the cranial division of the autonomic system.

NEURONES OF THE SYMPATHETIC DIVISION AND ADRENAL SECRETION HAVE THE SAME ACTION

Lying anterior to each kidney is a small body—the adrenal gland. It is composed of an external portion or cortex, and a central portion or medulla. From the medulla can be extracted a substance, called variously suprarenin, adrenin, epinephrin or "adrenalin," * which, in extraordinarily minute amounts, affects the structures innervated by the sympathetic division of the autonomic system precisely as if they were receiving nervous impulses. For example, when adrenin is injected into the blood, it will cause pupils to dilate, hairs to stand erect, blood vessels to be constricted, the activities of the alimentary canal to be inhibited, and sugar to be liberated from the liver. These effects are not produced by action of the substance on the central nervous system, but by direct action on the organ itself.[7] And the effects occur even after the structures have been removed from the body and kept alive artificially.

The adrenals are glands of internal secretion, i. e.,

---

* The name, "adrenalin" is proprietary. "Epinephrin" and "adrenin" have been suggested as terms free from commercial suggestions. As *adrenin* is shorter and more clearly related to the common adjectival form, *adrenal*, I have followed Schäfer in using *adrenin* to designate the substance produced physiologically by the adrenal glands.

like the thyroid, parathyroid, and pituitary glands, for example; they have no connection with the surface of the body, and they give out into the blood the material which they elaborate. The blood is carried away from each of them by the lumbo-adrenal vein which empties either into the vein from the kidney or directly into the large abdominal vein, the inferior vena cava, just anterior to the openings of the kidney veins. The adrenal glands are supplied by preganglionic fibers of the autonomic group,[8] shown in solid line in Fig. 1. This seems an exception to the general rule that gland cells have an outlying neurone between them and the neurones of the central nervous system. The medulla of the adrenal gland, however, is composed of modified nerve cells, and may therefore be regarded as offering exceptional conditions.

The foregoing brief sketch of the organization of the autonomic system brings out a number of points that should be of importance as bearing on the nature of the emotions which manifest themselves in the operations of this system. Thus it is highly probable that the sympathetic division, because arranged for diffuse discharge, is likely to be brought into activity as a whole, whereas the sacral and cranial divisions, arranged for particular action on separate organs, may operate in parts. Also, because antagonisms exist between the middle and either end division of the autonomic, affective states may be classified according to their expression in the middle or an end division and these states would be, like the nerves, antagonistic in character. And finally, since the adrenal glands are innervated by autonomic fibers of the mid-division, and since adrenal secretion stimulates the same activities that are stimulated nervously by this division, it is possible that disturbances in the realm of the sympathetic, although initiated by nervous discharges, are automatically augmented and prolonged through chemical effects of the adrenal secretion.

REFERENCES

1. CANNON, *American Journal of Psychology,* xxv (1914), p. 257.
2. For a summary of his studies of the organization of the autonomic system, see LANGLEY, *Ergebnisse der Physiologie* (Wiesbaden, 1903), ii², p. 818.
3. See CANNON, *American Journal of Physiology,* xiii (1905), p. xxii.
4. See SHERRINGTON, *The Integrative Action of the Nervous System* (New York, 1909), p. 19.
5. LANGLEY and ANDERSON, *Journal of Physiology,* xix (1895), see pp. 85, 122.
6. SHERRINGTON, *op. cit.,* p. 90.
7. ELLIOTT, *Journal of Physiology,* xxxii (1905), p. 426.
8. See ELLIOTT, *ibid.,* xlvi (1913), p. 289 ff.

CHAPTER III

As stated in the first chapter, the inhibition of gastric secretion produced by great excitement long outlasts the presence of the object which evokes the excitement. The dog that was enraged by seeing a cat for five minutes secreted only a few drops of gastric juice during the next fifteen minutes. Why did the state of excitation persist so long after the period of stimulation had ended? This question, which presented itself to me while reading Bickel and Sasaki's paper, furnished the suggestion expressed at the close of the last chapter, that the excitement might provoke a flow of adrenal secretion, and that the changes originally induced in the digestive organs by nervous impulses might be continued by circulating adrenin. The prolongation of the effect might be thus explained. Whether that idea is correct or not was not then tested. Its chief service was in leading to an inquiry as to whether the adrenal glands are in fact stimulated to action in emotional excitement. The preganglionic fibers passing to the glands are contained in the splanchnic nerves. What is the effect of splanchnic stimulation?

It was in 1891 that Jacobi [1] described nerve fibers derived from the splanchnic trunks which were distributed to the adrenal glands. Six years later Biedl [2] found that these nerves conveyed to the glands impulses which cause dilation of their blood vessels (vasodilator impulses), and he suggested that they probably conveyed also secretory impulses. Evidence in support of this suggestion was presented the following year by Dreyer,[3] who demonstrated that electrical excitation of the splanchnic nerves produced in the blood taken from the adrenal veins an increased amount of a substance having the power of raising arterial blood pressure—an effect which is produced by injecting "adrenalin" into the circulation—and that this result was independent of accompanying changes in the blood supply to the glands. The conclusion drawn by Dreyer that this substance was adrenin has been confirmed in various ways by later observers. Tscheboksaroff [4] repeated Dreyer's procedure and found in blood taken from the veins after splanchnic stimulation evidences of the presence of adrenin that were previously absent. Asher [5] observed a rise of blood pressure when the glands were stimulated in such a manner as not to cause constriction of the arteries—the rise was therefore assumed to be due to secreted adrenin. Dilation of the pupil was used by Meltzer and Joseph [6] to prove secretory action of the splanchnics on the adrenal

glands; they found that stimulation of the distal portion of the cut splanchnic nerve caused the pupil to
enlarge—an effect characteristic of adrenin circulating
in the blood. Elliott [7] repeated this procedure, but
made it a more rigorous proof of internal secretion of
the adrenals by noting that the effect failed to appear
if the gland on the stimulated side was removed. Additional proof was brought by myself and Lyman [8] when
we found that the typical drop in arterial pressure produced in cats by injecting small amounts of adrenin
could be exactly reproduced by stimulating the splanchnic nerves after the abdominal blood vessels, which
contract when these nerves are excited, were tied so
that no changes in them could occur to influence the
rest of the circulation.

The problem of splanchnic influence on the adrenal
glands Elliott attacked by a still different method.
Using, as a measure, the graded effects of graded
amounts of adrenin on blood pressure, he was able to
assay the quantity of adrenin in adrenal glands after
various conditions had been allowed to prevail. The
tests were made on cats. In these animals each adrenal
gland is supplied only by the splanchnic fibers of its
own side, and the two glands normally contain almost
exactly the same amount of adrenin. Elliott [9] found
that when the gland on one side was isolated by cutting
its splanchnic supply, and then impulses were sent
along the intact nerves of the other side, either by
disturbing the animal or by artificial excitation of the
nerves, the gland to which these fibers reached in-

variably contained less adrenin, often very much less, than the isolated gland. Results obtained by the method employed by Elliott have been confirmed with remarkable exactness in results obtained by Folin, Denis and myself,[10] using a highly sensitive color test after adding the gland extract to a solution of phosphotungstic acid.

All these observations, with a variety of methods, and by a respectable number of reliable investigators, are harmonious in bringing proof that artificial stimulation of the nerves leading to the adrenal glands will induce secretory activity in the central portion or medulla, and that in consequence adrenin will be increased in the blood. The fact is therefore securely established that in the body a mechanism exists by which these glands can be made to discharge this peculiar substance promptly into the circulation.

THE QUESTION OF ADRENAL SECRETION IN EMOTIONAL EXCITEMENT

As we have already seen, the phenomena of a great emotional disturbance in an animal indicate that sympathetic impulses dominate the viscera. When, for example, a cat becomes frightened, the pupil dilates, the activities of the stomach and intestines are inhibited, the heart beats rapidly, the hairs of the back and tail stand erect—from one end of the animal to the other there are abundant signs of nervous discharges along sympathetic courses. Do not the adrenal glands share in this widespread subjugation of the viscera to sympathetic control?

This question, whether the common excitements of an animal's life might be capable of evoking a discharge of adrenin, was taken up by D. de la Paz and myself in 1910. We made use of the natural enmity between two laboratory animals, the dog and the cat, to pursue our experiments. In these experiments the cat, fastened in a comfortable holder (the holder already mentioned as being used in X-ray studies of the movements of the alimentary canal), was placed near a barking dog. Some cats when thus treated showed almost no signs of fear; others, with scarcely a movement of defense, presented the typical picture. In favorable cases the excitement was allowed to prevail for five or ten minutes, and in a few cases longer. Samples of blood were taken within a few minutes before and after the period.

THE METHOD OF SECURING BLOOD FROM NEAR THE ADRENAL VEINS

The blood was obtained from the inferior vena cava anterior to the opening of the adrenal veins, i. e., at a point inside the body near the level of the notch at the lower end of the breastbone or sternum. To get the blood so far from the surface without disturbing the animal was at first a difficult problem. We found, however, that by making anesthetic with ethyl chloride the skin directly over the femoral vein high in the groin, the vein could be quickly bared, cleared of connective tissue, tied, and opened, without causing any general disturbance whatever. A long, fine flexible catheter (2.4 millimeters in diameter) which had previously been coated with vaseline inside and out, to lubricate it and to delay the clotting of blood within it, was now introduced into the opening in the femoral vein, thence through the iliac and on into the inferior cava to a point near the level of the sternal notch. A thread tied around this tube where, after being inserted to the proper distance, it disappeared into the femoral vein, marked the extent of insertion, and permitted a later introduction to the same extent. This slight operation—a venesection, commonly practiced on our ancestors—consumed only a few minutes, and as the only possibility of causing pain was guarded against by local anesthesia, the animal remained tranquil throughout. Occasionally it was necessary to stroke the cat's head gently to keep her quiet on the holder, and under such circumstances I have known her to purr during all the preparations for obtaining the blood, and while the blood was being taken.

The blood (3 or 4 cubic centimeters) was slowly drawn through the catheter into a clean glass syringe. Care was taken to avoid any marked suction such as might cause collapse of the vein near the inner opening of the tube. As soon as the blood was secured, the catheter was removed and the vein tied loosely, to prevent bleeding. The blood was at once emptied into a beaker, and in order to prevent it from clotting the fibrin was whipped from it by means of fringed rubber tubing fitted over a glass rod. Since this defibrinated blood was obtained while the animal was undisturbed, it was labeled "quiet blood."

The animal was then exposed to the barking dog, as already described, and immediately thereafter blood was again removed, from precisely the same region as before. This sample, after being defibrinated, was labeled "excited blood." The two samples, the "quiet" and the "excited," both obtained in the same manner and subsequently treated in the same manner, were now tested for their content of adrenin.

THE METHOD OF TESTING THE BLOOD FOR ADRENIN

It was desirable to use as a test tissues to which the blood was naturally related. As will be recalled, adrenin affects viscera even after they have been removed from the body, just as if they were receiving impulses via sympathetic fibers, and further, that sympathetic fibers normally deliver impulses which cause contraction of the internal genitals and relaxation of the stomach and intestines. The uterus has long been employed as a test for adrenin, the presence of which it indicates by increased contraction. That isolated strips of the longitudinal muscle of the intestine, which are contracting rhythmically, are characteristically inhibited by adrenin in dilutions of 1 part in 20 millions, had been shown by Magnus in 1905. Although, previous to our investigation in 1910, this extremely deli-

cate reaction had not been used as a biological signal
for adrenin, it possesses noteworthy advantages over
other methods.   The intestine is found in all animals
and not in only half of them, as is the uterus; it is
ready for the test within a few minutes, instead of the
several hours said to be required for the best use of the
uterus preparation; [11] and it responds by relaxing.
This last characteristic is especially important, for in
defibrinated blood there are, besides adrenin, other
substances capable of causing contraction of smooth
muscle,[12] and liable therefore to lead to erroneous conclusions when a structure which responds by contracting, such as uterus or artery, is used to prove whether
adrenin is present.   On the other hand, substances
producing relaxation of smooth muscle are few, and
are unusual in blood.[13]

We used, therefore, the strip of intestinal muscle as
an indicator.   Later Hoskins [14] modified our procedure
by taking, instead of the strip, a short segment of the
rabbit intestine.   The segment is not subjected to danger of injury during its preparation, and when fresh it
is almost incredibly sensitive.   It may be noticeably
inhibited by adrenin, 1 part in 200,000,000!

The strip, or the intestinal segment, was suspended
between minute wire pincers (*serres fines*) in a cylindrical chamber 8 millimeters in diameter and 5 centimeters deep.   By a thread attached to the lower *serre
fine* the preparation was drawn into the chamber, and
was held firmly; by the upper one it was attached to
the short end of a writing lever (see Fig. 2).   When

not exposed to blood, the strip was immersed in a normal solution of the blood salts (Ringer's solution). The blood or the salt solution could be quickly withdrawn from or introduced into the chamber, without disturbing the muscle, by means of a fine pipette passed down along the inner surface. The chamber and its contents, the stock of Ringer's solution, and the samples of "quiet" and "excited" blood were all sur-

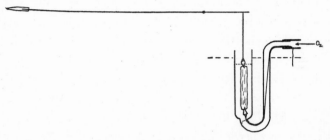

Fig. 2.—Diagram of the arrangements for recording contractions of the intestinal muscle.

rounded by a large volume of water kept approximately at body temperature (37° C.). Through the blood or the salt solution in the chamber oxygen was passed in a slow but steady stream of bubbles. Under these circumstances the strip will live for hours, and will contract and relax in a beautifully regular rhythm, which may be recorded graphically by the writing lever.

The first effect of surrounding the muscle with blood, whether "quiet" or "excited," was to send it into a strong contraction which might persist, sometimes with slight oscillations, for a minute or two (see Figs. 4 and

5). After the initial shortening, the strip, if in quiet blood, soon began to contract and relax rhythmically and with each relaxation to lengthen more, until a fairly even base line appeared in the written record. At this stage the addition of fresh "quiet" blood usually had no effect, even though the strip were washed once with Ringer's solution before the second portion of the blood was added. For comparison of the effects of "quiet" and "excited" blood on the contracting strip, the two samples were each added to the muscle immediately after the Ringer's solution had been removed, or they were applied to the muscle alternately and the differences in effect then noted.

Stewart and Rogoff [15] have argued that evidence obtained by this method is not valid because the rate of blood flow may be lessened by experimental procedures, and then, even if adrenin should be secreted constantly, it would appear to be increased in amount because less diluted by the slowly moving stream. They did not prove, however, that the flow was in fact retarded; and there is evidence that, under such conditions as we tested, the flow is actually accelerated, i. e., that the circulatory changes are unfavorable rather than favorable to a greater concentration of adrenin in the blood.[16]

The criticism of the catheter method led to the use of the "denervated" heart, the heart completely separated from connection with the central nervous system.[17] This method has the great advantage of not requiring the blood, which is being tested for its adrenin content, to be removed from the body. After severance of the cardiac nerves, the heart continues its service as a pump, but is now influenced only by agents brought to it in the blood stream. It is extremely sensitive to adrenin; the isolated heart responds with a faster beat when adrenin is added in the ratio of 1 part in 1,400,000,000 parts of the blood supplied to the organ! [18] The denervated heart may be used in acute experiments, performed wholly under ether; or the heart may be denervated by thorough surgical methods, and the tests made on the surviving animals after full recovery from the operation. The results obtained by these methods will next be presented.

REFERENCES

1. Jacobi, *Archiv für experimentelle Pathologie und Pharmakologie*, xxix (1891), p. 185.
2. Biedl, *Archiv für die gesammte Physiologie*, lxvii (1897), pp. 456, 481.
3. Dreyer, *American Journal of Physiology*, ii (1898-99), p. 219.
4. Tscheboksaroff, *Archiv für die gesammte Physiologie*, cxxxvii (1910), p. 103.
5. Asher, *Zeitschrift für Biologie*, lviii (1912), p. 274.
6. Meltzer and Joseph, *American Journal of Physiology*, xxix (1912), p. xxxiv.
7. Elliott, *Journal of Physiology*, xliv (1912), p. 400.
8. Cannon and Lyman, *American Journal of Physiology*, xxxi (1913), p. 377.
9. Elliott, *Journal of Physiology*, xliv (1912), p. 400.
10. Folin, Cannon and Denis, *Journal of Biological Chemistry*, xiii (1913), p. 477.
11. Fraenkel, *Archiv für experimentelle Pathologie und Pharmakologie*, lx (1909), p. 399.

12. See O'CONNOR, *ibid.*, lxvii (1912), p. 206.
13. GRUTZNER, *Ergebnisse der Physiologie,* iii² (1904), p. 66; MAGNUS, *ibid.*, p. 69.
14. HOSKINS, *Journal of Pharmacology and Experimental Therapeutics,* iii (1911), p. 95.
15. STEWART and ROGOFF, *Journal of Experimental Medicine,* xxvi (1917), p. 637.
16. BURTON-OPITZ, *American Journal of Physiology,* lviii (1921), p. 226.
17. CANNON, *American Journal of Physiology,* l (1919), p. 399; CANNON and RAPPORT, *ibid.*, lviii (1921), p. 308; CANNON, LEWIS and BRITTON, *ibid.*, lxxvii (1926), p. 326.
18. ANREP and DALY, *Proceedings of the Royal Society of London,* Bxcvii (1925), p. 454.

CHAPTER IV

IF the secretion of adrenin is increased in strong emotional states and in pain, that constitutes a fact of considerable significance, for, as already mentioned, adrenin is capable of producing many of the bodily changes which are characteristically manifested in emotional and painful experiences. It is a matter of prime importance for further discussion to determine whether the adrenal glands are in fact roused to special activity in times of stress.

THE EVIDENCE THAT ADRENAL SECRETION IS INCREASED IN EMOTIONAL EXCITEMENT

That blood from the adrenal veins causes the relaxation of intestinal muscle characteristic of adrenal extract or adrenin is shown in Fig. 3. The muscle was originally beating in blood which contained no demonstrable amount of adrenal secretion; this inactive blood was replaced by blood from the adrenal veins, obtained after quick etherization. Etherization, it will be recalled, is accompanied by a "stage of excitement." Relaxation occurred almost immediately (at b). Then the rhythm was renewed in the former blood, and thereupon the muscle was surrounded with blood from the vein leading away from the left kidney, i. e., blood obtained from the same animal and under the same conditions as the adrenal blood, but from a neighboring vein. No relaxation occurred. By this and other similar tests the reliability of the method was proved.

In no instance did blood from the inferior vena cava of the quiet normal animal produce relaxation. On the

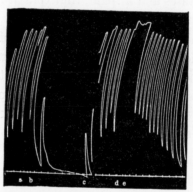

Fig. 3.—Intestinal muscle beating in inactive blood, which was withdrawn from the chamber at *a*. Blood from the *adrenal* vein of an animal excited by etherization was substituted at *b*, and withdrawn at *c*. Contractions were restored in the original inactive blood which was removed at *d*. Blood from the *renal* vein (same animal) was added at *e*.

In this and the next three records time is marked in half minutes.

other hand, blood from the animal after emotional excitement showed more or less promptly the typical relaxation. In Fig. 4 is represented the record of intestinal muscle which was beating regularly in Ringer's solution. At *a* the Ringer's solution was removed, and at *b* "excited" blood was added; after the preliminary shortening, which, as already stated, occurs at the first immersion in blood, the muscle lengthened gradually into complete inhibition. At *c* the "excited" blood was removed, and at *d* "quiet" blood was added in its place. The muscle at once began fairly regular rhythmic beats. At *e* the "quiet" blood was removed, and at *f* the "excited" blood was again applied. The muscle lengthened almost immediately into an inhibited state. In this instance the "excited" blood was taken

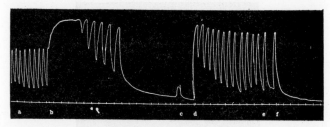

FIG. 4.—Alternate application of "excited" blood (at *b* and *f*) and "quiet" blood (at *d*), from the same animal, to intestinal muscle initially beating in Ringer's solution.

after the cat had been barked at for about fifteen minutes.

The inference that this inhibition of contraction of the intestinal muscle is due to an increased amount of adrenal secretion in the "excited" blood de la Paz and I justified on several grounds:

1. The inhibition was produced by "excited" blood taken from the inferior vena cava anterior to the mouths of the adrenal veins, when blood from the femoral vein, taken at the same time, had no inhibitory influence. Since blood from the femoral vein is typical of the cava blood below the entrance of the kidney veins, the conclusion is warranted that the difference

of effect of the two samples of blood is not due to any agent below the kidneys. But that blood from the kidneys does not cause the relaxation is shown in Fig. 3. The only other structures which could alter the blood between the two points at which it was taken are the adrenal glands, and the material secreted by them would produce precisely the inhibition of contraction which was in fact produced.

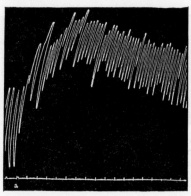

Fig. 5.—Failure of the cava blood (added at *a*) to produce inhibition when excitement has occurred after removal of the adrenal glands. The muscle later proved sensitive to adrenin in blood in the ratio 1:1,000,000.

2. If in ether anesthesia the blood vessels leading to and from the adrenal glands are first carefully tied, and then the glands are removed, excitement four or five hours later, before the weakness that follows the removal has become prominent, does not alter the blood so that the typical inhibition occurs (see Fig. 5). Thus, although the animal shows all the characteristic signs of sympathetic stimulation, the blood, in the absence of the adrenals, remains unchanged.

3. As already shown, sometimes the effect produced by the "excited" blood was prompt inhibition, sometimes the inhibition followed only after several beats, and sometimes a slowing and shortening of contractions, with a lower tone, were the sole signs of the action of adrenin. All these degrees of relaxation can be duplicated by adding to inactive blood varying

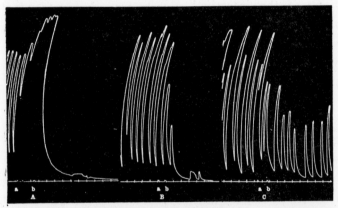

FIG. 6.—Effect of adding adrenin 1:1,000,000 (A), 1:2,000,000 (B), and 1:3,000,000 (C), to formerly inactive blood. In each case a marks the moment when the quiet blood was removed, and b, the time when the blood with adrenin was added.

amounts of adrenin. Fig. 6 shows the effects, on a somewhat insensitive muscle preparation, of adding adrenin, 1:1,000,000 (A), 1:2,000,000 (B), and 1:3,000,-000 (C), to different samples of blood previously without inhibitory influence. These effects of adrenin and the effects produced by blood taken near the opening of the adrenal veins are strikingly analogous.

4. Embden and von Furth [1] have reported that 0.1 gram of suprarenin chloride disappears almost com-

pletely in two hours if added to 200 cubic centimeters of defibrinated beef blood, and the mixture constantly aerated at body temperature. "Excited" blood which produces inhibition loses that power on standing in the cold for twenty-four hours, or on being kept warm and agitated with bubbling oxygen. We found that the power of the "excited" blood to inhibit the contractions of the intestinal muscle was destroyed after three hours of exposure to bubbling oxygen. The destruction of adrenin and the disappearance of the effect which adrenin would produce are thus closely parallel.

All these considerations, taken with the proof that sympathetic impulses increase secretion of the adrenal glands, and taken also with the evidence that, during such emotional excitement as was employed in these experiments, signs of sympathetic discharges appeared throughout the animal from the dilated pupil of the eye to the standing hairs of the tail-tip, led us to the conclusions that the characteristic action of adrenin on intestinal muscle was in fact, in our experiments, due to secretion of the adrenal glands, and that that secretion is increased in great emotion.

The foregoing observations, reported in 1911, were supported the next year by Elliott [2] who noted that the iris of a cat's eye, after being deprived of its sympathetic nerves, was dilated more widely than the normal iris when the animal became angry, and that this effect failed to occur if the adrenal glands were removed. Elliott's experiment was repeated and confirmed by

Kellaway[3] in 1919. On the other hand Stewart and
Rogoff[4] were unable to repeat any of these experiments, and threw doubt on the actual existence of an
emotional stimulation of adrenin.

The importance of bodily reactions in strong emotional states made desirable a confirmatory demonstration of secretion from the adrenal medulla by other
means than had previously been used. In 1927 Britton
and I[5] used animals (cats) surviving the denervation
of the heart to prove that adrenin is discharged when
strong emotion is aroused. While the animal was resting quietly on a cushion an aggressive dog was brought
near. The response of the cat included dilation of the
pupils, erection of hairs on the tail and back, retraction
of the ears, baring of the teeth, hissing, snarling, spitting and striking at the dog with claws protruding.
The skeletal movements were of minor character; the
visceral disturbance was widespread as shown by the
standing hairs. Such disturbances were associated
with accelerations of the completely denervated heart
varying roughly between 15 and 30 beats per minute;
the average rise in forty-five tests was 22. The variations of increment of heart rate corresponded with
variations in other signs of emotional reaction. After
inactivation of the adrenal glands repetition of the
same conditions with the same animals induced only
minor accelerations, or none at all: the average in
thirty-nine tests was a rise of 2 beats (see Fig. 7).

When great excitement is accompanied by vigorous
struggle, the maximal effect is produced; the dener-

vated heart may then beat faster by more than 100 beats per minute.

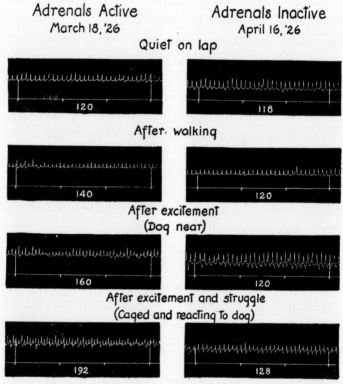

FIG. 7.—Original records of the rate of the denervated heart of cat 27 taken before (on March 18) and after (on April 16) adrenal secretion was excluded (on April 6). Time in 5-second intervals. The basal rate with the animal quiet on lap is to be compared with the rate after walking, after being excited by the presence of a dog, and after being caged and reacting to a barking dog.

The results just cited, which have been confirmed by the Japanese investigators, Sataké, Watanabé and Sugawara,[6] strongly support the results of the earlier experiments on the association of great emotional disturbance with an extra discharge of adrenin. Such disturbance is attended by inhibition of the digestive activities, erection of hairs from head to tail tip, sweating, and other changes, all signs of diffuse discharge of sympathetic impulses. It would indeed be astonishing if sympathetic impulses should be sent to every nook and cranny of the organism, except to the adrenal medulla. In view of the numerous facts demonstrating emotional secretion of adrenin there is no need for crediting that extraordinary assumption.

THE EVIDENCE THAT ADRENAL SECRETION IS INCREASED BY "PAINFUL" STIMULATION

As mentioned in the first chapter, stimulation of sensory fibers in one of the larger nerve trunks is known to result in such nervous discharges along sympathetic paths as to produce marked inhibition of digestive processes. Other manifestations of sympathetic innervation—e. g., contraction of arterioles, dilation of pupils, erection of hairs—are also demonstrable. And since the adrenal glands are stimulated to activity by sympathetic impulses, it was possible that they would be affected as are other structures supplied with sympathetic fibers, and that they would secrete in greater abundance when sensory nerves were irritated.

The testing of this possibility was undertaken by Hoskins and myself in 1911. Since bodily changes from "painful" stimulation can in large degree be pro-

duced in an anesthetized animal, without, however,
an experience of pain by the animal, it was possible
to make the test quite simply. The sensory stimulus
was a rapidly interrupted induced electric current

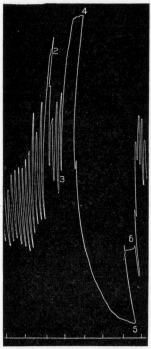

FIG. 8.—Intestinal muscle beating in normal **vena-cava** blood,
    removed at *1* and renewed at *2*. At *3* normal blood removed.
    At *4* contraction inhibited by vena-cava blood drawn after
    sensory stimulation; at *5* removed. At *6* Ringer's solution
    substituted.

(from an induction coil) applied to the sciatic nerve.
The current was increased in strength as time passed,
and thus the intensity of the effect, indicated by continuous dilation of the pupils, was maintained. There

was no doubt that such stimulation would have caused very severe pain if the animal had not been anesthetized. Indeed, the stimulus used was probably much stronger than would be necessary to obtain a positive result in the absence of the anesthetic (urethane), which notably lessens the irritability of visceral nerve fibers.[7] In different instances the stimulation lasted from three to six minutes. Throughout the period there was markedly increased rapidity and depth of breathing.

As Fig. 8 shows, the normal blood, removed from the vena cava before stimulation, caused no inhibition of the beating segment, whereas that removed afterwards produced a deep relaxation. Hoskins and I showed that the increased respiration which accompanies "painful" stimulation does not augment adrenal activity. We concluded, therefore, that when a sensory trunk is strongly excited the adrenal glands are reflexly stimulated, and that they pour into the blood stream an increased amount of adrenin.

CONFIRMATION OF OUR RESULTS BY OTHER OBSERVERS

Our experiments with use of the intestinal strip as an indicator, and the conclusions therefrom, were reported in 1911. They have since been abundantly confirmed by many other investigators who have employed a wide variety of methods. Most of these investigators have observed organs which have been disconnected from the central nervous system and which

thereafter have responded in a characteristic manner
to an increase of circulating adrenin. In 1912 Anrep [8]
reported that the denervated limb or kidney *contracted*
when he stimulated a sensory nerve—an effect which
disappeared after removal of the adrenal glands or
section of the splanchnic nerves. Since the only functional connection between the denervated limb or kidney and the rest of the body was the blood stream,
since the rise of blood pressure resulting from sensory
stimulation would naturally cause *distention* of the
denervated organs, and since in fact the contraction of
these organs did change to distention after adrenalec-
tomy, Anrep inferred that, when he stimulated an
afferent nerve, reflexly secreted adrenin produced the
constriction of the denervated vessels and thereby a
reduction of the size of the organ. Anrep's observation
on the denervated limb was supported in 1919 by Pearlman and Vincent.[9] This testimony was further corroborated in 1913 by Levy [10] who noted reflex acceleration of the denervated heart; in 1917 by Florovsky [11]
and in 1923 by Baschmakoff [12] who observed reflex increase of secretion from the denervated salivary gland
(in the cat); in 1924-25 by Houssay and Molinelli [13]
and in 1925 by Tournade and Chabrol [14] who let the
blood from the adrenal vein of animal A flow into animal B which manifested typical adrenin effects when a
sensory nerve of animal A was excited; and in 1923 by
Kodama [15] and in 1926 by Sugawara, Watanabé and
Saito [16] who used the "cava pocket" method of Stewart
and Rogoff.

Because Stewart and Rogoff [17] reported (in 1917) that they were unable to demonstrate any effects of sensory stimulation on adrenal activity, Rapport and I [18] in 1921 and later Carrasco-Formiguera and I [19] (1922) performed critical experiments with use of the denervated heart. Stewart and Rogoff attributed the acceleration of the denervated heart to a redistribution of blood in the body and to an increase of blood pressure, in consequence of sensory stimulation, rather than to any larger output of adrenin. Rapport and I showed that when the possibility of redistributing the blood in the body was reduced to a minimum the heart was accelerated as much as before, and further added to the already existing evidence that increase of blood pressure had no effect on the denervated heart. And Carrasco-Formiguera and I repeated for reflex stimulation the conditions which Stewart and Rogoff had demanded of themselves in bringing their proof that secretion from the adrenal medulla is augmented by direct stimulation of the splanchnic nerves—i. e., a failure of acceleration of the denervated heart if the blood from the adrenal glands was prevented from entering the general circulation during the stimulation, an acceleration when the pent blood was released, and approximately the same time interval between release of the pent blood and the start of the acceleration as that between the start of sensory stimulation and the effect on the heart (see Fig. 9). Thus Stewart and Rogoff were required to discredit their own evidence for direct nervous control of adrenal secretion or

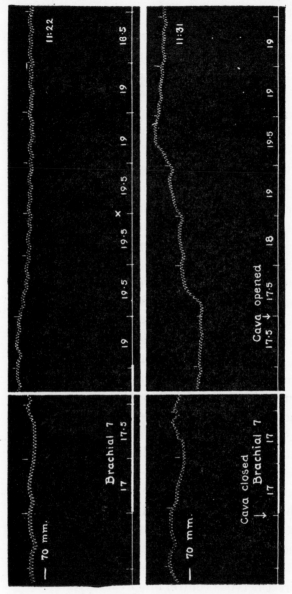

FIG. 9.—Beginning and end of two records of the beat of the denervated heart, when a sensory nerve (the right brachial) was stimulated for 30 seconds. In both the initial rate was 204 beats per minute (12 x 17). At 11:22, acceleration of the rate began within 10 seconds after the stimulus was started; at X, 45 seconds after the start, the rate was 234 beats per minute.   The point X corresponds in time to the opening of the cava in the record for 11:31. At 11:31, brachial stimulation (30 seconds) during closure of the inferior cava above the adrenal veins; when the cava was opened, 45 seconds after the start, the rate was 210. Acceleration of the heart began within 10 seconds thereafter and rose to 234 beats per minute.

accept our evidence for reflex control. This dilemma they have not solved. And the later corroboration of our results by Japanese investigators who used Stewart and Rogoff's own method leaves them without any support whatever for their contention that the discharge of adrenin is steady and invariable and wholly uninfluenced by sensory stimulation.

The logic of all these experiments may be briefly summed up. That the adrenal glands are subject to direct splanchnic influence has been demonstrated anatomically and by the physiological effects of their secretion after artificial stimulation of the splanchnic nerves. Impulses are normally sent along these nerves, in the natural conditions of life, when animals become greatly excited, as in fear and rage and pain. There is every probability, therefore, that these glands are stimulated to extra secretion at such times. Exceedingly delicate biological tests (intestinal muscle and denervated organs) and an examination of the glands themselves, afford clear evidence that in pain and deep emotion the glands do, in fact, pour out an excess of adrenin into the circulating blood.

Here, then, is a remarkable group of phenomena—a pair of glands stimulated to activity in times of strong excitement and by such nerve impulses as themselves produce at such times profound changes in the viscera; and a secretion given forth into the blood stream by these glands, which is capable of inducing by itself, or of augmenting the nervous influences which induce, the very changes in the viscera which accompany suffering and the major emotions. What may be the significance of these changes, occurring when conditions of pain and great excitement—experiences common to animals of most diverse types and probably known to their ancestors for ages past—lay hold of the bodily functions and determine the instinctive responses?

Certain noteworthy effects of injecting adrenin into the blood have for many years been more or less well recognized. For example, when injected it causes liberation of sugar from the liver into the blood stream. It relaxes the smooth muscle of the bronchioles. Some old experiments indicated that it acts as an antidote for muscular fatigue. It alters the distribution of the blood in the body, driving it from the abdominal viscera into the heart, lungs, central nervous system and limbs. And there was some evidence that it renders more rapid the coagulation of the blood. There may be other activities of adrenin not yet discovered— it may coöperate with the products of other glands of internal secretion. And other glands of internal secretion may be stimulated by sympathetic impulses. But we were not concerned with these possibilities. We wished to know whether the adrenin poured out in pain and emotional excitement produces or helps to produce the same effects that follow the injection of adrenin. Our later researches were directed towards securing answers to this question.

REFERENCES

1. EMBDEN and VON FURTH, *Hofmeister's Beiträge zur chemischen Physiologie und Pathologie*, iv (1904), p. 423.
2. ELLIOTT, *Journal of Physiology*, xliv (1912), p. 374.
3. KELLAWAY, *ibid.*, liii (1919), p. 211.
4. STEWART and ROGOFF, *Journal of Experimental Medicine* xxiv (1916), p. 709; *American Journal of Physiology*, xliv (1917), p. 543.
5. CANNON and BRITTON, *American Journal of Physiology*, lxxix (1927), p. 433.
6. SATAKÉ, WATANABÉ and SUGAWARA, *Tohoku Journal of Experimental Medicine*, ix (1927), p. 1.
7. ELLIOTT, *Journal of Physiology*, xxxii (1905), p. 448.
8. ANREP, *ibid.*, xlv (1912), p. 307.
9. PEARLMAN and VINCENT, *Endocrinology*, iii (1919), p. 121.
10. LEVY, *Heart*, iv (1913), p. 342.
11. FLOROVSKY, *Bulletin de l'Académie Impériale des Sciences*, ix (Petrograd, 1917), p. 119.
12. BASCHMAKOFF, *Archiv für die gesammte Physiologie*, cc (1923), p. 379.
13. HOUSSAY and MOLINELLI, *Revista de la Asociación Médica Argentina*, xxxvii (1924), p. 327; *Revista de la Sociedad Argentina de Biologia*, l (1925), p. 125.
14. TOURNADE and CHABROL, *Comptes rendus de la Société de Biologie*, xcii (1925), p. 418.
15. KODAMA, *Tohoku Journal of Experimental Medicine*, iv (1923), p. 166.
16. SUGAWARA, WATANABÉ and SAITO, *ibid.*, vii (1926), p. 1.
17. STEWART and ROGOFF, *Journal of Experimental Medicine*, xxvi (1917), p. 637.
18. CANNON and RAPPORT, *American Journal of Physiology*, lviii (1921), p. 308.
19. CANNON and CARRASCO-FORMIGUERA, *ibid.*, lxi (1922), p. 215.

CHAPTER V

THE INCREASE OF BLOOD SUGAR IN PAIN
AND GREAT EMOTION

SUGAR is the form in which carbohydrate material is transported in organisms; starch is the storage form. In the bodies of animals that have been well fed the liver contains an abundance of glycogen or "animal starch," which may be called upon in times of need. At such times the glycogen is changed, and set free in the blood as sugar. Ordinarily there is a small percentage of sugar in the blood—from 0.06 to 0.1 per cent. When only this small amount is present the kidneys are capable of preventing its escape in any noteworthy amount. If the percentage rises to the neighborhood of 0.18 per cent, however, the sugar passes over the obstacle set up by the kidneys, and is readily demonstrable in the urine by ordinary tests. This condition of "glycosuria," therefore, may properly be considered, in certain circumstances, as evidence of increased sugar in the blood. The injection of adrenin can liberate sugar from the liver to such an extent that glycosuria results. Does the adrenal secretion discharged in pain and strong emotional excitement play a rôle in producing glycosuria under such conditions?

In clinical literature scattered suggestions are to be found that conditions giving rise to emotional states

66

may be the occasion also of more or less permanent glycosuria. Great grief and prolonged anxiety during a momentous crisis have been regarded as causes of individual instances of diabetes, and anger or fright has been followed by an increase in the sugar excreted by persons who already have the disease. Kleen [1] cites the instance of a German officer whose diabetes and whose Iron Cross for valor both came from a stressful experience in the Franco-Prussian War. The onset of the disease in a man directly after his wife was discovered in adultery is described by Naunyn; [2] and this author also mentions two cases in his own practice— one started during the bombardment of Strassburg (1870), the other started a few days after a companion had shot himself. In cases of mental disease, also, states of depression have been described accompanied by sugar in the urine. Schultze [3] has reported that in these cases the amount of glycosuria is dependent on the degree of depression, and that the greatest excretion of sugar occurs in the fear-psychoses. Raimann [4] has reported that in both melancholia and mania the assimilation limit of sugar may be lowered. Similar results in the insane have recently been presented by Mita,[5] and by Folin and Denis.[6] The latter investigators found glycosuria in 12 per cent of 192 insane patients, most of whom suffered from depression, apprehension, or excitement. And Arndt [7] has observed glycosuria appearing and disappearing as alcoholic delirium appeared and disappeared in his patients.

Although clinical evidence thus indicates an emotional origin of some cases of diabetes and glycosuria, the intricacies of existence and the complications of disease in human beings throw some doubt on the value of that evidence. Both Naunyn[8] and Hirschfeld, although mentioning instances of diabetes apparently due to an emotional experience, urge a skeptical attitude toward such statements. It is desirable, therefore, that the question of an emotional glycosuria be tested under simpler and more controllable conditions. "Emotional glycosuria" in experimental animals has indeed been referred to by Waterman and Smit[9] and more recently by Henderson and Underhill.[10] Both these references, however, are based on the work of Böhm and Hoffmann,[11] reported in 1878.

GLYCOSURIA FROM PAIN

Böhm and Hoffmann found that cats, when bound to an operating board, a tube inserted into the trachea (without anesthesia), and in some instances a catheter inserted into the urethra through an opening above the pubis, had in about half an hour an abundance of sugar in the urine. In three determinations sugar in the blood proved slightly above "normal" so long as sugar was appearing in the urine, but returned to "normal" as the glycosuria disappeared. Since they were able to produce the phenomenon by simply binding animals to the holder, they called it "Fesselungs-diabetes."

As possible causes of this glycosuria in bound animals, they considered opening the trachea, cooling, and pain. The first two they readily eliminated, and still they found sugar excreted. Pain they could not obviate, and since, without binding the animals, they caused glycosuria by merely stimulating the sciatic nerves, they concluded that painful confinement was itself a sufficient cause. Other factors, however, such as cooling and circulatory disturbances, probably co-operated with pain, they believed, to produce the result. Their observations on cats have been proved true also of rabbits; [12] and recently it has been shown that an operation involving some pain increases blood sugar in dogs.[13] Temporary glycosuria has likewise been noted in association with intense pain in human beings.

Inasmuch as Böhm and Hoffmann did not recognize an emotional element in discussing their results, and inasmuch as they admitted that they could not obviate from their experimental procedure pain, which they themselves proved was effective in causing glycosuria, designating what they called "Fesselungsdiabetes" as "emotional glycosuria" is not justified.

EMOTIONAL GLYCOSURIA

The discovery that during strong emotion adrenal secretion is increased, and the fact that injection of adrenin gives rise to glycosuria, suggested that glycosuria might be called forth by emotional excitement, and then that even without the painful element of

Böhm and Hoffmann's experiments, sugar might be found in the urine. The testing of this possibility was undertaken by Shohl, Wright and myself in 1911.

Our first procedure was a repetition of Böhm and Hoffmann's experiments, freed from the factor of pain. The animals (cats) were bound to a comfortable holder, which left the head unfastened. This holder I had used hundreds of times in X-ray studies of digestion, with many different animals, without causing any signs of even so much as uneasiness. Just as in observations on the movements of the alimentary canal, however, so here, the animals reacted differently to the experience of being confined. Young males usually became quite frantic, and with eyes wide, pupils dilated, pulse accelerated, hairs of the tail more or less erect, they struggled, snarling and growling, to free themselves. Females, on the contrary, especially if elderly, were as a rule much more calm, and resignedly accepted the novel situation.

According to differences in reaction the animals were left in the holder for periods varying in length from thirty minutes to five hours. In order to insure prompt urination, considerable quantities of water were given by stomach tube at the beginning of the experiment and in some cases again later. Arrangements were made for draining the urine promptly, when the animal was on the holder or when afterwards in a metal metabolism cage, into a glass receiver containing a few drops of chloroform to prevent fermentation. The diet in all cases consisted of customary raw meat and milk. In every instance the urine was proved free from sugar before the animal was excited.

In our series of observations twelve cats were used, and in every one a well-marked glycosuria was developed. The shortest periods of confinement to the holder which were effective were thirty and forty minutes; the longest we employed was five hours. The average time required to bring about a glycosuria was less than an hour and a half; the average in seven of the twelve cases was less than forty minutes. In all cases no sugar was found in the urine passed on the day after the excitement.

The promptness with which the glycosuria developed was directly related to the emotional state of the animal. Sugar was found early in animals which early showed signs of being frightened or in a rage, and much later in animals which took the experience more calmly.

As cooling may result in increased sugar in the blood, and consequent glycosuria, the rectal temperature was observed from time to time, and it was found to vary so slightly that in these experiments it was a wholly negligible factor. In one cat the rectal temperature fell to 36° C. while the animal was bound and placed in a cold room (about 2° C.) for fifty minutes, but no sugar appeared in the urine.

Further evidence that the appearance of sugar in the urine may arise purely from emotional excitement was obtained from three cats which gave negative results when bound in the holder for varying periods up to four hours. It was noteworthy that these animals remained calm and passive in their confinement. When, however, they were placed, separately, in a small wire cage, and were barked at by an energetic little dog, which jumped at them and made signs of attack, the cats became much excited, they showed their teeth, humped their backs, and growled defiance. This sham fight was permitted to continue for a half hour in each of the three cases. Invariably the animal, which after four hours of bondage had exhibited no glycosuria, now had sugar in the urine. Pain, cooling, and bondage were not factors in these experiments. The animal was either frightened or enraged by the barking dog, and that excitement was attended by glycosuria.

The sugar excreted in the twenty-four hours which included the period of excitement was determined by the Bertrand method.[14] It ranged from 0.024 gram to 1.93 grams, or from 0.008 gram to 0.62 gram per kilo body weight, for the twenty-four hours' quantity.

As already stated, the presence of sugar in the urine may be used as an indication of increased sugar in the blood, for unless injury has been done to the cells of the kidneys, they do not permit sugar to escape until the percentage in the blood has risen to a considerable degree. Thus, though testing the urine reveals the instances of a high content of blood sugar, it does not show the fine variations that appear when the blood itself is examined. In 1914 Scott [15] reported an extensive and thorough investigation of the variations of blood sugar in cats; he found that merely incidental conditions, producing even mild excitement, as indicated by crying or otherwise, result in a noticeable rise in the amount. Indeed, so sensitive is the sugar-liberating mechanism that all the early determinations of the "normal" content of sugar in blood which has been drawn from an artery or vein in the absence of anesthesia, are of very doubtful value. Certainly when care is taken to obtain blood suddenly from a tranquil animal, the percentage (0.069, Scott; 0.088, Pavy) is much less than when the blood is drawn without anesthesia (0.15, Böhm and Hoffmann), or after light narcosis (0.282, Rona and Takahashi [16]).

Our observations on cats have since been found valid for rabbits. Rolly and Oppermann, Jacobsen, and Hirsch and Reinbach [17] have recently recorded that the mere handling of a rabbit preparatory to operating on it will increase the percentage of blood sugar (in some cases from 0.10 to 0.23 and 0.27 per cent). Dogs are said to be much less likely to be disturbed by the nature of their surroundings than are rabbits and cats. Nevertheless, pain and excitement are such fundamental experiences of animals that the same mechanism must be operative in all when these experiences occur. Gib has given an account of a bitch that became much agitated when shut up, and after such enforced seclusion, but never otherwise, she excreted small quantities of sugar in the urine.[18] And Hirsch and Reinbach [19] have reported a "psychic hyperglycemia" in dogs, that resulted from fastening the animals to a table. The blood sugar rose in one instance from 0.11 to 0.14 per cent, and in another from 0.09 to 0.16 per cent.

The results noted in these lower animals have been confirmed in human beings. One of my former students, W. G. Smillie, found that four of nine medical students, all normally without sugar in their urine, had glycosuria after a hard examination, and only one of the nine had glycosuria after an easier examination. The tests, which were positive with Fehling's solution, Nylander's reagent, and also with phenyl-hydrazine, were made on the first urine passed after the examination. Furthermore, C. H. Fiske and I examined the urine of twenty-five members of the Harvard University football squad immediately after the final and most exciting contest of the season of 1913, and found sugar in twelve cases. Five of these positive cases were among substitutes not called upon to enter the game. The only excited spectator of the Harvard victory whose urine was examined also had a marked glycosuria, which on the following day had disappeared.

Other tests made on students before and after important scholastic examinations have been published by Folin, Denis and Smillie.[20] Of thirty-four second-year medical students tested, one had sugar before the examination as well as afterwards. Of the remaining thirty-three, six, or 18 per cent, had small but unmistakable traces of sugar in the urine passed directly following the ordeal. A similar study was made on second-year students at a women's college. Of thirty-six students who had no sugar in the urine on the day before, six, or 17 per cent, eliminated sugar with the urine passed immediately after the examination.

From the foregoing results it is reasonable to conclude that just as in the cat, dog, and rabbit, so also in man, emotional excitement produces temporary increase of blood sugar.

THE RÔLE OF THE ADRENAL GLANDS IN EMOTIONAL GLYCOSURIA

Since artificial stimulation of the splanchnic nerves produces glycosuria,[21] and since major emotions, such as rage and fright, are attended by nervous discharges along splanchnic pathways, glycosuria as an accompaniment of emotional excitement would naturally be expected to occur. To what extent the adrenal glands which, as already mentioned, are stimulated to increased secretion by excitement, might play a part in this process, has been in dispute. Removal of these glands or cutting of the nerve fibers supplying them, according to some observers,[22] prevents glycosuria after puncture of the fourth ventricle of the brain (the "sugar puncture," which typically induces glycosuria) and also after stimulation of the splanchnics.[23] On the other hand, Wertheimer and Battez [24] have stated that removal of the glands does not abolish the effects of sugar puncture in the cat. It was questionable, therefore, whether removal of the adrenal glands would affect emotional glycosuria.

Evidence on this point I secured with Shohl and Wright in observations on three animals from which the adrenals were removed aseptically under ether.

The animals selected had all become quickly excited on being bound to the holder, and had manifested glycosuria after about an hour of confinement. In the operation, to avoid discharge of adrenin by handling, the adrenal veins were first tied, and then the glands freed from their attachments and removed as quickly and with as little manipulation as possible. In one cat the entire operation was finished in twenty minutes. In two of the cats a small catheter was introduced into the urethra through an incision, so that the bladder could be emptied at any time.

In all three cases urine that was free from sugar was obtained soon after the operation. Although the animals deprived of their adrenals manifested a general lessening of muscular tone, they still displayed much of their former rage or excitement when bound. Indeed, one was more excited after removal of the adrenals than before. That the animals might not be excessively cooled they were kept warm with coverings or an electric heating pad. Although they were now bound for periods from two to three times as long as the periods required formerly to cause glycosuria, no trace of sugar was found in the urine in any instance. The evidence thus reported tends, therefore, to support the view that the adrenal glands perform an important contributory rôle in the glycosuria resulting from splanchnic stimulation.

Later evidence has brought confirmation of the earlier. Griffith,[25] working in the Harvard Laboratory of Physiology, found that the reflex increase of blood sugar resulting from stimulation of a sensory nerve was practically as great after the liver nerves were severed as it was in normal animals.   In these circumstances secretion of adrenin could still affect the liver cells and set free sugar. On the other hand, if the adrenal glands were removed or inactivated and the liver nerves left intact, reflex hyperglycemia, though still considerable, averaged less than in normal animals. Observations corresponding to these were made by Bulatao and myself [26] on animals deprived of the cerebral cortex and exhibiting a sham rage (a "pseudaffective preparation").   If the adrenal glands had been removed or inactivated, the initial hyperglycemia of the pseudaffective state neither rose nor remained high; instead it declined. If, on the contrary, the hepatic nerves had been severed without disturbance of the adrenal glands the initial hyperglycemia was increased during the quasi-emotional activity.   Quite in harmony with our results Britton [27] has found that the usual emotional hyperglycemia of cats excited by a barking dog is only slightly modified from the normal after the liver nerves alone have been severed, whereas excitement for the same length of time, after removal of the medullary portion of the adrenal glands, is followed by a lowering of the blood-sugar level.   Furthermore Olmsted [28] has reported that tying off the adrenals or denervating them prevented such asphyxial hyperglycemia as he produced when they were present.   There seems to be little question, therefore, that the secreted adrenin, by working the same effects as sympathetic nerve impulses, is a prominent agency in bringing extra sugar into the blood stream.

Possibly the emotional element is in part accountable for the glycosuria observed after painful stimulation, but conditions causing pain alone will reasonably explain it. As we have already seen, strong stimulation of sensory fibers causes the discharge of impulses along the splanchnic nerves, and incidentally calls forth an increased secretion of the adrenal glands. In glycosuria resulting from painful stimulation, as well as in emotional glycosuria, the adrenal glands appear to be essential factors.

Later the evidence will be given that sugar is the optimum source of muscular energy. In passing, we may note that the liberation of sugar at a time when great muscular exertion is likely to be demanded of the organism may be interpreted as a highly interesting instance of biological adaptation.

REFERENCES

1. KLEEN, *On Diabetes Mellitus and Glycosuria* (Philadelphia, 1900), pp. 22, 37-39.
2. NAUNYN, *Der Diabetes Mellitus* (Vienna, 1898), p. 72.
3. SCHULTZE, *Verhandlungen der Gesellschaft deutscher Naturforscher und Aerzte,* ii (Cologne, 1908), p. 358.
4. RAIMANN, *Zeitschrift für Heilkunde,* xxiii (1902), Abtheilung iii, pp. 14, 19.
5. MITA, *Monatshefte für Psychiatrie und Neurologie,* xxxii (1912), p. 159.
6. FOLIN, DENIS and SMILLIE, *Journal of Biological Chemistry,* xvii (1914), p. 519.
7. ARNDT, *Zeitschrift für Nervenheilkunde,* x, (1897), p. 436.
8. NAUNYN, *op. cit.,* p. 73; HIRSCHFELD, *Die Zuckerkrankheit* (Leipzig, 1902), p. 45.

9. WATERMAN and SMIT, *Archiv für die gesammte Physiologie,* cxxiv (1908), p. 205.

10. HENDERSON and UNDERHILL, *American Journal of Physiology,* xxviii (1911), p. 276.

11. BÖHM and HOFFMANN, *Archiv für experimentelle Pathologie und Pharmakologie,* viii (1878), p. 295.

12. ECKHARD, *Zeitschrift für Biologie,* xliv (1903), p. 408.

13. LOEWY and ROSENBERG, *Biochemische Zeitschrift,* lvi (1913), p. 114.

14. See ABDERHALDEN, *Handbuch der biochemischen Arbeitsmethoden,* ii (Berlin, 1910), p. 181.

15. SCOTT, *American Journal of Physiology,* xxxiv (1914), p. 283.

16. Cited by SCOTT, *ibid.,* p. 296.

17. ROLLY and OPPERMANN, *Biochemische Zeitschrift,* xlix (1913), p. 201. JACOBSEN, *ibid.,* li (1913), p. 449. HIRSCH and REINBACH, *Zeitschrift für physiologische Chemie,* lxxxvii (1913), p. 122.

18. Cited by KLEEN, *op cit.,* p. 37.

19. HIRSCH and REINBACH, *Zeitschrift für physiologische Chemie,* xci (1914), p. 292.

20. FOLIN, DENIS and SMILLIE, *op. cit.,* p. 520.

21. See MACLEOD, *American Journal of Physiology,* xix (1907), p. 405, also for other references to literature.

22. See MEYER, *Comptes rendus de la Société de Biologie,* lviii (1906), p. 1123; NISHI, *Archiv für experimentelle Pathologie und Pharmakologie,* lxi (1909), p. 416.

23. GAUTRELET and THOMAS, *Comptes rendus de la Société de Biologie,* lxvii (1909), p. 233; and MACLEOD, *Proceedings of the Society for Experimental Biology and Medicine,* viii (1911), p. 110 (true for left adrenal and left splanchnic).

24. WERTHEIMER and BATTEZ, *Archives Internationales de Physiologie,* ix (1910), p. 392.

25. GRIFFITH, *American Journal of Physiology,* lxvi (1923), p. 618.

26. BULATAO and CANNON, *ibid.,* lxxii (1925), p. 309.

27. BRITTON, *ibid.,* lxxxvi (1928), p. 340.

28. OLMSTED, *ibid.,* lxxv (1926), p. 487.

CHAPTER VI

IMPROVED CONTRACTION OF FATIGUED MUSCLE AFTER SPLANCHNIC STIMULATION OF THE ADRENAL GLAND

In the older literature on the adrenal glands the deleterious effect of their absence, or the beneficial effect of injected extracts, on the contraction of skeletal muscle was not infrequently noted. As evidence accumulated, however, tending to prove an important relation between the extract of the adrenal medulla (adrenin) and the sympathetic nervous system, the relations with the efficiency of skeletal muscle began to receive less consideration.

The muscular weakness of persons suffering from diseased adrenals (Addison's disease) was well recognized before experimental work on the glands was begun. Experiments on rabbits were reported in 1892 by Albanese,[1] who showed that muscles which were stimulated after removal of the glands were much more exhausted than when stimulated the same length of time in the same animal before the removal. Similarly Boinet [2] reported, in 1895, that rats recently deprived of their adrenals were much more quickly exhausted in a revolving cage than were normal animals.

That extract of the adrenal glands has the power of increasing and prolonging the contraction of normal resting skeletal muscle, was noted by Oliver and Schaefer,[3] in their classic original study of the action of adrenal substance. But a recent examination of this effect by Takayasu,[4] who employed adrenin alone, has failed to confirm the earlier observations. It should be understood that these observations, however, were made on resting and not on fatigued muscle. On fatigued muscle a beneficial effect of adrenal extract, even when applied to the solution in which the isolated muscle was contracting, was claimed by Dessy and Grandis,[5] who studied the phenomenon in a salamander.* Further evidence leading to the same conclusion was offered in a discriminating paper by Panella.[6] He found that in cold-blooded animals the active principle of the adrenal medulla notably reënforced skeletal muscle, prolonging its ability to do work, and improving its contraction when fatigued. In warm-blooded animals the same effects were observed, but only after certain experimental procedures, such as anesthesia and section of the bulb, had changed them to a condition resembling the cold-blooded.

The foregoing evidence indicates that removal of the adrenals has a debilitating effect on muscular power,

---

* These earlier investigations, in which an extract of the entire gland was used, made no distinction between the action of the medulla and that of the cortex. It seems certain that the weakness following removal or disease of the adrenals is due to absence of the cortex (see Hoskins and Wheelon, *American Journal of Physiology*, xxxiv, 1914, p. 184). Such a possible effect, however, should not be confused with the demonstrable influence of injected adrenin (derived from the adrenal medulla alone) and the similar effects from adrenal secretion caused by splanchnic stimulation.

and that injection of extracts of the glands has an invigorating effect. It seemed possible, therefore, that increased secretion of the adrenal glands, whether from direct stimulation of the splanchnic nerves or as a reflex result of pain or the major emotions, might act as a dynamogenic factor in the performance of muscular work. With this possibility in mind L. B. Nice and I [7] first concerned ourselves in a research which we conducted in 1912.

The general plan of the investigation consisted primarily in observing the effect of stimulating the splanchnic nerves, isolated from the spinal cord, on the contraction of a muscle whose nerve, also isolated from the spinal cord, was rhythmically and uniformly excited with break shocks from an induction coil. When a muscle is thus stimulated it at first responds by strong contractions, but as time passes the contractions become weaker, the degree of shortening of the muscle becomes less, and in this state of lessened efficiency it may continue for a long period to do work. The tired muscle which is showing continuously and evenly its inability to respond as it did at first, is said to have reached the "fatigue level." This level serves as an excellent basis for testing influences that may have a beneficial effect on muscular performance, for the benefit is at once manifested in greater contraction.

In the experimental arrangement which we used, only a connection through the circulating blood existed between the splanchnic region and the muscle—all nervous relations were severed. Any change in muscular ability, therefore, occurring when the splanchnic nerve is stimulated, must be due to an alteration in the quantity or quality of the blood supplied to the laboring muscle.

Cats were used for most experiments, but results obtained with cats were confirmed on rabbits and dogs. To produce anesthesia in the cats and rabbits, and at the same time to avoid the fluctuating effects of ether, urethane (2 grams per kilo body-weight) was given by a stomach tube. The animals were fastened, back downward, over an electric warming pad, to an animal holder. Care was taken to maintain the body temperature at its normal level throughout each experiment.

THE NERVE-MUSCLE PREPARATION

The muscle selected to be fatigued was usually the extensor of the right hind foot (the *tibialis anticus*), though at times the common extensor muscle of the digits of the same foot was employed. The anterior tibial nerve which supplies these muscles was bared for about two centimeters, severed toward the body, and set in shielded electrodes, around which the skin was fastened by spring clips. Thus the nerve could be protected, kept moist, and stimulated without stimulation of neighboring structures. By a small slit in the skin the tendon of the muscle was uncovered, and after a strong thread was tied tightly about it, it was separated from its insertion. A nerve-muscle preparation was thereby made which was still connected with its proper blood supply. The preparation was fixed firmly to the animal holder by thongs looped around the hock and the foot, i. e., on either side of the slit through which the tendon emerged.

The thread tied to the tendon was passed over a pulley and down to a pivoted steel bar which bore a writing point. Both the pulley and this steel writing lever were supported in a rigid tripod. In the earliest experiments the contracting muscle was made to lift weights (125 to 175 grams); in all the later observations, however, the muscle pulled against a spring attached below the steel bar. The tension of the spring as the muscle began to lift the lever away from the support was, in most of the experiments, 110 grams, with an increase of 10 grams as the writing point was raised 4.5 millimeters. The magnification of the lever was 3.8.

The stimuli delivered to the anterior tibial nerve were, in most experiments, single break shocks of a value barely maximal when applied to the fresh preparation. The rate of stimulation varied between 60 and 300 per minute, but was uniform in any single observation. A rate which was found generally serviceable was 180 per minute.

Since the anterior tibial nerve contains fibers affecting blood vessels, as well as fibers causing contraction of skeletal muscle, the possibility had to be considered that stimuli applied to it might disturb the blood supply of the region. Constriction of the blood vessels would be likely to produce the most serious disturbance, by lessening the blood flow to the muscle. The observations of Bowditch and Warren,[8] that vasodilator rather than vasoconstrictor effects are produced by single induced shocks repeated at intervals of not more than five per second, reassured us as to the danger of diminishing the blood supply, for the rate of stimulation in our experiments never exceeded five per second and was usually two or three. Furthermore, in using these different rates we have never noted any result which could reasonably be attributed to a diminished circulation.

THE SPLANCHNIC PREPARATION

The splanchnic nerves were stimulated in various ways. At first only the left splanchnics in the abdomen were prepared. The nerves, separated from the spinal cord, were placed upon shielded electrodes. The form of electrodes which was found most satisfactory was that illustrated in Fig. 10. The instrument was made

Fig. 10.—The shielded electrodes used in stimulating the splanchnic nerves. For description see text.

of a round rod of hard wood, beveled to a point at one end, and grooved on the two sides. Into the grooves were pressed insulated wires ending in platinum hooks, which projected beyond the beveled surface. Around the rod was placed an insulating rubber tube which was cut out so as to leave the hooks uncovered when the tube was slipped downward.

In applying the electrodes the left splanchnic nerves were first freed from their surroundings and tightly ligated as close as possible to their origin. By means of strong compression the conductivity of the nerves was destroyed central to the ligature. The electrodes were now fixed in place by thrusting the sharp end of the wooden rod into the muscles of the back. This was so done as to bring the platinum hooks a few millimeters above the nerves. With a small seeker the nerves were next gently lifted over the hooks, and then the rubber tube was slipped downward until it came in contact with the body wall. Absorbent cotton was packed about the lower end of the electrodes, to take up any fluid that might appear; and finally the belly wall was closed with spring clips. The rubber tube served to keep the platinum hooks from contact with the muscles of the back and the movable viscera, while still permitting access to the nerves which were to be stimulated. This stimulating apparatus could be quickly applied, and, once in place, needed no further attention. In some of the experiments both splanchnic nerves were stimulated in the thorax. The rubber-covered electrode proved quite as serviceable there as in the abdomen.

The current delivered to the splanchnic nerves was a rapidly interrupted induced current of such strength that no effects of spreading were noticeable. That splanchnic stimulation causes secretion of the adrenal glands has been proved in many different ways which have already been described (see p. 38).

(see p. 38).

THE EFFECTS OF SPLANCHNIC STIMULATION ON THE CONTRACTION OF FATIGUED MUSCLE

As already stated, when skeletal muscle is repeatedly stimulated by a long series of rapidly recurring electric shocks, its strong contractions gradually grow weaker

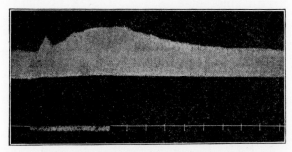

FIG. 11.—Upper record, contraction of the *tibialis anticus,* 80 times a minute, lifting a weight of 125 grams. Lower record, stimulation of the left splanchnic nerves, two minutes. Time, half minutes.

until a fairly constant condition is reached. The record then has an even top—the "fatigue level." The effect of splanchnic stimulation was tried when the muscle had been fatigued to this stage. The effect which was often obtained by stimulating the left splanchnic nerves is shown in Fig. 11. In this instance the muscle while relaxed supported no weight, and while contracting lifted a weight of 125 grams. The rate of stimulation was 80 per minute.

The muscle record shows a brief initial rise from the fatigue level, followed by a drop, and that in turn by another, prolonged rise. The maximum height of the record is 13.5 millimeters, an increase of 6 millimeters over the height recorded before splanchnic stimulation. Thus the muscle was performing for a short period 80 per cent more work than before splanchnic stimulation, and for a considerably longer period exhibited an intermediate betterment of its efficiency.

THE FIRST RISE IN THE MUSCLE RECORD

The brief first elevation in the muscle record when registered simultaneously with arterial blood pressure

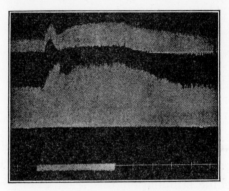

FIG. 12.—Top record, arterial blood pressure with membrane manometer. Middle record, contractions of *tibialis anticus* loaded with 125 grams and stimulated 80 times a minute. Bottom record, splanchnic stimulation, two minutes. Time, half minutes.

is observed to occur at the same time with the sharp initial rise in the blood-pressure curve (see Fig. 12). The first sharp rise in blood pressure is due to contraction of the vessels in the area of distribution of the splanchnic nerves, for it does not appear if the alimentary canal is removed, or if the celiac and the superior and inferior mesenteric arteries are ligated. The betterment of the muscular contraction is probably due directly to the better blood supply resulting from the increased pressure, for if the adrenal veins are clipped and the splanchnic nerves are stimulated, the blood pressure rises as before and at the same time there may be registered a higher contraction of the muscle.

THE PROLONGED RISE IN THE MUSCLE RECORD

As Fig. 12 shows, the initial quick uplift in the blood-pressure record is quickly checked by a drop. This rapid drop does not appear when the adrenal veins are obstructed. A similar difference in blood-pressure records has been noted before and after excision of the adrenal glands. As Elliott,[9] and as Lyman and I [10] have shown, this sharp drop after the first rise, and also the subsequent elevation of blood pressure, are the consequences of liberation of adrenal secretion into the circulation. Fig. 12 demonstrates that the prolonged rise of the muscle record begins soon after this characteristic drop in blood pressure.

If after clips have been placed on the adrenal veins so that no blood passes from them, the splanchnic nerves are stimulated, and later the clips are removed, a slight but distinct improvement in the muscular contraction occurs. As in the experiments of Young and Lehmann,[11] in which the adrenal veins were tied for a

time and then released, the release of the blood which
had been pent in these veins was quickly followed by
a rise of blood pressure. The volume of blood thus
restored to circulation was too slight to account for the
rise of pressure. In conjunction with the evidence that
splanchnic stimulation calls forth adrenal secretion,
the rise may reasonably be attributed to that secretion.
The fact should be noted, however, that in this instance the prolonged improvement in muscular contraction did not appear until the adrenal secretion
had been admitted to the general circulation.

Many variations in the improvement of activity in
fatigued muscle after splanchnic stimulation were
noted in the course of our investigation. The improvement varied in degree, as indicated by increased height
of the record. In some instances the height of contraction was doubled—a betterment by 100 per cent;
in other instances the contraction after splanchnic
stimulation was only a small fraction higher than that
preceding the stimulation; and in still other instances
there was no betterment whatever. Never, in our experience, were the augmented contractions equal to the
original strong contractions of the fresh muscle.

The improvement also varied in degree as indicated
by persistence of effect. In some instances the muscle
returned to its former working level within four or
five minutes after splanchnic stimulation ceased (see
Fig. 11); and in other cases the muscle continued working with greater efficiency for fifteen or twenty minutes after the stimulation.

THE TWO FACTORS: ARTERIAL PRESSURE AND ADRENAL
SECRETION

The evidence just presented has shown that splanchnic stimulation improves the contraction of fatigued muscle. Splanchnic stimulation, however, has two effects—it increases general arterial pressure and it also causes a discharge of adrenin from the adrenal glands. The questions now arise—Does splanchnic stimulation produce the improvement in muscular contraction by increasing the arterial blood pressure and thereby flushing the laboring muscles with fresh blood? Or does the adrenin liberated by splanchnic stimulation act itself, specifically, to improve the muscular contraction? Or may the two factors coöperate? These questions will be dealt with in the next two chapters.

REFERENCES

1. ALBANESE, *Archives Italiennes de Biologie,* xvii (1892), p. 243.
2. BOINET, *Comptes rendus de la Société de Biologie,* xlvii (1895), pp. 273, 498.
3. OLIVER and SCHAFER, *Journal of Physiology,* xviii (1895), p. 263. See also RADWANSKA, *Anzeiger der Akademie* (Krakau, 1910), pp. 728-736. Reviewed in *Zentralblatt für Biochemie und Biophysik,* xi (1911), p. 467.
4. TAKAYASU, *Quarterly Journal of Experimental Physiology,* ix (1916), p. 347.
5. DESSY and GRANDIS, *Archives Italiennes de Biologie,* xli (1904), p. 231.
6. PANELLA, *ibid.,* xlviii (1907), p. 462.
7. CANNON and NICE, *American Journal of Physiology,* xxxii (1913), p. 44.

8. BOWDITCH and WARREN, *Journal of Physiology*, vii (1886), p. 438.

9. ELLIOTT, *ibid.*, xliv (1912), p. 403.

10. CANNON and LYMAN, *American Journal of Physiology*, xxxi (1913), p. 376.

11. YOUNG and LEHMANN, *Journal of Physiology*, xxxvii (1908), p. liv.

CHAPTER VII

THE EFFECTS ON CONTRACTION OF FATIGUED MUSCLE OF VARYING THE ARTERIAL BLOOD PRESSURE

GREAT excitement is accompanied by sympathetic innervations which contract the small blood vessels, accelerate the heart rate and thus increase arterial pressure. In 100 cases studied by Gallavardin and Haour [1] the blood pressure at first, when the subjects were excited, was 25 to 35 millimeters of mercury higher than it was later when they became accustomed to the procedure. In a patient observed by Schrumpf [2] fear of a serious diagnosis was attended by a pressure 33 per cent higher than it was after the patient was reassured. In extreme pleasure, anger or fright a rise of 90 millimeters may occur. Great muscular effort, likewise, is accompanied by heightened arterial pressure and is avoided by persons likely to be injured by it. Both in excitement and in strong exertion the blood is forced in large degree from the capacious vessels of the abdomen into other parts of the body. In excitement the abdominal arteries and veins are contracted by impulses from the splanchnic nerves. In violent effort the diaphragm and the muscles of the belly wall are voluntarily and antagonistically contracted in order to stiffen the trunk as a support for the arms; and the increased abdominal pressure which

93

results forces blood out of that region and does not permit reaccumulation. The general arterial pressure in man, as McCurdy [3] has shown, may suddenly rise during extreme physical effort, from approximately 110 millimeters to 180 millimeters of mercury.

THE EFFECT OF INCREASING ARTERIAL PRESSURE

What effect the increase of arterial pressure, resulting from excitement or physical strain, may have on muscular efficiency, has received only slight consideration. Nice and I found there was need of careful study of the relations between arterial pressure and muscular ability, and, in 1913, one of my students, C. M. Gruber, undertook to make clearer these relations.

The methods of anesthesia and stimulation used by Gruber were similar to those described in the last chapter. The arterial blood pressure was registered from the right carotid or the femoral artery by means of a mercury manometer. A time marker indicating half-minute intervals was placed at the atmospheric pressure level of the manometer. And since the blood-pressure style, the writing point of the muscle lever, and the time signal were all set in a vertical line on the surface of the recording drum, at any given muscular contraction the height of blood pressure was simultaneously registered.

To increase general arterial pressure two methods were used: the spinal cord was stimulated in the neck

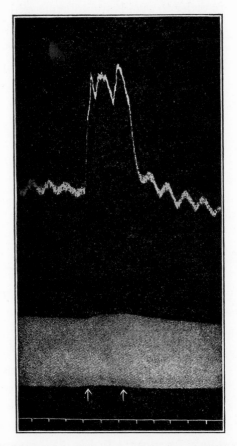

Fig. 13.—In this and four following records, the upper curve indicates the blood pressure, the middle line muscular contraction, and the lower line the time in 30 seconds (also zero blood pressure.) Between the arrows the exposed cervical spinal cord was stimulated.

region through platinum electrodes, or the left splanchnic nerves were stimulated after the left adrenal gland had been excluded from the circulation. This was done in order to avoid any influence which adrenal secretion might exert. It is assumed in these experiments that vessels supplying active muscles would be actively dilated, as Kaufmann[4] has shown, and would, therefore, in case of a general increase of blood pressure, deliver a larger volume of blood to the area they supply. The effects of increased arterial pressure are illustrated in Figs. 13, 14 and 15. In the experiment represented in Fig. 13, the rise of blood pressure was produced by stimulation of the cervical cord, and in Figs. 14 and 15 by stimulation of the left splanchnic nerves after the left adrenal gland had been tied off.

The original blood pressure in Fig. 13 was 120 millimeters of mercury. This was increased by 62 millimeters, with a rise of only 8.4 per cent in the height of contraction of the fatigued muscle.

In Fig. 14 the original blood pressure was 100 millimeters of mercury. By increasing this pressure 32 millimeters (A) there resulted a simultaneous betterment of 9.8 per cent in the height of muscular contraction. In Fig. 14 B the arterial pressure was raised 26 millimeters and the height of contraction increased correspondingly 7 per cent. In Fig. 14 C no appreciable betterment can be seen, although the blood pressure rose 18 millimeters.

In Fig. 15 the original blood pressure was low—68 millimeters of mercury. This was increased in Fig. 15 A by 18 millimeters (the same as in Fig. 14 C without effect), and there resulted an increase of 20 per cent in the height of contraction. In Fig. 15 B the pressure was raised 24 millimeters with a corresponding increase of 90 per cent in the muscular contrac-

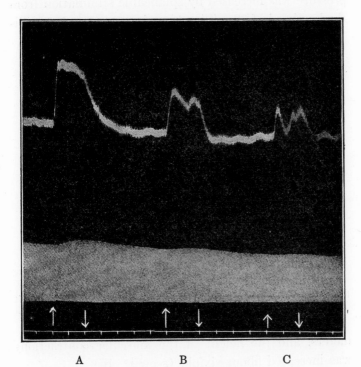

A   B   C

Fig. 14.—Stimulation of the left splanchnic nerves (left adrenal gland tied off) during the periods indicated by the arrows.

tion; and in Fig. 15 C, 30 millimeters with a betterment of 125 per cent.

Comparison of Figs. 13, 14 and 15 reveals that the improvement of contraction of fatigued muscle is much greater when the blood pressure is raised, even slightly,

from a low level, than when it is raised, perhaps to a
very marked degree, from a high level. In one of the
experiments performed by Nice and myself the arterial
pressure was increased by splanchnic stimulation from
the low level of 48 millimeters of mercury to 110 milli-

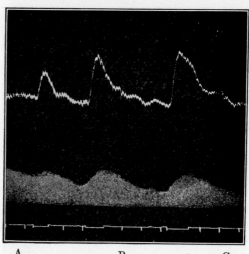

A   B   C
FIG. 15.—During the periods indicated in the time line the left
    splanchnic nerves were stimulated. The vessels of the left
    adrenal gland were tied off.

meters, and the height of the muscular contractions
was increased about sixfold (see Fig. 16).

Results confirming those described above were obtained by Gruber in a study of the effects of splanchnic
stimulation on the irritability of muscle when fatigued.
In a series of eleven observations the average value of
the barely effective stimulus (the "threshold" stimulus) had to be increased as the condition of fatigue
developed. It was increased for the nerve-muscle by

25 per cent and for the muscle by 75 per cent. The left splanchnic nerves, disconnected from the left adrenal gland, were now stimulated. The arterial pressure, which had varied between 90 and 100 millimeters of

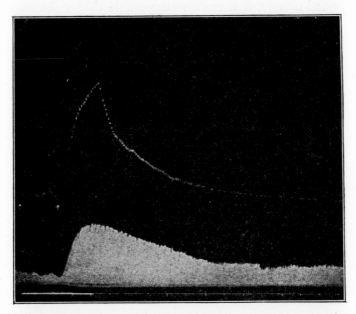

FIG. 16.—The bottom record (zero of blood pressure) shows stimulation of left splanchnics; between the arrows the pressure was kept from rising by compression of heart.

mercury, was raised at least 40 millimeters. As a result of splanchnic stimulation there was an average recovery of 42 per cent in the nerve-muscle and of 46 per cent in the muscle. The increased general blood pressure was effective, therefore, quite apart from any possible action of adrenal secretion, in largely restoring to the fatigued structures their normal irritability.

THE EFFECT OF DECREASING ARTERIAL PRESSURE

Inasmuch as an increase in arterial pressure produces an increase in the height of contraction of fatigued muscle, it is readily supposable that a decrease

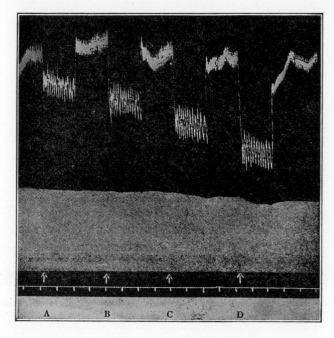

FIG. 17.—The arrows indicate the points at which the thorax began to be compressed in order to lessen the output of blood from the heart.

in the pressure would have the opposite effect. Such is the case only when the blood pressure falls below the region of 90 to 100 millimeters of mercury. Thus if the arterial pressure stands at 150 millimeters of mercury, it has to fall approximately 55 to 65 milli-

meters before causing a decrease in the height of contraction. Fig. 17 is the record of an experiment in
which the blood pressure was lowered by lessening the
output of blood from the heart by compressing the
thorax. The record shows that when the pressure was
lowered from 120 to 100 millimeters of mercury (A),
there was no appreciable decrease in the height of contraction; when lowered to 90 millimeters (B), there
resulted a decrease of 2.4 per cent; when to 80 millimeters of mercury (C), a decrease of 7 per cent; and
when to 70 millimeters (D), a decrease of 17.3 per
cent. Results similar to those represented in Fig. 17
were obtained by pulling on a string looped about the
aorta just above its iliac branches, thus lessening the
flow to the hind limbs.

The region of 90 to 100 millimeters of mercury may
therefore be regarded as the *critical region* at which a
falling blood pressure begins to be accompanied by a
concurrent lessening of the efficiency of muscular contraction, when the muscle is kept in continued activity.
It is at that region that the blood flow is dangerously
near to being inadequate.

AN EXPLANATION OF THE EFFECTS OF VARYING THE
ARTERIAL PRESSURE

How are these effects of increasing and decreasing
the arterial blood pressure most reasonably explained?
There is abundant evidence that fatigue products (e.g.,
lactic acid) accumulate in a muscle which is continu-

ously doing work, and also that these metabolites interfere with efficient contraction. As Ranke [5] long ago
demonstrated, if a muscle, deprived of circulating
blood, is fatigued to a standstill and then the circulation is restored, the muscle again responds for a short
time to stimulation, because the waste has been neu-
tralized or swept away by the fresh blood. When the
blood pressure is at its normal height for warm-blooded
animals (about 120 millimeters of mercury, see Fig.
13), the flow appears to be adequate to wash out the
depressive metabolites, at least in the single muscle
used in these experiments, because a large rise of pressure produces but little change in the fatigue level.
On the other hand, when the pressure is abnormally
low the flow is inadequate, and the waste products are
permitted to accumulate and clog the action of the
muscle. Under such circumstances a rise of pressure
has a very striking beneficial effect.

It is noteworthy that the best results of adrenin on
fatigued muscle reported by previous observers were
obtained from studies on cold-blooded animals. In
these animals the circulation is maintained normally
by an arterial pressure about one-third that of warm-
blooded animals. Injection of adrenin in an amount
which would not shut off the blood supply would, by
greatly raising the arterial pressure, markedly increase
the circulation of blood in the active muscle. In short,
the conditions in cold-blooded animals are quite like
those in the pithed mammal with an arterial pressure
of about 50 millimeters of mercury (see Fig. 16).

Under these conditions the improved circulation causes a remarkable recovery from fatigue. That notable results of adrenin on fatigue are observed in warm-blooded animals only when they are deeply anesthetized or are deprived of the medulla was claimed by Panella.[6] He apparently believed that in normal mammalian conditions adrenin has little effect because quickly destroyed, whereas in the cold-blooded animals and in mammals whose respiratory, circulatory, and thermogenic states are made similar to the cold-blooded by anesthesia or pithing, the contrary is true. In accordance with our observations on the effects of blood pressure on fatigued muscle, we would explain Panella's results not as he has done but as due to two factors. First, the efficiency of the muscle, when blood pressure is low, follows the ups and downs of pressure much more directly than when the pressure is high. And second, a given dose of adrenin always raises a low blood pressure in atonic vessels. The improvement of circulation is capable of explaining, therefore, the main results obtained in cold-blooded animals and in pithed mammals.

Oliver and Schäfer reported unusually effective contractions in muscles removed from the body after adrenal extract had been injected. As shown in Fig. 16, however, the fact that the circulation *had been* improved results in continued greater efficiency of the contracting muscle. Oliver and Schäfer's observation may perhaps be accounted for on this basis.

THE VALUE OF INCREASED ARTERIAL PRESSURE IN PAIN
AND STRONG EMOTION

As stated in a previous paragraph, there is evidence
that the vessels supplying a muscle dilate when the
muscle becomes active. And although the normal
blood pressure (about 120 millimeters of mercury) may
be able to keep adequately supplied with blood the
single muscle used in our investigation, a higher pressure might be required when more muscles are involved in activity, for a more widely spread dilation
might then reduce the pressure to the point at which
there would be insufficient circulation in active organs.
Furthermore, with many muscles active, the amount
of waste would be greatly augmented, and the need for
abundant blood supply would thereby to a like degree
be increased. For both reasons a rise of general arterial pressure would prove advantageous. The high
pressure developed in excitement and pain, therefore,
might be specially serviceable in the muscular activities which are likely to accompany excitement and
pain.

In connection with the foregoing considerations, the
action of adrenin on the distribution of blood in the
body is highly interesting. By measuring alterations
in the volume of various viscera and the limbs, Oliver
and Schäfer [7] proved that the viscera of the splanchnic area—e. g., the spleen, the kidneys, and the intestines—suffer a considerable decrease of volume when
adrenin is administered, whereas the limbs into which

the blood is forced from the splanchnic region actually increase in size. These observations were refined by Hartman [8] who found that whereas a small dose of adrenin constricts the splanchnic vessels it causes an actual dilation of the vessels of the limbs. Furthermore, Hoskins, Gunning and Berry [9] showed, and their work has been confirmed by others,[10] that with nerves intact adrenin causes active dilation of the vessels in muscles and constriction of cutaneous vessels. This evidence Gley appears to have overlooked, for he [11] has criticized the view that adrenin takes part in emotional reactions because in them the vascular effects are localized, and adrenin, he argues, must necessarily have a general effect on all vessels (except the pulmonary and coronary). The differential action of adrenin indicates differences in the degree or character of sympathetic innervations. In other words, at times of pain and excitement sympathetic discharges, probably aided by the adrenal secretion simultaneously liberated, will drive the blood out of the vegetative organs of the interior, which serve the routine needs of the body, into the skeletal muscles which have to meet by extra action the urgent demands of struggle or escape.

But there are exceptions to the general statement that by adrenin the viscera are emptied of their blood. It is well attested that addition of adrenin to the blood causes an increased flow through the beating heart. And although recent studies by Forbes and Wolff [12] have proved that cerebral vessels can be made to constrict somewhat on stimulating the cervical sympathetic nerve or on applying adrenin directly to them, there are no observations to offset the older experiments which showed that in the presence of a normally high arterial pressure adrenin affects the blood flow through the brain only slightly if at all. Conditions are similar in the lungs. Although vaso-constrictor effects can be demonstrated in the pulmo-nary vessels, they are comparatively feeble and are readily overpowered by changes in the discharge per minute through the right heart.[13] From this evidence we may infer that sympathetic impulses, though caus-ing constriction of the arteries of the abdominal vis-cera, have no effective influence on those of the pul-monary and intracranial areas and actually increase the blood supply to the heart. Thus the absolutely and immediately essential organs—those the ancients called the "tripod of life"—the heart, the lungs, the brain (as well as its instruments, the skeletal muscles)—are in times of excitement abundantly supplied with blood taken from organs of less importance in critical mo-ments. This shifting of the blood so that there is an assured adequate supply to structures essential for the preservation of the individual may reasonably be inter-preted as a fact of prime biological significance. It will be placed in its proper setting when the other evi-dence of bodily changes in pain and excitement have been presented.

REFERENCES

1. GALLAVARDIN and HAOUR, *Archives de Mal du Cœur,* v (1912), p. 81.
2. SCHRUMPF, *Deutsche medizinische Wochenschrift,* xxxvi (1910), p. 2385.
3. McCURDY, *American Journal of Physiology,* v (1901), p. 98.
4. KAUFMANN, *Archives de Physiologie,* xxiv (1892), p. 283.
5. RANKE, *Archiv für Anatomie* (1863), p. 446.
6. PANELLA, *Archives Italiennes de Biologie,* xlviii (1907), p. 462.
7. OLIVER and SCHAFER, *Journal of Physiology,* xviii (1895), p. 240.
8. HARTMAN, *American Journal of Physiology,* xxxviii (1915), p. 438.
9. HOSKINS, GUNNING and BERRY, *ibid.,* xli (1916), p. 513.
10. HARTMAN and FRASER, *ibid.,* xliv (1917), p. 353; GRUBER, *ibid.,* xlv (1918), p. 302; and PEARLMAN and VINCENT, *Endocrinology,* iii (1919), p. 121.
11. GLEY, *Revue de Médicine,* xl (1923), p. 208.
12. FORBES and WOLFF, *Archives of Neurology and Psychiatry,* xix (1928), p. 1057.
13. WIGGERS, *Physiological Reviews,* i (1921), p. 262.

CHAPTER VIII

THE SPECIFIC ROLE OF ADRENIN IN COUNTERACTING THE EFFECTS OF FATIGUE

As a muscle approaches its fatigue level, its contractions are decreased in height. Higher contractions of the muscle will again be elicited if the stimulus is increased. Although these phenomena are well known, no adequate analysis of their causes has been advanced.

A number of factors are probably operative in decreasing the height of contraction: (1) the using up of available energy-producing material; (2) the accumulation of metabolites in the fatigued muscle; (3) polarization of the nerve at the point of repeated electrical stimulation; and (4) a decrease of irritability. It may be that there are interactions between these factors within the muscle, e. g., the second may cause the fourth.

VARIATIONS OF THE THRESHOLD STIMULUS AS A MEASURE OF IRRITABILITY

The last of the factors mentioned above—the effect of fatigue on the irritability of the nerve-muscle combination, or on the muscle alone—can be tested by determining variations in the least stimulus capable of causing the slightest contraction, the so-called "threshold stimulus." As the irritability lessens, the threshold stimulus must necessarily be higher. The height of the threshold is therefore a measure of irritability. How does fatigue affect the irritability of nerve-muscle and muscle? How is the irritability of fatigued structures affected by rest? How is it influenced by adrenin or by adrenal secretion? Answers to these questions were sought in researches carried on by Gruber [1] in 1913.

THE METHOD OF DETERMINING THE THRESHOLD STIMULUS

The neuro-muscular arrangements used in these researches were in many respects similar to those already described in the account of experiments by Nice and myself. To avoid the influence of an anesthetic some of the animals were decerebrated under ether and then used as in the experiments in which urethane was the anesthetic. The nerve (the *peroneus communis*) supplying the *tibialis anticus* muscle was bared and severed; and near the cut end shielded platinum electrodes were applied. These electrodes were used in fatiguing the muscle. Between these electrodes and the muscle other platinum electrodes could be quickly applied to determine the threshold stimulus and the tissue resistance. These second electrodes were removed except when in use, and when replaced were set always in the same position. Care was taken, before replacing them, to wipe off moisture on the nerve or on the platinum points.

For determining the threshold stimulus of the muscle the skin and other overlying tissues were cut away from the *tibialis anticus* in two places about 5 centimeters apart. Through these openings platinum needle electrodes could be thrust into the muscle whenever readings were to be taken. Local polarization was avoided by reinserting the needles into fresh points on the exposed areas whenever new readings were to be taken.

The tendon of the *tibialis anticus* was attached, as in the previous experiments, by a strong thread passing about pulleys to a lever which when lifted stretched a spring. During the determination of the threshold the spring was detached from the lever, so that only the pull of the lever itself (about 15 grams) was exerted on the muscle.

The method of measuring the stimulating value of the electric current which was used in testing the threshold was that devised by E. G. Martin * then in the Harvard Laboratory—a method by which the strength of an induced electric shock is calculable in definite units. If the tissue resistance enters into the calculation these are called β units. When the threshold of the nerve-muscle was taken, the apparatus for the determination was connected with the nerve

* For a full account of Dr. Martin's method of calculating the strength of electric stimuli, see Martin, *The Measurement of Induction Shocks* (New York, 1912).

through the electrodes nearer the muscle. They were separated from the fatiguing electrodes by more than 3 centimeters, and arranged so that the kathode was next the muscle. When the threshold of the muscle was taken directly the apparatus was connected with the muscle through platinum needle electrodes thrust into it. The position of the secondary coil of the inductorium, in every case, was read by moving it away from the primary coil until the very smallest possible contraction of the muscle was obtained. Four of these readings were made, one with tissue resistance, the others with 10,000, 20,000, and 30,000 ohms additional resistance in the secondary circuit. Only break shocks were employed—the make shocks were short-circuited. Immediately after the determination of the position of the secondary coil, and before the electrodes were removed or disconnected, three readings of the tissue resistance were made. From these data four values for β were calculated.

The strength of the primary current for determining the threshold of the nerve-muscle was usually .01 ampere, but in a few cases .05 ampere was used. For normal muscle it was .05 ampere and for denervated muscle 1.0 ampere. The inductorium, which was used throughout, had a secondary resistance of 1400 ohms. This was added to the average tissue resistance in making corrections—corrections were made also for core magnetization.

THE LESSENING OF NEURO-MUSCULAR IRRITABILITY
BY FATIGUE

The threshold for the *peroneus communis* nerve in decerebrate animals varied from 0.319 to 2.96 units, with an average in sixteen experiments of 1.179.* This average is the same as that found by E. L. Porter [2] for the radial nerve in the spinal cat (i. e., with the brain removed). For animals under urethane anesthesia a higher average was obtained. In these it varied from .644 to 7.05, or an average in ten experiments of 3.081.

The threshold for the *tibialis anticus* muscle varied in the decerebrate animals from 6.75 units to 33.07, or an average in fifteen experiments of 18.8. Ten experiments were performed under urethane anesthesia and the threshold varied from 12.53 to 54.9, with an average of 29.84 β units. From these results it is evident that anesthesia notably affects the threshold.

E. L. Porter proved, by experiments carried on in the Harvard Physiological Laboratory, that the threshold of an undisturbed nerve-muscle remains constant for hours, and his observation was confirmed by Gruber (see Fig. 19). If, therefore, after fatigue, a change exists in the threshold, this change is necessarily the result of alterations set up by the fatigue process in the nerve-muscle or muscle.

After fatigue the threshold of the nerve-muscle, in sixteen decerebrate animals, increased from an average

---

* For the detailed data of these and other quantitative experiments, the reader should consult the tables in the original papers.

of 1.179 to 3.34—an increase of 183 per cent. In ten animals under urethane anesthesia the threshold after fatigue increased from a normal average of 3.08 to 9.408—an increase of 208 per cent.

An equal increase in the threshold stimulus was ob-

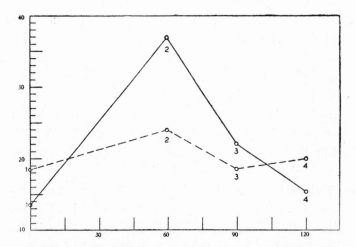

FIG. 18.—A record plotted from the data of one experiment. The time intervals in minutes are registered on the abscissa; the value of the threshold in units is registered on the ordinate. The continuous line is the record of the muscle, the broken line that of the nerve-muscle. The values for the nerve-muscle have been magnified ten times, those for the muscle are normal.

1, normal values of the threshold. 2, fatigue thresholds after one hour's work, lifting 120 grams 240 times a minute. 3 and 4, the threshold after rest.

tained from the normal muscle directly. In decerebrate animals the normal threshold of 18.8 units was increased by fatigue to 69.54, or an increase of 274 per cent. With urethane anesthesia the threshold increased from 29.849 to 66.238, or an increase of 122 per cent.

Fig. 18, plotted from the data of one of the many experiments, shows the relative heights of the threshold before and after fatigue. The correspondence of the two readings of the threshold, one from the nerve supplying the muscle and the other from the muscle directly, served as a check on the electrodes. The broken line in the figure represents the threshold (in units) of the nerve-muscle, and the continuous line that of the muscle. The threshold values of the nerve-muscle have been magnified ten times in order to bring the two records close together. In this experiment the threshold of the muscle after fatigue (i.e., at 2) is 167 per cent higher than the normal threshold (at 1), while that of the nerve-muscle after fatigue is 30.5 per cent higher than its normal.

Evidently a direct relation exists between the duration of work and the increase of threshold. For instance, the threshold is higher after a muscle is fatigued for two hours than it is at the end of the first hour. The relation between the work done and the threshold is not so clear. In some animals the thresholds were higher after 120 grams had been lifted 120 times a minute for 30 minutes than they were in others in which 200 grams had been lifted 240 times a minute for the same period. The muscle in the latter instances did almost four times as much work, yet the threshold was lower. The difference may be due to the general condition of the animal.

A few experiments were performed on animals in which the nerve supplying the muscle was cut seven to fourteen days previous to the experiment. The muscle, therefore, had within it no living nerve fibers. The average normal threshold for the denervated muscle in 6 animals was 61.28 units. As in the normal muscle, the percentage increase due to fatigue was large.

THE SLOW RESTORATION OF FATIGUED MUSCLE TO NORMAL IRRITABILITY BY REST

That rest decreases the fatigue threshold of both nerve-muscle and muscle can be seen in Fig. 18. The time taken for total recovery, however, is dependent upon the amount of work done, but this change, like that of fatigue, varies widely with different individuals. In some animals the threshold returned to normal in 15 minutes; in others, in which the same amount of work was done, it was still above normal even after 2 hours of rest. This may be due to the condition of the animals—in some the metabolites are probably eliminated more rapidly than in others. There were also variations in the rate of restoration of the normal threshold when tested on the nerve and when tested on the muscle in the same animal. In Fig. 18 (at 3) the nerve-muscle returned to normal in 30 minutes, whereas the muscle (at 4) after an hour's rest had not returned to normal by a few β units. This, however, is not typical of all nerve-muscles and muscles. The opposite condition—that in which the muscle returned to normal before the nerve-muscle—occurred in as many cases as did the condition just cited. The failure of the two tissues to alter uniformly in the same direction may be explained as due to variations in the location of the electrodes when thrust into the muscle at different times (e. g., whether near nerve filaments or not). The results from observations made on the nerve are more likely to be uniform and reliable than are those from the muscle.

The time required for the restoration of the threshold from fatigue to normal, in denervated muscles, is approximately the same as that for the normal muscle.

THE QUICK RESTORATION OF FATIGUED MUSCLE TO NORMAL IRRITABILITY BY ADRENIN

The foregoing observations showed that fatigue raises the normal threshold of a muscle, on the average, between 100 and 200 per cent (it may be increased more than 600 per cent); that this increase is dependent on the time the muscle works, but also varies with the animal; that rest, 15 minutes to 2 hours, restores the normal irritability; and that this recovery of the threshold depends upon the time given to rest, the duration of the work, and also upon the condition of the animal. The problem which was next attacked by Gruber was that of learning whether the higher contractions of fatigued muscle after splanchnic stimulation could be attributed to any influence which adrenal secretion might have in restoring the normal irritability. To gain insight into the probabilities he tried first the effects of injecting slowly into the jugular vein physiological amounts of adrenin.*

The normal threshold of the *peroneus communis* nerve varied in the animals used in this series of observations from 0.35 to 5.45 units, with an average in nine experiments of 1.3, a figure close to the 1.179 found in the earlier series on the effect of fatigue. For the *tibialis anticus* muscle, in which the nerve-endings were intact, the threshold varied from 6.75 to 49.3 units, with an average in the nine experiments of 22.2. This is slightly higher than that cited for this same muscle in the earlier series. By fatigue the threshold of the nerve-muscle was increased from an average of 1.3 to an average of 3.3 units, an increase of 154 per cent. The muscle increased from an average of 22.2 to an average of 59.6, an increase of 169 per cent. After an injection of 0.1 to 0.5 cubic centimeters of adrenin (1:100,000) the fatigue threshold was decreased *within five minutes* in the nerve-muscle from an average of 3.3 to 1.8, a recovery of 75 per cent, and in the muscle from an average of 59.6 to 42.4, a recovery of 46 per cent. To prove that this effect of adrenin is a *counteraction of the effects of fatigue,* Gruber determined the threshold for muscle and nerve-muscle in non-fatigued animals before and after adrenin injection. He found that in these cases no lowering of threshold occurred, a result in marked contrast with the pronounced and prompt

---

* The form of adrenin used in these and in other injections was fresh adrenalin made by Parke, Davis & Co.

lowering induced by this agent in muscles when fatigued.

Figs. 19 and 20, plotted from the data of two of the experiments, show the relative heights of the threshold before and after an injection of adrenin. The close correspondence of the two readings of the threshold, one from the nerve supplying the muscle, the other from the muscle directly, served to show that there was no fault in the electrodes. The continuous line in the figures represents the threshold (in units) of the muscle, the broken line that of the nerve-muscle. The threshold of the nerve-muscle is magnified 100 times in Fig. 19 and 10 times in Fig. 20. In Fig. 19 (at 2 and 4) the threshold was taken after an intravenous injection of 0.1 and 0.2 cubic centimeter of adrenin respectively.

These examples show that adrenin does not affect the threshold of the normal non-fatigued muscle when tested either on the muscle directly or on the nerve-muscle. In Fig. 19 (at 3) the observation taken after two hours of rest illustrates the constancy of the threshold under these circumstances.

In Fig. 19 the normal threshold was increased by fatigue (at 5)—the muscle had been pulling 120 times a minute for one hour on a spring having an initial tension of 120 grams—from 30.0 to 51.6 units, an increase of 72 per cent; and in the nerve-muscle from 0.62 to 0.89 units, an increase of 46 per cent. The threshold (at 6) was taken *five minutes* after injecting 0.1 cubic centimeter of adrenin (1:100.000). The

threshold of the muscle was lowered from 51.6 to 38.0
units, a recovery of 62 per cent; that of the nerve-
muscle from 0.89 to 0.79 units, a recovery of 37 per
cent. After another injection of 0.5 cubic centimeter

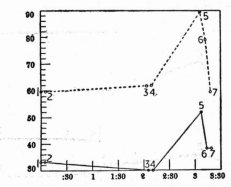

FIG. 19.—A record plotted from the data of one experiment. The
  time intervals in hours and minutes are represented on the
  abscissa; the values of the threshold in β units are represented
  on the ordinate. The continuous line is the record of the
  muscle, the broken line that of the nerve-muscle. The nerve-
  muscle record is magnified 100 times; that of the muscle is
  normal.

  1, normal threshold stimulus. *2*, threshold five minutes after
  an intravenous injection of 0.1 cubic centimeter of adrenin
  (1:100,000) without previous fatigue. *3*, threshold after a rest
  of two hours. *4*, threshold five minutes after an injection of
  0.2 cubic centimeter of adrenin (1:100,000) without previous
  fatigue. *5*, threshold after one hour's fatigue. The muscle
  contracted 120 times per minute against a spring having an
  initial tension of 120 grams. *6*, threshold five minutes after an
  injection (0.1 cubic centimeter) of adrenin (1:100,000). *7*,
  threshold five minutes after another injection of adrenin (0.5
  cubic centimeter of a 1:100,000 solution).

of adrenin the thresholds (at 7) were taken; that of
the nerve-muscle dropped to normal—0.59 units—a
recovery of 100 per cent, and that of the muscle remained unaltered—26 per cent above its normal
threshold.

In Fig. 20 the threshold (at 5) was taken five minutes after an injection of 0.1 cubic centimeter of adrenin.   The drop here was as large as that shown in
Fig. 19.   The threshold taken from the muscle directly
was lowered from 30.6 to 18 units, a recovery of 61 per

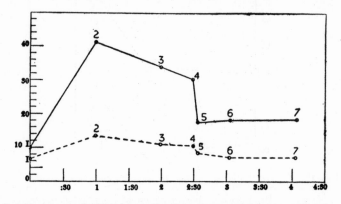

FIG. 20.—A record plotted from the data of one experiment.   The time
intervals in hours and minutes are registered on the abscissa;
the values of the threshold in units are registered on the ordinate.   The continuous line is the record of the muscle, the
broken line that of the nerve-muscle.   The record of the nerve-
muscle is magnified ten times; that of the muscle is normal.

1, normal threshold.   *2*, the threshold after one hour's fatigue.
The muscle contracted 120 times per minute against a spring
having an initial tension of 120 grams.   *3* and *4*, thresholds after
rest; after 60 minutes (*3*), and after 90 minutes (*4*).   *5*, threshold
five minutes after an injection of adrenin (0.1 cubic centimeter of
a 1:100,000 solution).   *6* and *7*, thresholds after rest; after 60
minutes (*6*), and after 90 minutes (*7*).

cent; the nerve-muscle from 1.08 to 0.87 units, a recovery of 51 per cent.   That this sudden decrease cannot be due to rest is shown in the same Figure (at 3
and 4).   These readings were made after 60 and 90
minutes' rest respectively.   The sharp decline in the
record (at 5) indicates distinctly the remarkable re-

storative influence of adrenin in promptly lowering the
high fatigue threshold of neuro-muscular irritability.

THE EVIDENCE THAT THE RESTORATIVE ACTION OF
ADRENIN IS SPECIFIC

As stated in describing the effects of arterial blood
pressure, an increase of pressure is capable of causing
a decided lowering of the neuro-muscular threshold
after fatigue. Is it not possible that adrenin produces
its beneficial effects by bettering the circulation?

Nice and I had argued that the higher contractions
of fatigued muscle, that follow stimulation or injection of adrenin, could not be wholly due to improved
blood flow through the muscle, for when by traction on
the aorta or compression of the thorax arterial pressure
in the hind legs was prevented from rising, splanchnic stimulation still caused a distinct improvement,
the initial appearance of which coincided with the
point in the blood-pressure curve at which evidence
of adrenal secretion appeared. And, furthermore, the
improvement was seen also when adrenin was given
intravenously in such weak solution (1:100,000) as to
produce a *fall* instead of a rise of arterial pressure.
Lyman and I had shown that this fall of pressure was
due to a dilator effect of adrenin. Since the blood vessels of the fatigued muscle were dilated by severance
of their nerves when the nerve trunk was cut, and, besides, as previously stated (see p. 85), were being stimulated through their nerves at a rate favorable to re-

laxation, it seemed hardly probable that adrenin could produce its beneficial effect by further dilation of the vessels and by consequent flushing of the muscle with an extra supply of blood.[3] The lowering of blood pres-

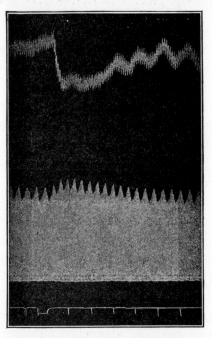

FIG. 21.—Top record, blood pressure with mercury manometer. Middle record, contractions of the *tibialis anticus* muscle 240 times per minute against a spring with an initial tension of 120 grams. Bottom record (zero blood pressure), injection of 0.4 cubic centimeter of adrenin (1:100,000). Time in half minutes.

sure had been proved to have no other effect than to impair the action of the muscle (see p. 100). Although the chances were thus against an interpretation of the beneficial influence of adrenin through action on the circulation, it was thought desirable to test the possibility by comparing its effect with that of another vasodilator—amyl nitrite.

Figs. 21 and 22 are curves obtained from the left

FIG. 22.—Top record, blood pressure with mercury manometer. Middle record, contractions of *tibialis anticus* muscle 240 per minute against a spring with an initial tension of 100 grams direct load. Bottom record (zero blood pressure), time in half minutes. The arrow indicates the point at which a solution of amyl nitrite was injected.

tibialis anticus muscle. The rate of stimulation was 240 times a minute.

The muscle in Fig. 21 contracted against a spring

having an initial tension of 120 grams, and that in Fig. 22 against an initial tension of 100 grams. In Fig. 21, at the point indicated on the base line, 0.4 cubic centimeter of adrenin (1:100,000) was injected into the left external jugular vein. There resulted a fall of 25 millimeters of mercury in the arterial pressure and a concurrent betterment of 15 per cent in the height of contraction, requiring two minutes and fifteen seconds of fatigue (about 540 contractions) before it returned to the former level. In Fig. 22, at the point indicated by the arrow, a solution of amyl nitrite was injected into the right external jugular vein. There resulted a fall of 70 millimeters of mercury in arterial pressure and a betterment of 4.1 per cent in the height of muscular contraction, requiring fifteen seconds of fatigue (about 60 contractions) to decrease the height of contraction to its former level. In neither case did the blood pressure fall below the critical region (see p. 101).*

Although the fall in arterial pressure caused by dilation of the vessels due to amyl nitrite was almost three times as great as that produced by the adrenin, yet the resultant betterment was only about one-fourth the percentage height and lasted but one-ninth

---

* In some cases after injection of amyl nitrite the normal blood pressure, which was high, dropped sharply to a point below the critical level. There resulted a primary increase in muscular contraction due to the betterment in circulation caused by the dilation of the vessels before the critical level was reached. During the time that the pressure was below the critical level the muscle contraction fell. As the blood pressure again rose to normal the muscle contraction increased coincidentally.

the time. In all cases in which these solutions caused
an *equal* fall in arterial pressure, adrenin caused higher
contractions, whereas amyl nitrite caused *no appreciable change.*

THE POINT OF ACTION OF ADRENIN IN MUSCLE

From the evidence presented in the foregoing pages
it is clear that adrenin somehow is able to bring about
a rapid recovery of normal irritability of muscle after
the irritability has been much lessened by fatigue, and
that the higher contractions of a fatigued muscle after
an injection of adrenin are due, certainly in part, to
some specific action of this substance and not wholly
to its influence on the circulation. Some of the earlier
investigators of adrenal function, notably Albanese,[4]
and also Abelous and Langlois [5] inferred from experiments on the removal of the glands that the rôle they
played in the bodily economy was that of neutralizing,
destroying or transforming toxic substances produced
in the organism as a result of muscular or nervous
work. These early observers did not distinguish between the adrenal cortex and the adrenal medulla
which alone discharges adrenin. It seemed possible
that the metabolites might have a checking or blocking influence at the junction of the nerve fibers with
the muscle fibers, and might thus, like curare, lessen
the efficiency of the nerve impulses. And Radwánska's observation [6] that the beneficial action of adrenin
is far greater when the muscle is stimulated through

its nerve than when stimulated directly, and Panella's discovery [7] that adrenin antagonizes the effect of curare, were favorable to the view that adrenin improves the contraction of fatigued muscle by lessen-

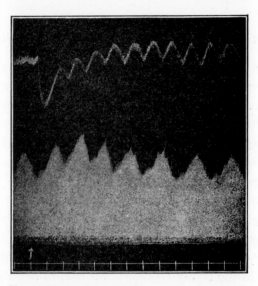

Fig. 23.—Top record, blood pressure with mercury manometer. Middle record, contractions of a denervated muscle (*tibialis anticus*) 240 per minute against a spring having an initial tension of 120 grams (*peroneus communis* nerve was cut nine days before this record was taken). Bottom record (zero blood pressure), time in half minutes. At the point indicated by an arrow 0.1 cubic centimeter of adrenin (1:100,000) was injected intravenously.

ing or removing a block established by accumulated metabolites.

The high threshold of fatigued denervated muscle, however, Gruber found was quite as promptly lowered by adrenin as was that of normal muscles stimulated through their nerves. Fig. 23 shows that the height of contraction, also, of the fatigued muscle is increased when adrenin is administered. In this experiment the left *tibialis anticus* muscle was stimulated directly by thrusting platinum needle electrodes into it. The *peroneous communis* nerve supplying the muscle had been cut and two centimeters of it removed nine days previous to the experiment. The rate of stimulation was 120 times per minute and the initial tension of the spring about 120 grams. At the point indicated by the arrow an injection of 0.1 cubic centimeter of adrenin (1:100,000) was made into a jugular vein. A fall in arterial pressure from 110 to 86 millimeters of mercury and a simultaneous betterment of 20 per cent in the height of contraction were obtained. It required four minutes of fatigue (about 480 contractions) to restore the muscle curve to its former level. Results similar to this were obtained from animals in which the nerve had been cut 7, 9, 12, 14, and 21 days. In all instances the nerve was inexcitable to strong faradic stimulation.

In Radwánska's experiments, mentioned above, the muscle was stimulated directly when the nerve endings were intact. It seems reasonable to suppose, therefore, that in all cases he was stimulating nerve tissue. Since a muscle is more irritable when stimulated through its nerve than when stimulated directly (nerve and muscle), a slight change in the irritability of the muscle by adrenin would naturally result in a greater contraction when the nerve was stimulated. Panella's results also are not inconsistent with the interpretation that the effect of adrenin is on the muscle substance rather than on the nerve endings. A method which has long been used to separate muscle functionally from nerve is that of blocking the nervous impulses by the drug curare. Gruber found that when curare is injected the threshold of the normal muscle is increased, as was to be expected from the removal of the highly efficient nervous stimulations. And also, as was to be expected on that basis, curare did not increase the threshold in a muscle in which the nerve endings had degenerated. Adrenin antagonizes curare with great promptness, decreasing the heightened threshold of a curarized muscle, in five minutes or less, in some cases to normal. From this observation it might be supposed that curare and fatigue had the same effect, and that adrenin had the single action of opposing that effect. But fatigue raises the threshold of a *curarized* muscle, and adrenin then antagonizes this fatigue. Langley [8] has argued that curare acts upon a hypothetical "receptive substance" in muscle. If so, probably curare acts upon a substance, or at a point, different from that upon which fatigue acts; for, as the foregoing evidence shows, fatigue increases the threshold of a muscle whether deprived of its nerve supply by nerve section and degeneration or by curare, whereas curare affects only the threshold of a muscle in which the nerve endings are normal. [9] And since adrenin can oppose the effects of both curare and fatigue, it may be said to have two actions, or to act on two different substances or at two different points in the muscle.

Gruber's earlier studies were extended when he and

Fellows [10] showed, in 1918, that after a muscle had been removed from the body for a long period, so that it was not responding when stimulated, the addition of a small amount of adrenalin to the salt solution which was being perfused through the vessels quickly resulted in a contraction for each stimulus. Of similar significance was the observation by Gruber and Kretschmer [11] that adrenin counteracts the fatigue induced by perfusing through a fresh muscle the fatigue products of muscular activity (lactic acid, and acid sodium and potassium phosphate). Recently Redfield and Hunt (in unpublished experiments in the Harvard Laboratory) have noted that heart muscle, worked to a standstill in an atmosphere of nitrogen, continues beating if only adrenin is added. And Campos, Lundin, Walker, and I [12] have found that when a dog has been extremely fatigued by running in a treadmill, the subcutaneous injection of a small amount of dilute adrenin has a striking influence in prolonging the animal's capacity to continue at work. In what manner adrenin may improve contraction is not yet clear. Gruber [13] noted that it markedly shortens the duration of the latent and contraction periods of a muscular contraction and induces a greater shortening of the muscle when stimulated, due possibly to increasing the irritability or liberating more available energy or acting catalytically on muscle metabolism.

In this connection the observations made by the Linton brothers and myself [14] are of interest. We found that if large muscles, which were completely disconnected from the nervous system, were made to contract vigorously so that their waste products, set free in the circulating blood, caused effects on the respiratory center, the center for adrenal secretion was also affected and adrenin was set free. Thus by its effects on the blood excessive muscular activity might help to call forth the very substance which would minimize the fatigue which would result from such activity.

The evidence adduced in the last chapter indicated that the greater "head" of arterial pressure produced during great excitement by a more rapid heart beat, and by a simultaneous constriction of the capacious splanchnic blood vessels, accompanied by dilation of the vessels in muscles, would be highly serviceable to the organism in any extensive muscular activity which the excitement might involve. By assuring an abundant flow of blood through the widened vessels of the working muscle, more oxygen would be delivered and the waste products resulting from the wear and tear in contraction would be more promptly burned or swept away and thus would be prevented from impairing the muscular efficiency. The adrenin discharge at such times would, as was pointed out, probably reënforce the effects of sympathetic impulses. The evidence presented in this chapter shows that adrenin has also another action, a very remarkable action, that of restoring to a muscle its original ability to respond to stimulation, after that has been largely lost by continued activity through a long period. What rest will do

only after an hour or more, adrenin will do in five
minutes or less.   The bearings of this striking phenomenon on the functions of the organism in times of
great need for muscular activity will be considered in
a later discussion.

REFERENCES

1. GRUBER, *American Journal of Physiology*, xxxii (1913),
   p. 437.
2. E. L. PORTER, *ibid.*, xxxi (1912), p. 149.
3. CANNON and NICE, *ibid.*, xxxii (1913), p. 55.
4. ALBANESE, *Archives Italiennes de Biologie*, xvii (1892),
   p. 239.
5. ABELOUS and LANGLOIS, *Archives de Physiologie*, xxiv
   (1892), pp. 269-278, 465-476.
6. RADWÁNSKA, *Anzeiger der Akademie* (Krakau, 1910), pp.
   728-736.   Reviewed in the *Centralblatt für Biochemie und
   Biophysik*, xi (1911), p. 467.
7. PANELLA, *Archives Italiennes de Biologie*, xlvii (1907), p. 30.
8. LANGLEY, *Proceedings of the Royal Society of London*,
   lxxviii (1906), B, p. 181.   *Journal of Physiology*, xxxiii
   1905-6), pp. 374-413.
9. See GRUBER, *American Journal of Physiology*, xxxiv (1914),
   p. 89.
10. GRUBER and FELLOWS, *ibid.*, xlvi (1918), p. 472.
11. GRUBER and KRETSCHMER, *ibid.*, xlvii (1918), pp. 178, 185.
12. CAMPOS, CANNON, LUNDIN and WALKER, *ibid.* (1929).
13. GRUBER, *Journal of Pharmacology and Experimental Thera-
    peutics*, xxiii (1924), p. 335.
14. CANNON, LINTON and LINTON, *American Journal of Phy-
    siology*, lxxi (1924), p. 153.

CHAPTER IX

THE HASTENING OF COAGULATION OF BLOOD
BY ADRENIN

THE primary value of blood to the body must have been one of the earliest observations of reasoning beings. When we consider the variety of fundamental services which this circulating fluid performs—the conveyance of food and oxygen to all the tissues, the removal of waste, the delivery of the internal secretions, the protection of the body against toxins and bacterial invasion, and the distribution of heat from active to inactive regions—the view of the ancient Hebrews that the "life of the flesh is in the blood" is well justified. It is naturally of the utmost importance that this precious fluid shall be safeguarded against loss. And its property of turning to a jelly soon after escaping from its natural channels assures a closure of the opening through which the escape occurred, and thus protection of the body from further bleeding. The slight evidence that adrenin hastens the clotting process has already been hinted at. When we found that adrenin is set free in pain and intense emotion, it seemed possible that there might exist in the body an arrangement for making doubly sure the assurance against loss of blood, a process that might nicely play its rôle precisely when the greatest need for it would be likely to arise.

It was in 1903, while tracing in dogs the rise and fall of sugar in the blood after administering adrenin, that Vosburgh and Richards[1] first noted that simultaneously with the increase of blood sugar there occurred more rapid coagulation. In some cases the diminution was as much as four-fifths the coagulation time of the control. Since this result was obtained by painting "adrenalin" on the pancreas, as well as by injecting it into the abdominal cavity, they concluded that "the phenomenon appears to be due to the application of adrenalin to the pancreas." Six years later, during a study of the effect of adrenalin on internal hemorrhage, Wiggers[2] examined incidentally the evidence presented by Vosburgh and Richards, and after many tests on five dogs found "never the slightest indication that adrenalin, either when injected or added to the blood, appreciably hastened the coagulation process." In 1911 von den Velden[3] reported that adrenin (about 0.007 milligram per kilo of body weight) decreased the coagulation time in man about one-half—an effect appearing 11 minutes after administration by mouth, and 85 minutes after subcutaneous injection. He affirmed also, but without describing the conditions or giving figures, that adrenin decreases coagulation time *in vitro*. He did not attribute the coagulative effect of adrenin in patients to this direct action on the blood, however, but to vasoconstriction disturbing the normal circulation and thereby the normal equilibrium between blood and tissue. In consequence, the tissue juices with their coagulative prop-

erties enter the blood, so he assumed. In support of
this theory he offered his observation that coagulation
time is decreased after the mucous membrane of the
nose has been rendered anemic by adrenin pledgets.
Von den Velden's claim [3] for adrenin given by mouth
was subjected to a single test on man by Dale and
Laidlaw,[4] but their result was completely negative.

The importance of Vosburgh and Richards' observation, the thoroughly discordant testimony of later
investigators, as well as the meager and incidental nature of all the evidence that has been adduced either
for or against the acceleration of clotting by adrenin
made desirable a further study of this matter.
Especially was this further study desirable because of
the discharge of adrenin into the blood in pain and
emotional excitement. Accordingly, in 1914, Gray and
I [5] undertook an investigation of the question. In
doing so we employed cats as subjects. Usually they
were quickly decerebrated under ether, and then continuance of the drug became unnecessary. Body temperature was maintained by means of an electric heating pad. Respiration proceeded normally except in a
few instances (in which, presumably, there was hemorrhage into the medulla), when artificial respiration had
to be given.

THE GRAPHIC METHOD OF MEASURING THE COAGULATION TIME

In order to avoid, so far as possible, the personal element in determining when the blood was clotted, the

blood was made to record its own clotting. The instrument by means of which this was done was the graphic coagulometer devised by Mendenhall and myself,[6] and illustrated diagrammatically in Fig. 24. It consists essentially of a light aluminum lever with the long arm nearly counterpoised by a weight W. The long arm is prevented from falling by a support S, and is prevented from rising by a horizontal right-angled rod reaching over the lever at R^1 and fixed into the

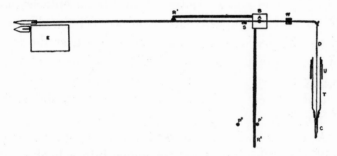

Fig. 24.—Diagram of the graphic coagulometer. The cannula at the right rests in a water bath not shown in this diagram. For further description see text.

block B which turns on the axis A. Into the same block is fixed the vertical rod R^2. When this rod is moved from the post P^1, against which it is held by the weight of the horizontal rod R^1, towards the other post P^2, the check on the long arm of the lever is lifted, and if the short arm is heavier, the long arm will then rise.

The cannula C, into which the blood is received, is two centimeters in total length and slightly more than two millimeters in internal diameter. It is attached by a short piece of rubber tubing to the tapered glass tube T, 5 centimeters long and 5 millimeters in internal diameter. The upper end of this tube is surrounded by another piece of rubber which supports the tube when it is slid into the U-shaped support U, fixed directly below the end of the short arm of the lever.

By drawing the cannulas from a single piece of glass tubing and by making the distance from shoulder to upper end about twelve millimeters, receptacles of fairly uniform capacity are assured. All the dimensions, the reach of the rubber connection over the top of the cannula (2-3 millimeters), the distance of the upper rubber ring from the lower end of the glass chamber (4 centimeters), etc., were as nearly standard as possible.

A copper wire D, 8 centimeters long and 0.6 millimeters in diameter, bent above into a hook and below into a small ring slightly less than two millimeters in diameter, is hung in a depression at the end of the short arm of the lever. The small ring then rests in the upper part of the cannula (see Fig. 24). The weight of the copper wire makes the short arm of the lever heavier than the long arm by 30 milligrams, when the delicate writing point is moving over a lightly smoked drum. Half a dozen of these standard wires are needed.

For accurate determination of the coagulation time Addis [7] has defined the following conditions as essential:

1. The blood must always be obtained under the same conditions.

2. Estimates must all be made at the same temperature.

3. The blood must always come in contact with the same amount and kind of foreign material.

4. The end point must be clear and definite and must always indicate the same degree of coagulation.

The precautions taken to fulfill these conditions were as follows:

1. *Drawing the blood.*—The blood was taken from the femoral artery in the groin. The artery (usually the right) was laid bare and freed from surrounding tissue. A narrow artery clip, with each limb enclosed in soft rubber tubing (to prevent injury of the tissues), and with its spring exerting gentle pressure, was placed on the artery immediately below the deep femoral branch, thus allowing no blood to stagnate above the clip. Between the clip and a ligature applied about 1.5 centimeters below, an opening was made. The blood was carefully milked out of the vessel between a blunt dissector moved beneath, and a small forceps, twisted into a pinch of absorbent cotton, moved above.

The cannula, cleaned in water, alcohol, and ether, was set in the rubber connection of the glass tube; the point of the cannula was then lubricated with vaseline and slipped into the artery. The pressure of the clip on the artery was next very slightly released and blood was allowed to flow into the cannula up to the lower border of the rubber connection. Only a good-sized

drop of blood was needed. Sometimes the blood ran
one or two millimeters above or below, but without
appreciably changing the result. Since the clip was
situated on the femoral immediately below a branch in
which the circulation persisted, *the blood received in
the cannula was always fresh from the moving stream.*
As soon as the clip gripped the artery again, the cannula was slipped out. A helper then promptly milked
the vessel in the manner described above, and covered
it with a pad of absorbent cotton smeared with vaseline
to prevent drying. Thereby blood was not permitted
to stagnate; and when a new sample was to be taken,
the vessel was clean and ready for use.

The tip of the cannula was at once plugged by
plunging it into a flat mound of plasticine about three
millimeters high. It was drawn off sidewise lest the
plasticine plug be pulled out again. One of the copper
wires D was now slid into the tube and cannula, the
tube slipped into the U-support, and the wire lifted
and hung on the lever. This procedure, from the moment blood began to flow until the wire was hung,
consumed usually about twenty seconds.

2. *Uniform temperature.*—Under the U-support was
placed a large water bath, in which the cannula and
the tapering part of the tube were submerged. A
thermometer was fixed to the U-support so that the
bulb came near the cannula in the bath. The water
was kept within a degree of 25° C. This temperature
was chosen for several reasons. (*a*) The cannula has
room temperature and rapidly cools the small volume

of blood that enters it. To heat blood and cannula to body temperature would take time. A bath near room temperature, therefore, seemed preferable to one near body temperature. (b) The test of clotting was conveniently made at intervals of a half-minute, and if the clotting process were hastened by higher temperatures, this interval would become relatively less exact. (c) A temperature of 25° C. rather than lower was selected because, as Dale and Laidlaw [8] have shown, the coagulation time is much slower for a given change in temperature below 25° than for the same change above. And with slowing of the process the end point, when the determination depends on supporting a weight, is less likely to be sharp. (d) The researches undertaken with use of this coagulometer were concerned with factors hastening the process. For that reason and for reason (b) a long rather than a short coagulation time for normal conditions was desirable.

3. *Uniformity in the amount and kind of contact with foreign surface.*—The capacity of the cannulas was fairly uniform, as stated above; the amount received in them was fairly constant; and the wire hanging in the blood presented approximately the same surface in different observations.

A further condition for insuring consistent treatment of the blood in different cases was that of making the tests for coagulation always at the same intervals. Below the writing point of the lever was set an electromagnetic signal *E,* which recorded half-minutes. At the moment a record was made by the signal (see first

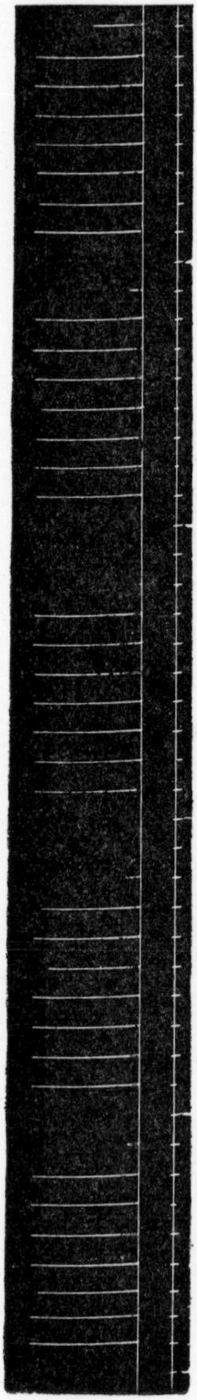

Fig. 25.—Record (reduced two-fifths) of five successive tests of coagulation, with the animal in a uniform condition. The lower line records intervals of 30 seconds. The marks below the time record indicate the moments when the blood samples were drawn.

signal mark, Fig. 25) the clip on the artery was opened, the blood taken, and the process thus begun. In about twenty seconds the cannula was suspended in the water bath and the wire was hanging on the lever. At the next record by the signal and at every subsequent record the vertical rod R^2 was pushed with the index finger from post P^1 to post P^2 and allowed to move back. This motion was uniform and lasted about one second. The check R^1 on the long arm of the lever was thus raised, and as the wire sank in the blood the writing point rose, recording that coagulation had not taken place (see Fig. 25).

4. *Definite end point.*—As soon as the blood clotted, the weight of 30 milligrams was supported, and the failure of the lever to rise to the former height in the regular time allowed, recorded that the change had occurred.

Very rarely the swing of the lever would be checked for a moment and would then begin to move rapidly, indicating that a strand of fibrin had formed but not sufficiently strong to support the weight, and that when the strand broke, the weight quickly sank in the blood. If this occurred, the next record almost always was the short line, which signified that the weight was well supported.

A very slight strand of fibrin was able to prevent the weight from dropping, though at different times the amount of support differed, as shown by the varying length of the final lines (compare first and last series, Fig. 25). These variations are probably a rough indication of the degree of coagulation. In our experiments, however, the length of the final line was disregarded, and merely the fact that the lever failed to swing through its usual distance was taken as evidence of a clot, and the consequent short record was taken as the end point.

As soon as this end point was registered, the tube. wire and cannula were lifted out of the bath; the cannula was then separated from the tube and pulled away from the wire. The clot was thus disclosed, confirming the graphic record.

The method, at least when used at half-minute intervals, did not reveal in all instances the same degree of clotting. Usually, when the process was very rapid, the revealed clot was a thick jelly; whereas, when the process was slow, a strand of fibrin or at most a small amount of jelly was found. This difference in the *degree* of coagulation introduced, of course, an element of inexactness. In our experiments, however, this in-exactness was unfavorable to the result we were seek-ing for, i. e., the acceleration of the process—because the jelly is a later stage than the fibrin strand; and since we nevertheless obtained good evidence of ac-celeration, we did not in these experiments attempt to determine more accurately differences in the stage of the clotting process.

5. *Cleaning of apparatus.*—After the wire was re-moved from the tube, the clot attached to its ring-tip was carefully brushed away under cool running water. Under the running water, also, a trimmed feather was introduced into the cannula and the tube to push out the plasticine and to wash out the blood. Wire, can-nula and tube were then dropped into a beaker receiv-ing running hot water (about 80° C.) and there al-lowed to remain for about five minutes. On removal from this the parts were shaken free of water, passed through 95 per cent alcohol and again shaken free, passed through ether and let dry.

By having a half-dozen cannulas and wires of stand-ard size, it was possible to save trouble by cleaning a number at one time.

Not infrequently the first few samples of blood taken from an animal showed rapid or somewhat irregular rates of clotting. Some causes for these initial varia-tions will be presented in following pages. The fairly uniform rate of clotting in any individual after the initial stage varied in twenty-one different animals from an average of 3 to an average of 10.6 minutes, with a combined average of 5.9 minutes. The conditions for these variations among the individuals have not been wholly determined.

THE EFFECTS OF SUBCUTANEOUS INJECTIONS OF ADRENIN

The first observations were of this class.

October 27. A cat weighing about 3 kilos was given 3 cubic centimeters of adrenin 1:1,000, i. e., 1 milligram per kilo, under the skin. The animal, in this instance, was kept in uniform ether anesthesia. Following is a record showing when blood was taken, and the coagulation time in each instance:

2:56	injection made		*3:27*	3.5	minutes
:59	6	minutes	*:44*	2	"
3:07	5.5	"	*:55*	2.5	"
:13	5	"	*4:07*	3	"
:20	6.5	"	*:20*	2	"

Average 5.7 minutes   Average 2.6 minutes

4:44	6	minutes
5:00	4.5	"
5:50	5	"

Average 5.2 minutes

In this case the coagulation time remained at its usual level for about twenty minutes after the subcutaneous injection.* Thereafter for about an hour the

---

* This period is longer than is expected after the subcutaneous injection of any drug. As will be shown later, *strong* doses of adrenin, if injected rapidly, may not at first shorten the clotting process. Probably in some instances of subcutaneous injection of these strong doses, the drug enters the circulation more rapidly than in others and in consequence coagulation is not at first accelerated.

coagulation time averaged 45 per cent of its previous duration. And widely separated tests made during the following hour indicated that approximately the initial rate of clotting had been regained.

The rather long period (nearly thirty minutes), in the case just cited, between the injection and the first appearance of rapid clotting was not the rule. As the following figures show, the coagulation time may become shortened quite promptly after subcutaneous injection.

October 29

3:30	5.5 minutes	*3:53*	4	minutes
:36	5.5 "	*4:01*	3.5	"
:44	adrenin, 3 cubic cen-	*:08*	3.5	"
	timeters, 1:1,000, in-	*:16*	4.5	"
	jected subcutaneously	*:23*	5	"
:46	5.5 minutes	*:30*	5.5	"

In this case nine minutes after the injection the change in the rate of clotting had begun, and it continued more rapid for the subsequent half-hour.

We did not attempt to find the minimal *subcutaneous* dose which would shorten clotting. A dose of 0.01 milligram per kilo, however, has proved effective, as shown by the following figures:

February 3

11:34	10 minutes	*:55*	10 minutes
:45	9 "	*12:06*	7 "
:50 to :52		*:14*	4 "
	adrenin, 2.8 cubic	*:19*	5.5 "
	c e n t i m e t e rs,		
	1:100,000, injected	*:31*	6 "
	under skin of		
	groin in cat weigh-	*:37*	7 "
	ing 2.8 kilos	*:45*	9 "

As will be shown later, the dose in this instance was ten times the minimal effective *intravenous* dose.   On the basis of these figures, less than a milligram of adrenin given subcutaneously would be necessary to shorten clotting to a marked degree in a man of average weight (70 kilograms).

Not many observations were made by us on the effects of adrenin administered subcutaneously.   The amount reaching the vascular system and the rate of its entrance into the blood could be so much more accurately controlled by intravenous than by subcutaneous introduction that most of our attention was devoted to the former method.

THE EFFECTS OF INTRAVENOUS INJECTIONS

In this procedure a glass cannula was fastened in one of the external jugular veins and filled with the same solution as that to be injected.   A short rubber tube was attached and tightly clamped close to the glass. Later, for the injection, the syringe needle was inserted through the rubber and into the fluid in the cannula, the clip on the vein was removed, and the injection made.

The solutions employed intravenously were adrenin 1:10,000, 1:50,000, and 1:100,000, in distilled water.

The smallest amount which produced any change in clotting time was 0.1 cubic centimeter of a dilution of 1:100,000 in a cat weighing 2 kilos, a dose of 0.0005 milligram per kilo.   Four tests previous to the injection averaged 5 minutes, and none was shorter than 4

minutes. Immediately after the injection the time was
2 minutes, but at the next test the effect had disappeared. Doubling the dose in the same cat—i. e., giving
0.2 cubic centimeter (0.001 milligram per kilo)—
shortened the coagulation time for about forty minutes:

December 23

10:30	4	minutes	10:53	3.5	minutes
:35	4	"	11:00	1.5	"
:41	4	"	:05	1.5	"
:46	adrenin, 0.001		:10	3	"
	milligram per kilo		:15	2	"
:47	2.5 minutes		:20	4	"
:50	3 "		:26	4.5	"
			:31	5	"

From 10:47, immediately after the second injection,
till 11:20 the average time for clotting was 2.5 minutes,
whereas both before and after this period the time was
4 minutes or longer. At 11:00 o'clock and 11:05, when
the end point was reached in 1.5 minutes (a reduction
of 63 per cent), a thick jelly was found on examining
the cannula. The changes in clotting time in this case
are represented graphically in Fig. 26.

In another case a dose of 0.0005 milligram per kilo
failed to produce any change, but 0.001 milligram per
kilo (0.28 cubic centimeter of adrenin, 1:100,000, given
a cat weighing 2.8 kilos) brought a sharp decline in the
record, as follows:

January 9

11:32	6	minutes	11:48	5.5	minutes
:40	6	"	:55	4	"
:47	adrenin, 0.001		12:00	5.5	"
	milligram per kilo		:06	7	"

In these instances the animals were decerebrated.
For decerebrate cats, the least amount of adrenin, intravenously, needed to produce shortening of coagulation time is approximately 0.001 milligram per kilo.

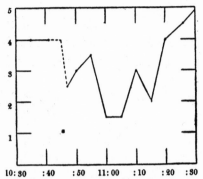

FIG. 26.—Shortening of coagulation time after injection of adrenin,
0.2 cubic centimeter, 1:100,000, (0.001 milligram per kilo), at
10:46. In this and following Figures a scale for coagulation
time is given in minutes at the left.

In the above cases rapid clotting was manifest directly after minute doses. Larger doses, however, may
produce primarily not faster clotting but slower, and
that may be followed in turn by a much shorter coagulation time. The figures below present such an instance:

November 25

2:36	3	minutes	*3:00*	2.5	minutes
:40	3	"	:03	1.5	"
:43	adrenin, 0.5 cubic		:05	1.5	"
	centimeter, 1:10,000		:07	2.5	"
:44	4	minutes	:10	1.5	"
:49	3.5	"	:14	1.5	"
:53	1.5	"	:16	2.5	"
:55	1.5	"	:19	3	"
:58	2	"	:23	3	"
			:30	3	"

This unexpected primary increase of coagulation time, lasting at least six minutes, is in striking contrast to the later remarkable shortening of the process from 3 to an average of 1.7 minutes for more than twenty minutes (see Fig. 27, A).

If a strong solution, i. e., 1:10,000, is injected rapidly, the process may be prolonged as above, but not followed as above by shortening, thus:

November 28

9:59	3	minutes	10:14	3.5	minutes
10:03	3	"	:18	3.5	"
:08	adrenin, 0.5 cubic		:22	3.5	"
	centimeter, 1:10,-		:26	3	"
	000		:29	3	"
:10	3	minutes	:33	3	"

There was in this case no decrease in coagulation time at any test for a half-hour after the injection, but instead a lengthening (see Fig. 27, B). Howell [9] has reported the interesting observation that repeated massive doses of adrenin given to dogs may so greatly retard coagulation that the animals may be said to be hæmophilic. These two instances show that on coagulation large doses have the contrary effect to small, just as Hoskins [10] showed was true for intestinal smooth muscle and Lyman and I [11] showed was true for arterial blood pressure.

In a few experiments the brain and the cord to midthorax were destroyed through the orbit. Artificial respiration then maintained the animal in uniform condition. Under these circumstances, adrenin intravenously had more lasting effects than when given to the usual decerebrate animals with intact cord. Fig. 28 illustrates such a case. For thirty minutes before injection the clotting time averaged 5.4 minutes. Then, about ten minutes after one cubic centimeter of adrenin, 1:50,000, had been slowly injected, clotting began to quicken; during the next twenty minutes the average was 3.4 minutes, and during the following forty-five

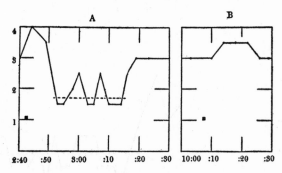

Fig. 27.—*A*, primary lengthening followed by shortening of the coagulation time when adrenin, 0.5 cubic centimeter 1:10,000 (0.05 milligram), was injected slowly at 2:43. *B*, lengthening of the coagulation time without shortening when the same dose was injected rapidly at 10:08.

minutes the average was 1.9 minutes—only 35 per cent as long as it had been before the injection.

In another case in which the brain and upper cord were similarly destroyed, the clotting time, which for a half-hour had averaged 3.9 minutes, was reduced by one cubic centimeter of adrenin, 1:100,000, to an average for the next hour and forty minutes of 2.3 minutes, with 1.5 and 3 minutes as extremes. During the first forty minutes of this period of one hour and forty minutes of rapid clotting all of eight tests except two

showed a coagulation time of two minutes or less. The
explanation of this persistent rapid clotting in animals
with spinal cord pithed is not yet clear.

As indicated in Figs. 26, 27 and 28, the records of
coagulation show oscillations. Some of these ups and
downs are, of course, within the limits of error of the

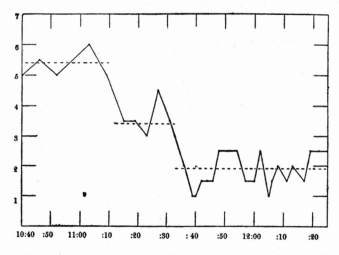

FIG. 28.—Persistent shortening of the coagulation time after injecting
(in an animal with brain and upper cord pithed) adrenin, 1
cubic centimeter, 1:50,000 (0.02 milligram), at 11:01-02. The
dash lines represent averages.

method, but in our experience they have occurred so
characteristically after injection of adrenin, and so
often have appeared in a rough rhythm, that they have
given the impression of being real accompaniments of
faster clotting. It may be that two factors are operating, one tending to hasten, the other to retard the
process, and that the equilibrium disturbed by adrenin

is recovered only after interaction to and fro between the two factors.

The oscillations in coagulation time after the injections suggest that clotting might vary with changes in blood pressure, for that also commonly oscillates after a dose of adrenin (e. g., Fig. 23). Simultaneous recording of blood pressure and determining of coagulation time have revealed that each may vary without corresponding variation in the other. Within ordinary limits, therefore, changes of blood pressure do not change the rate of clotting.

THE HASTENING OF COAGULATION BY ADRENIN NOT A DIRECT EFFECT ON THE BLOOD

As previously stated, von den Velden has contended that shortening of coagulation time by adrenin is due to exudation of tissue juices resulting from vasoconstriction. The amount of adrenin which produces markedly faster clotting in the cat is approximately 0.001 milligram per kilo. As Lyman and I [12] showed, however, this amount when injected slowly, as in the present experiments, results in brief vasodilation rather than vasoconstriction. Von den Velden's explanation can therefore not be applied to these experiments.

He has claimed, furthermore, that adrenin added to blood *in vitro* makes it clot more rapidly, but, as already noted, he gives no account of the conditions of his experiments and no figures. It is impossible, therefore, to criticize them. His claim, however, is contrary to Wiggers's [13] earlier observations that blood with added adrenin coagulated no more quickly than blood with an equal amount of added physiological salt solution. Also contrary to this claim are the following two experiments which we performed: (1) Ligatures were tied around the aorta and inferior vena cava immediately above the diaphragm, and thus the circulation was confined almost completely to the anterior part of the animal. Indeed, since the posterior part ceases to function in the absence of blood supply, the preparation may be called an "anterior animal." When such a preparation was made and 0.5 cubic centimeter of adrenin, 1:100,000 (half the usual dose, because, roughly, half an animal), was injected slowly into one of the jugulars, coagulation was not shortened. Whereas for a half-hour before the injection the clotting time averaged 4.6 minutes, for an hour thereafter the average was 5.3 minutes—a prolongation which may have been due, not to any influence of adrenin, but to failure of the blood to circulate through the intestines and liver.[14] In another experiment after the gastro-intestinal canal and liver had been removed from the animal, the average time for coagulation during twenty-five minutes before injecting adrenin (0.23 cubic centimeter, 1:100,000, in an animal weighing originally 2.3 kilos) was 5.5 minutes, and during forty minutes after the injection it was 6.8 minutes, with no case shorter than 6 minutes. In the absence of circulation through the abdominal viscera, therefore, adrenin fails to shorten the clotting time. (2) The cannulas

were filled with adrenin, 1:1,000, and emptied just before being introduced into the artery. The small
amount of adrenin left on the walls was thus automatically mixed with the drawn blood. Alternate
observations with these cannulas wet by adrenin and
with the usual dry cannulas showed no noteworthy
distinction.

February 19

2:21	6	minutes,	with	usual	cannula
:30	6.5	"	"	"	"
:36	6.5	"	"	adrenin	"
:49	6	"	"	"	"
:56	7	"	"	usual	"
3:04	6	"	"	adrenin	"

The results of these experiments have made it impossible for us to concede either of von den Velden's
claims, i. e., that clotting occurs faster because adrenin
is added to the blood, or because adrenin by producing
vasoconstriction causes tissues to exude coagulant
juices.

Vosburgh and Richards found that coagulation became more rapid as the blood sugar increased. Conceivably faster clotting might result from this higher
percentage of blood sugar. Against this assumption,
however, is the fact that clotting is greatly accelerated
by 0.001 milligram adrenin per kilo of body weight,
much less than the dose necessary to increase the sugar
content of the blood.[15] And furthermore, when dextrose (3 cubic centimeters of a 10 per cent solution) is
added to the blood of an anterior animal, making the
blood sugar roughly 0.3 per cent, the coagulation time

is not markedly reduced. Adrenin appears to act, therefore, in some other way than by increasing blood sugar.

Since adrenin makes the blood clot much faster than normally in the intact animal, and fails to have this effect when the circulation is confined to the anterior animal, the inference is justified that in the small doses here employed adrenin produces its remarkable effects, not directly on the blood itself, not through change in the extensive neuro-muscular, bony, or surface tissues of the body, but through some organ in the abdomen.

That exclusion of the liver from the bodily economy, by ligature of its vessels or by phosphorus poisoning, will result in great lengthening of the coagulation time has been clearly shown. The liver, therefore, seems to furnish continuously to the blood a factor in the clotting process which is being continuously destroyed in the body. It is not unlikely that adrenin makes the blood clot more rapidly by stimulating the liver to discharge this factor in greater abundance. From Grabfield's [16] evidence it would appear that the factor in question is prothrombin, for he found that the administration of small doses of adrenin induced an increase of that element in the group which coöperates in forming the clot, without markedly affecting other elements, i. e., antithrombin and fibrinogen.

The general results detailed in the foregoing pages have had confirmation in the researches of various investigators. In 1922, Takasaki [17] reported that he had found invariably a shortening of the coagulation time of the blood of rabbits after subcutaneous injection of adrenin, and in 1925 Hirayama [18] found that intravenous doses had the same effect in most cases unless the doses were too small or too large. La Barre [19] studied the clotting of blood plasma to which calcium was restored after it had been removed by an oxalate solution; the intravenous injection of adrenin in "moderate" doses accelerated the clotting, whereas large doses retarded it. Furthermore Hartman [20] and also Mills, Necheles and Chu [21] have incidentally noted the same effect—a faster coagulation when natural conditions (e. g., exercise) set free adrenin in the body or when adrenin is injected subcutaneously. This concordance of testimony warrants the conclusion that adrenin is an agent which, acting in the organism, induces faster clotting of blood.

REFERENCES

1. VOSBURGH and RICHARDS, *American Journal of Physiology*, ix (1903), p. 39.
2. WIGGERS, *Archives of Internal Medicine*, iii (1909), p. 152.
3. VON DEN VELDEN, *Münchener medizinische Wochenschrift*, lviii (1911), p. 187.
4. DALE and LAIDLAW, *Journal of Pathology and Bacteriology*, xvi (1912), p. 362.
5. CANNON and GRAY, *American Journal of Physiology*, xxxiv (1914), p. 321.
6. CANNON and MENDENHALL, *ibid.*, xxxiv (1914), p. 225.
7. ADDIS, *Quarterly Journal of Experimental Physiology*, i (1908), p. 314.
8. DALE and LAIDLAW, *op. cit.*, p. 359.
9. HOWELL, *American Journal of Physiology*, xxxiii (1914), p. xiv.
10. HOSKINS, *ibid.*, xxix (1912), p. 365.

11. CANNON and LYMAN, *ibid.*, xxxi (1913), p. 376.
12. CANNON and LYMAN, *ibid.*, p. 381.
13. WIGGERS, *op. cit.*, p. 152.
14. See PAVLOV, *Archiv für Physiologie* (1887), p. 458. BOHR, *Centralblatt für Physiologie*, ii (1888), p. 263. MEEK, *American Journal of Physiologie*, xxx (1912), p. 173. GRAY and LUNT, *ibid.*, xxxiv (1914), p. 332.
15. CANNON, *ibid.*, xxxiii (1914), p. 396.
16. GRABFIELD, *ibid.*, xlii (1917), p. 46.
17. TAKASAKI, *Mitteilungen aus der medizinischen Fakultät der kaiserlichen Universität zu Tokyo*, xxx (1922-23), p. 315.
18. HIRAYAMA, *Tohoku Journal of Experimental Medicine*, vi (1925), p. 160.
19. LA BARRE, *Archives Internationelles de Physiologie*, xxv (1925), p. 205.
20. HARTMAN, *American Journal of Physiology*, lxxx (1927), p. 716.
21. MILLS, NECHELES and CHU, *Chinese Journal of Physiology*, ii (1928), p. 219.

CHAPTER X

THE HASTENING OF COAGULATION OF BLOOD IN PAIN AND GREAT EMOTION

In the foregoing chapter evidence was presented that the intravenous injection of minute amounts of adrenin hastens the clotting of blood. The doses used lay between the ordinary discharge under experimental conditions and the increased discharge resulting from afferent stimulation,[1] and may therefore be regarded as physiological. Since injected adrenin is capable of shortening the coagulation time, may not the increased secretion of the adrenals likewise have that effect? The answer to this question was the object of an investigation by W. L. Mendenhall and myself.[2]

The blood was taken and its coagulation was recorded graphically in the manner already described. In some instances the cats were etherized, in others they were anesthetized with urethane, or were decerebrated. The splanchnic nerves always were stimulated after being cut away from connection with the spinal cord. Sometimes the nerves were isolated unilaterally in the abdomen; sometimes, in order to avoid manipulation of the abdominal viscera, they were isolated in the thorax and stimulated singly or together. A tetanizing current was used, barely perceptible on the tongue and too weak to cause by spreading any contraction of skeletal muscles.

COAGULATION HASTENED BY SPLANCHNIC STIMULATION

That splanchnic stimulation accelerates the clotting of blood, and that the effects vary in different animals, are facts illustrated in the following cases:

October 25.—A cat was etherized and maintained in uniform ether anesthesia. After forty minutes of preliminary observation the left splanchnic nerves were stimulated in the abdomen. Following are the figures which show the effects on the coagulation time:

3:00	4	minutes	*4:03*	2.5	minutes
:07	5.5	"	*:07*	2.5	"
:14	4	"	*:11*	3	"
:32	4.5	"	*:16*	2	"
:39 to :40		stimulation of	*:20*	1.5	"
		left splanchnic	*:23*	4	"
:42	5	minutes	*:29*	5.5	"
:49	5	"	*:40*	5.5	"
:56	2	"	*:50*	5	"
4:00	1	"			

In this instance at least ten minutes elapsed between the end of stimulation and the beginning of faster clotting. The period of faster clotting, however, lasted for about a half-hour, during which the coagulation time average 2.1 minutes, only 43 per cent of the previous average of 4.8 minutes. It is noteworthy that the curve (see Fig. 29), while lower, shows oscillations not unlike those which follow injection of adrenin (see p. 150).

The primary delay of the effect is not always, indeed it is not commonly, present:

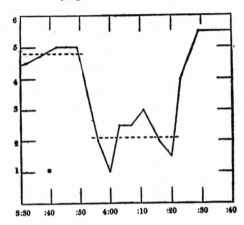

FIG. 29.—Shortening of coagulation time after stimulation of the left splanchnic nerves, 3:39–40.

November 6.—A cat was anesthetized (1:40 P.M.) with urethane, and later (3:05) its brain was pithed. The following observations on the coagulation time show the prompt effect of splanchnic stimulation:

3:36 7   minutes
  :46 6   "
4:02 to :05 stimulation of left splanchnic in abdomen
  :08 4   minutes
  :10 3   "
  :18 3.5   "
  :23 6.5   "

In Fig. 30 is presented the original record of the shortening of the coagulation after stimulation of the

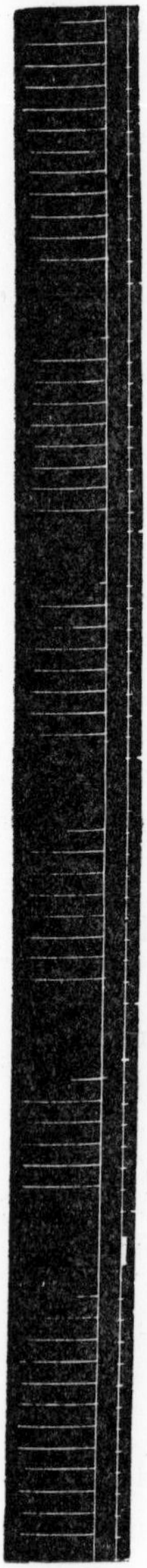

Fig. 30.—About one-third original size. Record of shortening of coagulation time after stimulation of the left splanchnic nerves, 4:33-:35. The time before stimulation was 6 minutes, and afterwards, 3, 4, 4, 4.5, and 6 minutes.

left splanchnic nerve (November 8) in a cat with brain pithed.

In the foregoing instances the coagulation time was reduced after splanchnic stimulation to less than half what it was before. The reduction was not always so pronounced.

November 7.—A cat * maintained in uniform ether anesthesia with artificial respiration had the following changes in the clotting time of its blood as the result of stimulating the left splanchnic nerve in the thorax:

3:40	5	minutes	*4:06*	3.5	minutes
:45	5	"	*:11*	4	"
:51	5.5	"	*:16*	3.5	"
:58	to *4:00* stimulation		*:21*	4	"
	of left splanchnic		*:26*	4.5	"
4:01	4.5 minutes		*:31*	5	"
			:36	6.5	"

In this case the average for about fifteen minutes before stimulation was slightly over five minutes, and for twenty-five minutes thereafter it was four minutes.

In all cases thus far the period of shortened coagulation lasted from ten to thirty minutes. In other cases, however, the effect was seen only in a

* This animal had just passed through a period of excitement with rapid clotting.

single observation. If this had occurred only once after splanchnic stimulation, it might be attributed to accident, but it was not an infrequent result, e. g.:

October 28.—A cat was etherized and decerebrated, and the splanchnic nerves were isolated in the thorax. Following are two instances of brief shortening of coagulation after splanchnic stimulation:

3:36	4.5 minutes		*4:07*	4.5 minutes
:42	4.5 "		:12	5.5 "
:47	*to* :49 splanchnic stimulation		:19	*to* :22 splanchnic stimulation
:51	4.5 minutes		:23	3.5 minutes
:57	2 "		:27	4 "
4:01	4 "		:33	5 "

In the foregoing instance it is noteworthy that the degree of acceleration is not so great after the second stimulation of the splanchnics as it was after the first. This reduction of effect as the nerves were repeatedly stimulated was frequently noted. The following case presents another illustration:

November 12.—A cat was etherized (2:35 P.M.) and the medulla was punctured (piqûre) at 3:12. The operation was without effect. The loss or lessening of effectiveness on second stimulation of the left splanchnic nerves is to be compared with the persistence of effectiveness on the right side:

3:40	4.5 minutes		*4:00*	3 minutes
:45	4.5 "		:05	2 "
:54	*to* :56 stimulation of left splanchnic in abdomen		:10	5.5 "
			:16	5 "

4:22 to :27 stimulation of left splanchnic in abdomen		:55 to :57 stimulation of right splanchnic	
		:59	3 minutes
:30	4 minutes	5:02	2.5 "
:34	4 minutes	:07	3 "
:39	4 "	:11	3 "
:44	4 "	:15	5.5 "
:48	4 "	:22	5.5 "

The experiments above recorded show that stimulation of the splanchnic nerves results immediately, or after a brief delay, in a shortening of the coagulation time of the blood—an effect which in different animals varies in duration and intensity, and diminishes as the stimulation is repeated. The next question was whether this effect is produced through the adrenal glands.

COAGULATION NOT HASTENED BY SPLANCHNIC STIMULATION IF THE ADRENAL GLANDS ARE ABSENT

The manner in which splanchnic stimulation produces its effects is indicated in the following experiments:

November 28.—A cat was etherized, and through the orbit the central nervous system was destroyed to the midthorax. The blood vessels of the *left* adrenal gland were then quickly tied and the gland removed. The readings for a half hour before the left splanchnic nerve was stimulated averaged seven minutes, then—

4:38 to :40 stimulation of left splanchnic (glandless)
:42   7 minutes

:50   7   minutes
5:02 to :04 stimulation of right splanchnic
:06   4   minutes
:10   7   "
:18   7   "
:26   7   "

December 4.—A cat was etherized and pithed through the orbit to the neck region. The right and left splanchnic nerves were tied and cut in the thorax. The *left* adrenal gland was then carefully removed. These operations consumed about a half-hour. The following records show the effect of stimulating the left and right splanchnic nerves:

4:10 5 minutes	5:00 2.5 minutes
:16 4.5 "	:14 6 "
:25 to :28 stimulation of	:23 to :25 stimulation of
left s p l a n c h n i c	right splanchnic
(glandless)	:26 6 minutes
:30 4.5 minutes	:33 4.5 "
:35 4.5 "	:38 3.5 "
:40 7.5 "	:43 4.5 "
:49 to :51 stimulation of	:49 5 "
right splanchnic	:55 6 "
:55 4.5 minutes	

The results in this experiment are represented graphically in Fig. 31.

Elliott's evidence that in the cat the splanchnic innervation of the adrenals is not crossed has already been mentioned. If the gland is removed on one side, therefore, stimulation of the nerves on that side causes no discharge from the opposite gland. As the above experiments clearly show, splanchnic stimulation on the glandless side results in no shortening of the coagulation time; whereas, in the same animals, stimulation of the nerves on the other side (still connected

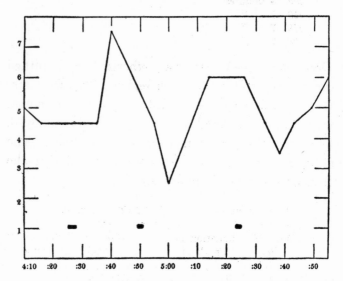

Fig. 31.—Results of stimulating the left splanchnic nerves, 4:25:28, after removal of the left adrenal gland; and of stimulating the right splanchnic nerves, 4:49–:51 and 5:23–:25, with right adrenal gland present.

with the adrenal gland) produces a sharp hastening of the clotting process.

The splanchnics innervate the intestines and liver even though the adrenal gland is removed. The foregoing experiments indicate that the nerve impulses delivered to these organs do not influence them in any direct manner to accelerate the speed of coagulation. Indeed, in one of the experiments (December 4, see Fig. 31) a high reading about ten minutes after splanchnic stimulation on the glandless side suggests the possibility of an opposite effect. Direct stimulation of the hepatic nerves on one occasion was followed by a change of the clotting time from 4.5, 5, 4.5, 4.5 minutes during twenty-five minutes before stimulation to 4.5, 7, and 6 minutes during twenty minutes after stimulation.

Since with the adrenals present stimulation of hepatic nerves induces alteration of glycogen in the liver and quick increase of blood sugar,[3] just as splanchnic stimulation does, the failure of the blood to clot faster after stimulation of the hepatic nerves confirms the evidence already offered that faster clotting when adrenin is increased in the blood is not due to a larger amount of sugar present (see p. 153).

The liver and intestines cannot be made to shorten clotting time by stimulation of their nerves, but, as has already been shown (see p. 152) neither can adrenin act by itself to hasten the clotting process. Apparently the effect is produced by coöperation between the adrenals and the liver (and possibly also the intestines). Somewhat similar coöperation is noted in the organization of sugar metabolism; in the absence of the adrenal glands stimulation of the liver nerves has little or no effect in raising the blood-sugar level (see p. 77),[4] and in the absence of the liver adrenin is without influence.[5]

The variations of effect noted after splanchnic stimulation can be accounted for by variations in the adrenin content of the glands. Elliott[6] found, as previously stated, that animals newly brought into strange surroundings may have a considerably reduced amount of adrenin in their adrenals. The animals used in our experiments had been for varying lengths of time in an animal house in which barking dogs also were kept, and were therefore subject to influences which would be likely to discharge the glands.

The evidence that stimulation of splanchnic nerves, with accompanying increase of adrenal secretion, results in more rapid clotting of blood is especially interesting in relation to the experiments previously described, which showed that in pain and emotional excitement there is an increased secretion of adrenin into the blood. Does the adrenin thus liberated have any effect on the rate of coagulation? The observations here recorded were made in order to obtain an answer to that question.

COAGULATION HASTENED BY "PAINFUL" STIMULATION

In the experiments on the action of stimuli which in the unanesthetized animal would cause pain, it will be recalled that faradic stimulation of a large nerve trunk (the stump of the cut sciatic) and operation under light anesthesia were the methods used to affect the sensory nerves. Elliott[6] found that repeated excitation of the sciatic nerve was especially efficient in exhausting the adrenal glands of their adrenin content, and also that this reflex persisted after removal of the cerebral hemispheres. It was to be expected, therefore, that with well-stored glands, sciatic stimula-

tion, even in the decerebrate animal, would call forth
an amount of adrenal secretion which would decidedly
hasten clotting.   The following case illustrates such
a result:

December 12.—A cat was anesthetized with ether at

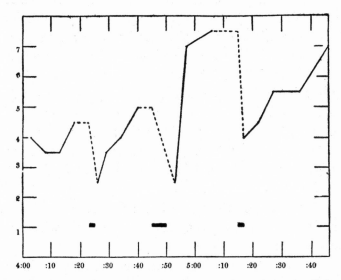

Fɪɢ. 32.—Three shortenings of coagulation time after stimulation
   of the left sciatic nerve, at 4:23–:25, at 4:45–:50 (stronger),
   and at 5:15–:17.

3:45 and the left sciatic nerve was bared. Decerebration was completed at 3:57. The clotting time of the
blood began to be tested six minutes later:

4:03	4	minutes	*4:26*	2.5 minutes	
:08	3.5	"	:29	3.5	"
:13	3.5	"	:34	4	"
:18	4.5	"	:40	5	"
:23 *to* :25	stimulation of		:45 to :50	stimulation of	
	left sciatic			left sciatic	

4:53	2.5 minutes		5:17	4	minutes
:57	7	"	:22	4.5	"
5:06	7.5	"	:27	5.5	"
:15 to :17	stimulation of		:36	5.5	"
	left sciatic		:46	7	"

The results obtained in this case, which were similar to results in other cases, are represented graphically in Fig. 32. The coagulation time was becoming gradually more prolonged, but each excitation of the sciatic nerve was followed by a marked shortening. The strength of stimulation was not determined with exactness, but it is worthy of note that the current used in the first and the third stimulations was weaker than could be felt on the tongue, whereas that used in the second was considerably stronger, though it did not produce reflex spasms.

Mere tying of the nerve is capable of producing a marked shortening of coagulation, as the following figures show:

October 21.—10:57, cat under ether, and urethane given:

11:11	8.5 minutes
:23	8.5 "
:32 to :35	left sciatic bared and tied
:37	1.5 minutes
:41	5.5 "
:50	7 "
12:02	8.5 "

Stimulation of the crural nerve had similar effects, reducing the clotting time in one instance from a succession of 3, 3, and 3.5 minutes to 1.5 minutes

shortly after the application of the current, with a
return to 3.5 minutes at the next test.

Operative procedures performed under light anesthesia (i. e., with the more persistent reflexes still
present), or reduction of anesthesia soon after operation, resulted in a remarkable shortening of the coagulation time:

November 8.—A cat was etherized and tracheotomized. The abdomen was then opened and a ligature
was drawn around the hepatic nerves. The operation
was completed at 2:25. At 2:50 the etherization became light and the rate of clotting began to be faster:

2:50	6	minutes	*3:15*	3.5 minutes	
3:00	5.5	"	*:20*	4.5	"
:10	3.5	"	*:30*	7.5	"

November 11.—A female cat, very quiet, was placed
in the holder at 1:55. The animal was not excited.
At 2:10 etherization was begun; the animal was then
tracheotomized, and the femoral artery was exposed.

2:21	4.5	minutes	
:26	4.5	"	anesthesia lessened
:32	3.5	"	" light
:35		abdomen opened	
:47	1.5	minutes	
:52	1	"	
:55		ligature passed around hepatic nerves	
:57	1.5	minutes; anesthesia light; corneal reflex present	
3:02	3	"	
:07	3	"	some hepatic nerves cut
:12	4.5	"	rest of hepatic nerves cut
:22	5	"	

The results of this experiment are shown graphically
in Fig. 33.

November 13.—A cat was etherized at 1:55, tracheotomized, and the femoral artery laid bare. As soon as these preparations were completed, the ether was

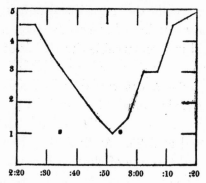

Fig. 33.—Shortening of coagulation time during an operation under light anesthesia. At 2:35 the abdomen was opened, at 2:55 a ligature was passed around the hepatic nerves.

removed and anesthesia became light. The blood clotted thus:

2:08	6	minutes	
:15	4	"	anesthesia light
:20	2		
:24	1	"	etherization begun again
:27	2.5	"	
:30	3.5	"	
:35	5.5	"	
:50	5.5	"	

In the foregoing and in other similar instances, a condition of surgical injury, whether just made or being made, was accompanied by more rapid clotting of blood when the degree of anesthesia was lessened. This condition was one which, if allowed to go further in the same direction, would result in pain. Both direct electrical stimulation and also surgical operation of a nature to give pain in the unanesthetized animal result, therefore, in faster clotting.

It is worthy of note that after decerebration clotting apparently occurred no faster because the abdomen had been opened, although in the decerebrate state etherization was suspended. The mechanism for reflex control of the adrenals lies near the anterior border of the medulla oblongata, as Rapport and I [7] have shown, and it is possible that the act of decerebration resulted in such damage to the central mechanism that it could not perform its functions.

COAGULATION HASTENED IN EMOTIONAL EXCITEMENT

The evidence for emotional secretion of the adrenal glands has already been presented. As was noted in my earlier observations on the motions of the alimentary canal (see p. 13), cats differ widely in their emotional reaction to being bound; some, especially young males, become furious; others, especially elderly females, take the experience quite calmly. This difference of attitude was used with positive results, the reader will recall, in the experiments on emotional glycosuria; there seemed a possibility likewise of using it to test the effect of emotions on blood clotting. To plan formal experiments for that purpose was not necessary, because in the ordinary course of the researches here reported, the difference in effects on the blood between the violent rage of vigorous young males and the quiet complacency of old females was early noted. Indeed, the rapid clotting which accompanied excitement not infrequently made necessary an annoying wait till slower clotting would permit the use of experimental methods for shortening the process.

The animals used on November 11 and 13 (see pp. 169, 170) are examples of calm acceptance of being placed on the holder; and furthermore, these animals were anesthetized without much disturbance. As the figures indicate, the clotting from the first occurred at about the average rate.

In sharp contrast to these figures are those obtained when a vigorous animal is angered:

October 30.—A very vigorous cat was placed on the holder at 9:08. It at once became stormy—snarling, hissing, biting, and lashing its big tail. At 9:12 etherizing was begun and that intensified the excitement. By 9:15 the femoral artery was tied. The clotting time of the blood for an hour after the ether was first given was as follows:

9:18	0.5	minute		*9:43*	1	minute
:19	1	"		*:45*	0.5	"
:22	1	"		*:49*	0.5	"
:24	1	"		*:52*	0.5	"
:26	1	"		*:54*	0.5	"
:28	1.5	"		*:57*	1	"
:31	1	"		*10:00*	0.5	"
:33	0.5	"		*:02*	0.5	"
:35	0.5	"		*:06*	1	"
:38	0.5	"		*:09*	0.5	"
:39	0.5	"		*:11*	0.5	"
:41	1	"		*:13*	1	"

Twenty-four observations made during the hour showed that the clotting time in this enraged animal averaged three-fourths of a minute and was never longer than a minute and a half. The clots were invariably a solid jelly. The persistence of the rapid clotting for so long a period after anesthesia was started may have been in part due to continued, rather light, etherization, for Elliott [8] found that etherization itself could reduce the adrenin content of the adrenal glands.

The shortened clotting did not always persist so long as in the foregoing instance. The brief period of faster clotting illustrated in the following case was typical of many:

November 18.—A cat that had been in stock for some time was placed on the holder at 2:13, and was at once enraged. Two minutes later etherization was started. The hairs on the tail were erect. The clotting was as follows:

2:25	1	minute	*2:31*	4.5 minutes
:27	0.5	"	:37	3.5 "
:28	2	"	:47	4.5 "

It seems probable that in this case, just as in some of the cases in which the splanchnic nerves were stimulated (see p. 161), the adrenals had been well-nigh exhausted because of the cat's being caged near dogs, and that the emotional flare-up practically discharged the glands, for repeated attempts later to reproduce the initial rapid clotting by stimulation of the splanchnic nerves were without result.

Evidence presented in previous chapters makes wholly probable the correctness of the inference that

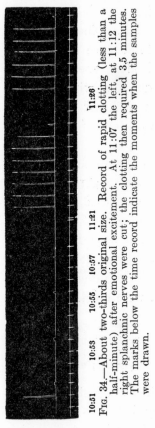

the faster coagulation which follows emotional excitement is due to adrenal discharge from splanchnic stimulation. In this relation the effect of severance of the splanchnics on emotional acceleration of the clotting process is of interest. The following cases are illustrative:

October 29.—A cat was left on the holder for ten minutes while the femoral artery was uncovered under local anesthesia. The blood removed was clotted in a half-minute. The animal was much excited. It was now quickly etherized and the brain pithed forward from the neck. The tests resulted as follows:

FIG. 34.—About two-thirds original size. Record of rapid clotting (less than a half-minute) after emotional excitement. At 11:07 the left, at 11:12 the right splanchnic nerves were cut; the clotting then required 3.5 minutes. The marks below the time record indicate the moments when the samples were drawn.

10:51	1	minute	11:07	cut left splanchnic
:53	0.5	"	:12	" right splanchnic
:55	0.5	"	:21	3.5 minutes
:57	0.5	"	:26	3.5 "

The original record of this case is given in Fig. 34. *November 5.*—A cat was etherized at 2:35. At 2:39

artificial respiration by tracheal cannula was begun, the air passing through an ether bottle. The clotting occurred thus:

2:53	1.5	minutes
:57	1.5	"
3:05	1.5	"
:15	1.5	"
:25		both splanchnics cut and tied in thorax
:35	4.5	minutes
:55	4.5	"

November 7.—A cat was etherized at 1:55 under excitement and with tail hairs erect. At 2:13 the animal was showing reflexes. The figures show the course of the experiment:

2:15	1.5	minutes		*3:11*	2.5	minutes
:21	1	"		*:26*		cut left splanchnic in thorax
:26	1	"				
:31	1	"		*:35*		cut right splanchnic in thorax
:36	1	"				
:41	1	"		*:40*	5	minutes
:46	2	"		*:45*	5	"
:51	2	"		*:51*	5.5	"
3:06	2	"				

In this instance the subsequent stimulation of the splanchnic nerves resulted again in faster clotting—a reduction from 5.5 minutes to 3.5 minutes (see experiment November 7, p. 160). The results from this experiment are expressed graphically in Fig. 35.

The data presented in this chapter show that such stimulation as in the unanesthetized animal would cause pain, and also such emotions as fear and rage, are capable of greatly shortening the coagulation time of blood. These results are quite in harmony with the evidence previously offered that injected adrenin and secretion from the adrenal glands induced by splanchnic stimulation hasten clotting, for painful

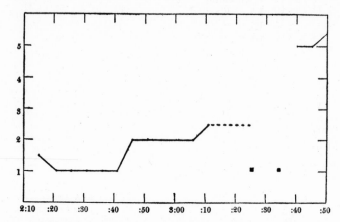

FIG. 35.—Rapid clotting after emotional excitement, with slowing of the process when the splanchnic nerves were cut in the thorax (the left at 3:26, the right at 3:35).

stimulation and emotional excitement also evoke activity of the adrenal medulla. Here, then, is another fundamental change in the body, a change tending to the conservation of its most important fluid, wrought through the adrenal glands in times of great perturbation.

REFERENCES

1. See CANNON, *Ergebnisse der Physiologie*, xxvii (1928), p. 380.
2. CANNON and MENDENHALL, *American Journal of Physiology* xxxiv (1914), p. 251.

3. MACLEOD, *Diabetes: Its Pathological Physiology* (London, 1913), pp. 68-72.
4. GAUTRELET and THOMAS, *Comptes Rendus de la Société de Biologie,* lxvii (1909), p. 233.
5. BANG, *Der Blutzucker* (*Wiesbaden,* 1913), p. 87.
6. ELLIOTT, *Journal of Physiology,* xliv (1912), pp. 406. 407.
7. CANNON and RAPPORT, *American Journal of Physiology.* lxiii (1921), p. 338.
8. ELLIOTT, *op. cit.,* p. 388.

CHAPTER XI

THE constriction of blood vessels and the acceleration of the heart beat, which attend emotional excitement and which result in a heightened arterial pressure, have been repeatedly referred to in foregoing
pages. The higher blood pressure causes a faster blood
flow through relaxed or non-contracted vascular channels. Thus the number of red blood corpuscles (erythrocytes) carrying oxygen from the lungs to the heart,
the brain and the active muscles, that would pass in
a given time, would be increased and the oxygen delivery would be increased correspondingly. Not only
is there a greater usage of these oxygen carriers, however,—there is also a greater number of them as a
consequence of excitement.

Ferrari [1] appears to have been first to study directly
the influence of emotional excitement on the blood
count. In students just after an examination he found
an average of 457,000 more erythrocytes per cubic millimeter than in the same students before the examination
—the higher counts corresponding to the most excited,
the lowest to an "indifferent and phlegmatic" member
of the group. The observations by Lamson [2] were of
similar import. He allowed cats to be frightened by a
barking dog. A great increase in the number of red

178

corpuscles resulted: in one experiment the figures rose from 10,720,000 per cubic millimeter to 14,920,000 in five minutes and in another from 11,576,000 to 14,464,-000 in five minutes. Such increases (39 and 25 per cent, respectively) were taken as clear proof of an emotional polycythemia. Lamson attributed to the liver an essential rôle in the acute polycythemia which he observed; there was, he inferred, either a liberation of erythrocytes from an hepatic reservoir or an escape of the fluid portion of the blood (the plasma) through hepatic capillaries so that the blood corpuscles became concentrated.

New light has been thrown on Lamson's data by recent developments of knowledge of the spleen. Although that organ has long been known to be muscular and to contract and expand (see Krumbhaar,[3] Barcroft[4]), and although the view had been expressed that it is a reservoir for red blood corpuscles, its service to the organism as a means of quickly increasing the number of circulating erythrocytes and of storing them away again was not clearly appreciated until the past few years. Between 1923 and 1927, a number of investigators, chief among whom were Barcroft and his co-workers[5] proved abundantly, by various methods, that the spleen is much larger during life than after death, that various circumstances which affect the organism cause the spleen to contract, and that when it contracts it discharges into the circulation an extra supply of erythrocytes. Among such circumstances are carbon monoxide poisoning, hemorrhage, lessening of partial pressure of oxygen (i. e., varieties of asphyxia), muscular exercise and injections of adrenin and pituitrin. Furthermore, Hargis and Mann [6] noted that slight affective stimuli (e. g., clapping the hands, pinching his skin, display of food) caused in the dog contractions of the spleen; and recently Barcroft and Stephens [7] have noted that indications of anxiety and jealousy were associated with diminution of spleen volume. Do not these observations on the influence of emotional states on the size of the spleen suggest that that organ, instead of the liver, is the source of emotional polycythemia? A research was undertaken by J. J. Izquierdo and myself [8] with the hope of answering that question.

As a rule, vigorous young cats, previously selected because of their energetic reaction to a barking dog (by erection of hairs, arching of the back, dilation of the pupils, hissing, spitting, etc.), were used as subjects.

Most of our examinations were made on blood taken from a small cut on the edge of the ear. For the preliminary or basal count the animal must be as quiet and undisturbed as possible, a condition which is favored by acquaintance with the observer, his assistant and the natural surroundings. If the animal is excited at this time the initial count may be so high that it will differ little from other counts made later. After the first count was completed the cat was confined in a small wire cage where it was protected from injury and where its motions were so limited that the effects of muscular activity (struggle) were minimized as much as possible. Thereupon a lively dog was brought near and allowed to bark at the cat for one minute. Immediately the dog was removed and a second sample of blood was secured as soon as possible from the cat's ear. In some cases three or four additional sam-

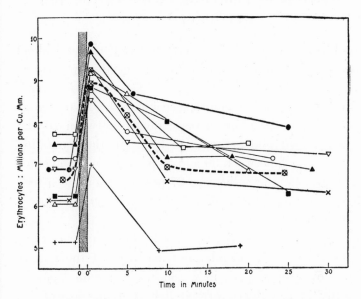

Fig. 36.—The course of emotional polycythemia. The vertical, shaded band represents the one-minute period of emotional excitement; the thick dash-line, the average of the nine cases.

ples were examined, from five to thirty minutes after the period of excitement, in order to follow the course of the polycythemia. When samples were repeatedly taken from the cat, the animal was each time carefully returned to the familiar surroundings which were not disturbing.

In all the tests the blood was diluted (with Hayem's solution, 0.5:100) in the same pipette and counted in the same Thoma-Zeiss chamber. Pains were taken to keep all the operations as uniform as possible.

In twenty-one observations on the peripheral blood of eighteen different animals the erythrocyte count immediately after excitement was invariably much higher than it was before (see Fig. 36). In fifteen of the observations the increase ranged between 10 and 30 per cent above the basal level; in the remaining six it ranged between 30 and 50 per cent. The average increase for the series was 27 per cent; for the fifteen cases with increases of 30 per cent or below it was 20 per cent.

That such increases are far beyond any variations occurring in the usual quiet existence of the animal is shown by Fig. 37, in which are represented graphically in the thick vertical lines the increase of red corpuscles per cubic millimeter after excitement in five animals, together with the results of repeated counts of blood samples taken for about a week from the same animals when undisturbed. With the exception of one count in the total of 27 (the first one of cat 203), the figures varied hardly more than a million corpuscles during the period. On the other hand, as a consequence of one minute of excitement the number of erythrocytes usually rose suddenly between 2 and 3 millions.

The additional counts made at various intervals after the period of excitement showed that the maximal height of the emotional polycythemia was present

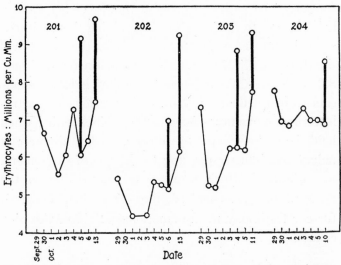

Fig. 37.—Graphic record of the daily variations of the erythrocyte count of five cats, and the rises due to one minute of emotional excitement (thick vertical lines). The high basal count of 203 on October 11 was associated with an angry reaction: it is noteworthy that the first counts, made when the animals were new to the strange procedure, as a rule were high.

as soon after the period of excitement as the blood could be collected. A fall in the numbers was notable at the end of five minutes, and within a half-hour the corpuscle count had come back to its former level (see Fig. 36).

Repetition of the excitement occasionally resulted in a gradually increasing indifference of the cat, safe in its cage, to the barking dog outside. Thus cat 207, an elderly female, which had had on October 22 a blood count of 10,308,000 after excitement, became indifferent to the dog, and was undisturbed even when fastened down—a check on free motion which is sometimes resisted with much vigor. On November 1, after being bound to the holder and remaining there without struggle for ten minutes, the rise in the count was slight, from 5,732,000 to 6,232,000—an increase of only 8.7 per cent. It will be recalled that elderly female cats were selected for X-ray observations of gastrointestinal movements because of their serenity when held back-downward by thongs. The absence of polycythemia corresponding to absence of excitement, in an animal which previously had manifested the concomitant presence of the two phenomena, is further testimony to the emotional origin of the high counts.

INDICATIONS THAT SMALL CORPUSCLES ARE LIBERATED DURING POLYCYTHEMIA

Larger amounts of blood obtained in some cases permitted observations to be made not only on the numbers of erythrocytes, but also on their volume. Comparison of the percentage increases of the counts with the percentage increases of erythrocyte volumes after excitement revealed at once a marked difference. The volumes did not rise nearly so much as the counts. Observations on the hemoglobin increases showed

PERCENTAGE OF ERYTHROCYTES OF VARIOUS DIAMETERS, CAT 207
OCTOBER 22, 1927

DIAMETERS (MICRA)	NUMBERS OF ERYTHROCYTES IN 100	
	Under Anesthesia	After Excitement
3-4	. . .	5
4-5	10	25
5-6	30	47
6-7	60	23
TOTAL	100	100

closer correspondence of these values with the volumes than with the counts. These results indicated a discrepancy so great that it could only be accounted for by the appearance of smaller corpuscles in the blood after excitement than were there before. Some measurements of the sizes of the corpuscles before and after excitement were made, therefore, to learn whether the microscope would reveal the presence of small sizes as the numbers increased. In the accompanying table are shown the size distribution of 100 red corpuscles from heart blood, that were kept in their own plasma, sealed under a thin coverglass. The size limits for cats has been given as 5–7 micra by Hayem [9] and 4–7.1 micra by Bethe [10]. Lamson [2] calculated that after giving adrenalin and increasing the erythrocyte count about 2 million corpuscles in each of two dogs, the average volume of the corpuscles was diminished 13.4 per cent during the polycythemia. He cited a number of previous investigators who had noted that the relative increase of hemoglobin was not so great as the relative increase of red corpuscles. Our results harmonize with these earlier observations.

ABSENCE OF EFFECT OF EMOTIONAL EXCITEMENT AFTER REMOVAL OF THE UPPER ABDOMINAL SYMPATHETIC INNERVATIONS

The animals used in this test were all in excellent physical condition. Twelve observations on six different animals showed that when the upper abdominal viscera are deprived of their sympathetic innervation, the usual emotional excitement is not followed by any prominent change in the erythrocyte count. The average count before excitement was 6,701,000; immediately after one minute of exposure to the dog it was 6,101,000; five to ten minutes later it was 6,412,000.

As a further test under these conditions, the cats were taken to the kennels where the barking dog was joined by a chorus of his fellows; the excitement continued for two or three minutes and then the cats were fastened to the holder where they were excited for five to ten minutes more. Even with such extra stimulation the usual effects did not occur; instead the erythrocyte count fell. In cat 302, for example, the figures were as follows:

Before excitement 7,064,000
After excited by dog 6,320.000
After tied down 5 minutes 5,728,000

EFFECT OF LEAVING ONLY THE LIVER INNERVATED

In this series of experiments the left splanchnic and the splenic nerves were severed, and the right adrenal gland and the upper abdominal sympathetic strands were removed. The effect of this operation is to exclude nervous and possible humoral (adrenin) agencies from action on the spleen while leaving the nervous system still connected with the liver through the right splanchnic nerves. After the animals had fully recovered from the operation and were in vigorous health, they were excited as before for one minute.

In three out of seven observations the figures showed no increase in the number of corpuscles after the period of excitement. In the other four cases, the increases were relatively slight. Of course it may be argued that if the sympathetic strands and the *left* splanchnics had not been severed the liver would have had richer innervation and the results would have been different. The results obtained, however, were so little indicative of any important rôle played by the liver that we did not take the trouble to try demedullating the left adrenal and leaving the left splanchnics. The data do not lend support to the view that the liver or any other organ still innervated is of noteworthy significance in producing emotional polycythemia. This conclusion is confirmed by a considerable number of cases in which the erythrocyte count did not increase, although the nerves of the spleen

were sectioned. In these animals the splanchnic and
the hepatic nerves were intact. If the emotional increase of red blood corpuscles was due in any noteworthy degree to the liver, they should have become
regularly more numerous as a result of the excitement.
This did not take place.

EFFECTS OF SECTIONING THE SPLENIC NERVES

A number of investigators have shown that adrenalin in small amounts causes the spleen to contract (cf.
Hoskins and Gunning,[11] Tournade and Chabrol [12]). It
has been observed also that adrenalin causes increase of
the erythrocyte count both in lower animals (see Lamson [12]) and in man (Schneider and Havens [13]). With
the spleen denervated, therefore, the possibility still
remains that adrenin, set free from the adrenal medulla, would cause contraction of the spleen similar to
that caused by the nerve impulses and thereby would
increase the percentage of red corpuscles. To de-
nervate the spleen the organ was exposed through a
mid-line or left-side section of the abdominal wall,
the splenic artery was isolated, and the nerves were
separated from the artery before it branched. The
larger bundles of nerves are there clearly visible and
can be thoroughly removed. In order to make sure
that all possible nervous connections were destroyed,
we bared likewise the splenic vein, the gastro-splenic
vessels and pancreatico-splenic artery, and, after clear-
ing a short extent of each one, touched it with phenol

The results of emotional excitement in these cases (in all except one the observations were made within six weeks after the operation) disclosed two striking features. First, brief excitement (i. e., for 1 minute) rarely produced a noteworthy positive effect. This was in marked contrast to the results obtained when the spleen was normally innervated. Second, longer excitement, lasting from 5 to 10 minutes, and attended by struggle, evoked occasional rises in the number of erythrocytes as great as 16 and 20 per cent, but also occasional drops nearly as great. The effects were quite inconstant and irregular; in two animals, 213 and 216, even long and very marked excitement did not yield positive results. That such displays, indeed that much less extreme displays, are attended by augmented adrenal secretion is well attested. When the normal spleen contracts under emotional conditions, therefore, two agencies are at hand and both may be operating—a greater concentration of adrenin in the blood and a discharge of sympathetic nerve impulses. The experiments indicate that in the absence of the nerve impulses the secreted adrenin is not markedly effective in causing polycythemia. This may not be due, however, to inability of adrenin to cause the spleen to contract; it may be due to greater or less failure of the denervated spleen to concentrate the blood gathered within its confines. Barcroft and Poole [14] report that the denervated portion of the spleen yields blood which shows not more than the most trifling sign of concentration—a process possibly due to rhythmic squeezing of the plasma out of the blood and dependent on intact nerve connections—whereas the innervated portion soon concentrates its corpuscular contents. It is clear that if the blood of the spleen is not concentrated, contraction of the organ must merely add to the volume of circulating blood without augmenting the percentage of corpuscles. Most of the cases of this series are consistent with that possibility. On the other hand, in a few of the cases, when struggle and excitement were prolonged, an augmentation occurred, usually slight, but in one instance rising to 20 per cent. These cases suggest that the blood may have been concentrated in these spleens and that under such conditions the greater output of adrenin during emotional stress can cause contraction though nerve impulses are no longer delivered.

Whatever may be the explanation for the irregular results obtained when the spleen was denervated and the adrenal glands were active, the regular results obtained under the natural conditions of normal innervation of both the spleen and the adrenals show clearly that excitement increases the erythrocyte count. The spleen is an organ where blood is concentrated and stored. When the spleen contracts it discharges its contents into the general circulation. The smooth muscle in the organ is subject to sympathetic impulses, and they are roused in great emotional disturbance. The experiments detailed in the foregoing pages prove that emotional polycythemia is dependent on the nervous control of the spleen. The significance of this function we shall consider in the next chapter.

Still another effect of excitement on the blood is the relative increase in mononuclear forms of white blood corpuscles. Menkin [15] has shown that an average increase of 13 per cent can be thus induced after a brief period of emotional disturbance and that a gradual subsidence to the original level is reached in about a half-hour just as in emotional polycythemia. The increase in mononuclears fails to appear after excitement if the spleen has been removed or has been disconnected from the central nervous system. Again a subtle change is demonstrated as a consequence of powerful affective states. The significance of this change is not yet clear.

REFERENCES

1. FERRARI, *Rivista di Patologia Nervosa e Mentale,* ii (1897), p. 306.
2. LAMSON, *Journal of Pharmacology and Experimental Therapeutics,* vii (1915), p. 169.
3. KRUMBHAAR, *Physiological Reviews,* vi (1926), p. 160.
4. BARCROFT, *The Lancet,* ccx (1926), p. 544.
5. BARCROFT and BARCROFT, *Journal of Physiology,* lviii (1923), p. 138. BARCROFT, HARRIS, ORAHOVATS and WEISS, *ibid.,* lx (1925), p. 443. BARCROFT, MURRAY, ORAHOVATS, SANDS and WEISS, *ibid.,* lx (1925), p. 79.
6. HARGIS and MANN, *American Journal of Physiology,* lxxv (1925), p. 180.
7. BARCROFT and STEPHENS, *Journal of Physiology,* lxiv (1927), p. 1.
8. IZQUIERDO and CANNON, *American Journal of Physiology,* lxxxiv (1928), p. 545.
9. HAYEM, *Du Sang et de ses Alterations Anatomiques,* Paris (1889), p. 172.

10. Bethe, *Schwalbe's Morphologische Arbeiten,* i (1891), p. 209.
11. Hoskins and Gunning, *American Journal of Physiology,* xliii (1917), p. 298.
12. Tournade and Chabrol, *Comptes Rendus de la Société de Biologie,* xc (1924), p. 835; *ibid.,* xcii (1925), p. 418.
13. Schneider and Havens, *American Journal of Physiology,* xxxvi (1915), pp. 239, 380.
14. Barcroft and Poole, *Journal of Physiology,* lxiv (1927), p. 23.
15. Menkin, *American Journal of Physiology,* lxxxv (1928), p. 489.

CHAPTER XII

WE now turn from a consideration of the data secured in our experiments to an interpretation of the data. One of the most important lessons of experience is learning to distinguish between the facts of observation and the inferences drawn from those facts. The facts may remain unquestioned; the explanation, however, may be changed by additional facts or through the influence of more extensive views. Having given this warning, I propose to discuss the bearings of the results reported in the earlier chapters.

Our inquiry thus far has revealed that the adrenin secreted in times of stress has all the effects in the body that are produced by injected adrenin. It coöperates with sympathetic nerve impulses in calling forth stored carbohydrate from the liver, thus flooding the blood with sugar; it helps in distributing the blood to the heart, lungs, central nervous system and limbs, while taking it away from the inhibited organs of the abdomen; it quickly abolishes the effects of muscular fatigue; and it renders the blood more rapidly coagulable. These remarkable facts are, furthermore, associated with some of the most primitive experiences in the life of higher organisms, experiences common to

193

all, both man and beast—the elemental experiences of pain and fear and rage that come suddenly in critical emergencies. What is the significance of these profound bodily alterations? What are the *emergency functions* of the sympathico-adrenal system?

THE REFLEX NATURE OF BODILY RESPONSES IN PAIN AND THE MAJOR EMOTIONS, AND THE USEFUL CHARACTER OF REFLEXES

The most significant feature of these bodily reactions in pain and in the presence of emotion-provoking objects is that they are of the nature of reflexes —they are not willed movements, indeed they are often distressingly beyond the control of the will. The pattern of the reaction, in these as in other reflexes, is deeply inwrought in the workings of the nervous system, and when the appropriate occasion arises, typical organic responses are evoked through inherent automatisms.

It has long been recognized that the most characteristic feature of reflexes is their "purposive" nature, or their utility either in preserving the welfare of the organism or in safeguarding it against injury. The reflexes of sucking, swallowing, vomiting and coughing, for instance, need only to be mentioned to indicate the variety of ways in which reflexes favor the continuance of existence. When, therefore, these automatic responses accompanying pain and fear and rage—the increased discharge of adrenin and sugar—

are under consideration, it is reasonable to inquire first as to their utility.

Numerous ingenious suggestions have been offered to account for the more obvious changes accompanying emotional states—as, for example, the *terrifying* aspect produced by the bristling of the hair and by the uncovering of the teeth in an access of rage.[1] The most widely applicable explanation proposed for these spontaneous reactions is that during the long course of racial experience they have been developed for quick service in the struggle for existence. Earlier writers on organic evolution pointed out the anticipatory character of these responses. According to Spencer,[2] "Fear, when strong, expresses itself in cries, in efforts to hide or escape, in palpitations and tremblings; and these are just the manifestations that would accompany an actual experience of the evil feared. The destructive passions are shown in a general tension of the muscular system, in gnashing of the teeth and protrusion of the claws, in dilated eyes and nostrils, in growls; and these are weaker forms of the actions that accompany the killing of prey." McDougall [3] has developed this idea systematically and has suggested that an association has become established between particular emotions and particular instinctive reactions; thus the emotion of fear is associated with the instinct for flight, and the emotion of anger or rage with the instinct for fighting or attack. Crile [4] likewise in giving recent expression to the same view has emphasized the importance of adaptation and natural selection, operative through myriads of years of racial experience, in enabling us to account for the already channeled responses which we find established in our nervous organization. And on a principle of "phylogenetic association" he assumes that fear, born of innumerable injuries in the course of evolution, has developed into portentous foreshadowing of possible injury and has become, therefore, capable of arousing in the body all the offensive and defensive activities that favor the survival of the organism.

Because the increase of adrenin and the increase of sugar in the blood, following painful or strong emotional experiences, are reflex in character, and because reflexes as a rule are useful responses, we are justified in the surmise that under these circumstances these reactions may be useful. What, then, is their possible value?

In order that these reactions may be useful they must be *prompt*. Such is the case. Carrasco-Formiguera and I [5] have shown that the denervated heart begins to beat faster within 10 seconds after adrenin is reflexly evoked, and Britton [6] has reported that blood sugar may be largely increased—not infrequently as much as 20 to 30 per cent—within three to six minutes after a brief emotional experience. The two secretions are, therefore, almost instantly ready for service.

Conceivably the two secretions might act in conjunction, or each might have its own function alone.

Thus adrenin might serve in coöperation with nervous impulses to produce an increase of blood sugar, or it might have that function and other functions quite apart from that.   Before these possibilities are considered, however, the value of the increased blood sugar itself will be discussed.

THE UTILITY OF THE INCREASED BLOOD SUGAR AS A SOURCE OF MUSCULAR ENERGY

When we were working on emotional glycosuria a clue to the significance of the increase of sugar in the blood was found in McDougall's suggestion of a relation between "flight instinct" and "fear emotion," and "pugnacity instinct" and "anger emotion."   And the point was made that, since the fear emotion and the anger emotion are, in wild life, likely to be followed by activities (running or fighting) which require contraction of great muscular masses in supreme and prolonged struggle, a mobilization of sugar in the blood might be of signal service to the laboring muscles. Pain—and fighting is almost certain to involve pain —would, if possible, call forth even greater muscular effort.   "In the agony of pain almost every muscle of the body is brought into strong action," Darwin [1] wrote, for "great pain urges all animals, and has urged them during endless generations, to make the most violent and diversified efforts to escape from the cause of suffering." *

---

* It is recognized that both pain and the major emotions may

That muscular work is performed by energy supplied in carbonaceous material is shown by the great increase of carbon dioxide output in severe muscular work, which may exceed twenty times the output during rest.

---

have at times depressive rather than stimulating effects. For example, Martin and Lacey have shown (*American Journal of Physiology*, xxxiii, 1914, p. 212) that such stimuli as would induce pain may cause a fall of blood pressure, and they suggest that the rise of blood pressure commonly reported at times of painful experience is due to the psychic disturbance that is simultaneously aroused. Conceivably there is a relation between recognizing the possibility of escape (with the psychic consequences of that possibility) and the degree of stimulating effect. Thus pain originating from the interior of the body, or from injuries sure to be made more painful by action, would not likely lead to action. On the other hand, the whip and spur illustrate the well-known excitant effect of external painful stimuli.

Similarly in relation to the strong emotions, the effect may be paralyzing until there is a *definite deed to perform*. Thus terror may be the most depressing of all emotions, but, as Darwin pointed out (*Op. cit.*, p. 81), "a man or animal driven through terror to desperation is endowed with wonderful strength, and is notoriously dangerous in the highest degree."

After a study of carefully described instances of emotional excitement in man, Stratton (*Psychological Review*, xxxv, 1928, p. 363) has recently drawn the following conclusion: *"Excitement and emotion generally are not primarily and usually causes of inadequacy, or reactions which reduce one's adequacy. They rather usually are reactions which increase our adequacy; they supplement our routine modes of response which at the moment appear inadequate.* They may arise when calm action *seems* inadequate, indeed when it actually *is* inadequate. But the emotion itself normally, at least in its sthenic phase, helps us on toward a condition in which we are more nearly equal to the occasion. It helps us to meet an emergency by making more easily available, and by more perfectly organizing, whatever is of promise for success, of promise in our entire equipment, native and acquired, and whether it be sensory, motor, intellectual, hedonic, or of impulse, whether instinctive or of habit. Behind and in support of a purpose enlivened by emotion, there is suddenly made ready for use an enlarged array of powers of most varied character. The study of such experiences thus reveals the fuller function of excitement and of each of the more specialized emotions as an elaborate device for meeting uncommon difficulties."

Furthermore, the storage of glycogen in muscle, and its disappearance from excised muscle stimulated to activity,[7] or its reduction after excessive contractions produced by strychnine[8] or by prolonged labor, and the lessened ability of muscles to work if their glycogen store has been reduced[9] or if the sugar of the blood falls to a low level,[10] and the simple chemical relation between glycogen and the lactic acid which appears when muscles are made to contract, are all indications that carbohydrate (sugar and glycogen) is the elective source of energy for contraction. Furthermore, although fat can be used in the performance of muscular work, that work is more economically performed on carbohydrate than on fat.[11] And if the extra metabolism required for a short vigorous effort is calculated by itself, above that required for mere maintenance of the body, it is found to be a carbohydrate metabolism.[12] The importance of blood sugar as a support for muscular activity is obvious.

Whether circulating sugar can be immediately utilized by active muscles has been a subject of dispute. The claim of Chauveau and Kaufmann[13] that a muscle uses about three and a half times as much blood sugar when active as when resting, although supported by Quinquaud,[14] and by Morat and Dufourt,[15] has been denied by Pavy,[16] who failed to find any difference between the sugar content of arterial and venous blood when the muscle was contracting; and also by Magnus-Levy,[17] who has estimated that the amount of change in sugar content of the blood passing through a muscle must be so slight as to be within the limits of the error of analysis. On the other hand, when blood or Ringer's solution is repeatedly perfused through contracting heart muscle, the evidence is clear that the contained sugar may more or less completely disappear. Thus Locke and Rosenheim [18] found that from 5 to 10 centigrams of dextrose disappeared from Ringer's solution repeatedly circulated through the rabbit heart for eight or nine hours. And in 1913, Patterson and Starling [19] demonstrated that if blood is perfused repeatedly through a heart-lung preparation for three or four hours, and the heart is continually stimulated by adrenin added to the blood, the sugar in the blood wholly vanishes; or if the supply of sugar is maintained, the consumption may rise as high as 8 milligrams per gram of heart muscle per hour—about four times the usual consumption. When an animal is eviscerated it may be regarded as a preparation in which the muscles are perfused with their proper blood, pumped by the heart and oxygenated by the lungs. Under these circumstances, the percentage of sugar in the blood steadily falls,[20] because the utilization by the tissues is not compensated for by further supply from the liver. The experiments of Mann and Magath [10] have a similar significance. They extirpated the liver and studied the effects; after an hour the animal appeared normal; after three to eight hours muscular weakness became prominent, associated with great reduction of blood sugar. Thus, although there may be doubt that analyses of sugar in the blood flowing into and out

from an active muscle during a brief period can be
accurate enough to prove a clear difference, the evidence from the experiments above cited shows that
when the supply of sugar is limited it disappears to
a greater or less degree if passed repeatedly through
muscular organs.

There is considerable evidence that increasing the
blood sugar directly increases muscular efficiency.
Locke [21] has proved that if oxygenated salt solution is
perfused through the isolated rabbit heart, the beats
begin to weaken after one or two hours; but if now 0.1
per cent dextrose is added to the perfusing liquid, the
beats at once become markedly stronger and may continue with very slow lessening of strength as long as
seven hours. And Schumberg [22] has noted that when
he performed a large amount of general bodily work
(thus using up blood sugar) and then tested flexion of
the middle finger in an ergograph, the ability of the
muscle was greater if he drank a sugar solution than if
he drank an equally sweet solution of "dulcin." He did
not know during the experiment which solution he was
drinking. These observations have been confirmed
by Prantner and Stowasser, and by Frentzel. [23] In experiments on cats, Lee and Harrold [24] found that when
sugar is removed from the animal by means of phlorhizin the *tibialis anticus* is quickly fatigued; but if,
after the phlorhizin treatment, the animal is given an
abundance of sugar and then submitted to the test, the
muscle shows a much larger capacity for work. And
the testimony of Mann and Magath [10] is most sig-

nificant of all. An animal, dying from the removal of the liver, had become comatose and flaccid and apparently unable to contract any muscle except the diaphragm; it was given an injection of glucose and in less than a minute thereafter it stood up, walked, wagged its tail, drank water and acted quite normally. All this evidence is, of course, favorable to the view that circulating sugar may be quickly utilized by contracting muscles.*

From the experimental results presented above it is clear that muscles work preferably by utilizing energy stored in carbohydrate, that great muscular labor is capable of considerably reducing the quantity of immediately available carbohydrate, stored glycogen and circulating sugar, and that under circumstances of a lessened sugar content the increase of blood sugar considerably augments the ability of muscles to continue contracting. The conclusion seems justified, therefore, that the increased blood sugar attendant on

---

* The recent studies by Cori and Cori (see *Journal of Biological Chemistry,* lxxix, 1928, pp. 309-355) have led them to conclude that adrenin produces hyperglycemia by "decreased utilization of blood sugar" and by the "mobilization of muscle glycogen" through a change to lactic acid which is remade into glycogen in the liver. They used, however, very large doses of adrenin—equivalent to 14 cubic centimeters of adrenin in a man of 70 k.—and for that reason their results should be regarded not as physiological but as pathological. No *physiological* mechanism exists for "mobilizing muscle glycogen" as sugar in the blood stream. Physiologically muscle glycogen changes to lactic acid when the muscle contracts. To "mobilize" it without activity and restore it to the liver is a perversion of the physiological process. Such "mobilization" would be analogous to removing forces from the firing line and settling them in barracks.

the major emotions and pain would be of direct
benefit to the organism in the strenuous muscular
efforts involved in flight or conflict or struggle to be
free.

THE UTILITY OF INCREASED ADRENIN IN THE BLOOD
AS AN ANTIDOTE TO THE EFFECTS OF FATIGUE

The function which the discharged adrenin itself
might have in favoring vigorous muscular contraction
has already been suggested in the chapter on the effect
of adrenin in restoring the irritability of fatigued muscle. Some of the earliest evidence proved that removal
of the adrenal glands has a debilitating effect on
muscular power, and that injection of adrenal extract
has an invigorating effect. For these reasons it seemed
possible that increased adrenal secretion, as a reflex
result of pain or the major emotions, might act in itself
as a dynamogenic factor in the performance of muscular
work. It was on the basis of that possibility that Nice
and I tested the effect of stimulating the splanchnic
nerves (thus causing adrenal secretion), or injecting
adrenin, on the contraction of the fatigued *tibialis
anticus*. We found, as already described, that when
arterial pressure was of normal height, and was prevented from rising in the legs while the splanchnic was
being stimulated, there was a distinct rise in the height
of contraction of the fatigued muscle. And we drew
the inference that adrenin set free in the blood may
operate favorably to the organism by preparing fa-

tigued muscles for better response to the nervous discharges sent forth in great excitement.

This inference led to the experiments by Gruber, who examined the effects of minute amounts of adrenin (0.1 or 0.5 cubic centimeter, 1:100,000), and also of splanchnic stimulation, on the threshold stimulus of fatigued neuro-muscular and muscular apparatus. Fatigue, the reader will recall, raises the threshold not uncommonly 100 or 200 per cent, and in some instances as much as 600 per cent. Rest will restore the normal threshold in periods varying from fifteen minutes to two hours, according to the length of previous stimulation. If a small dose of adrenin is given, however, the normal threshold may be restored in three to five minutes.

From the foregoing evidence the conclusion is warranted that adrenin, when freely liberated in the blood, not only aids in bringing out sugar from the liver's store of glycogen, but also has a remarkable influence in quickly restoring to fatigued muscles, which have lost their original irritability, the same readiness for response which they had when fresh. Thus the adrenin set free in pain and in fear and rage would put the muscles of the body unqualifiedly at the disposal of the nervous system; the difficulty which nerve impulses might have in calling the muscles into full activity would be practically abolished; and this provision, along with the abundance of energy-supplying sugar newly flushed into the circulation, would give to the animal in which these mechanisms are most efficient the best possible conditions for putting forth supreme muscular efforts.*

Some of the early observers, though noting that injections of adrenalin increased blood sugar, found no evidence that that condition was associated with a greater utilization of the sugar in metabolism. Since this occurs when sugar is directly injected, the conclusion was drawn (Wilenko [25]) that adrenin lessens the capacity of the organism to burn carbohydrate. These early results and conclusions, however, have not been supported by later investigators. Lusk and Riche [26] have reported that the subcutaneous administration of adrenin (one milligram per kilo body weight) to dogs, simultaneously with 50 grams of glucose by mouth, interferes not at all with the use of sugar—the respiratory quotient remains for several hours at 1.0, i. e., at the figure which glucose alone would have given. Tompkins, Sturgis and Wearn [27] studied in soldiers the effects of injecting adrenin; in 34 carefully controlled experiments the metabolism was increased by the injection and in 27 of these 34 the respiratory quotient rose towards 1.0. Sandiford [28] made similar studies on human beings; adrenalin invariably caused a rise of the metabolic rate, usually accompanied by a greater pulmonary ventilation rate, a faster respiration rate, a higher pulse rate, a larger volume output per heart beat, an increased pulse pres-

---

* If these results of emotion and pain are not "worked off" by action, it is conceivable that the excessive adrenin and sugar in the blood may have pathological effects. (Cf. Cannon, *Journal of the American Medical Association,* lvi, 1911, p. 742.)

sure, and a movement of respiratory quotient towards unity—again indicating an emphasis on carbohydrate metabolism.

We may conclude, therefore, that when both adrenin and sugar are increased in the blood as a result of excitement, the higher percentage of sugar is not due to adrenin inhibiting the use of sugar by the tissues, and that there is no evidence at present to show that the brief augmentation of adrenal discharge, following excitement or splanchnic stimulation, affects in any deleterious manner the utilization of sugar as a source of energy. Indeed, the observation of Patterson and Starling, above mentioned, that adrenin increases the use of sugar by the heart, may signify that a physiological discharge of the adrenals can have a favorable rather than an unfavorable effect on the employment of sugar by the tissues.

THE VASCULAR CHANGES PRODUCED BY THE SYMPATHICO-ADRENAL SYSTEM FAVORABLE TO SUPREME MUSCULAR EXERTION

Quite in harmony with a foregoing argument that sugar and adrenin, which are poured into the blood during emotional excitement, render the organism more efficient in the physical struggle for existence, are the vascular changes wrought by increased adrenin, probably in coöperation with sympathetic innervations. The studies of volume changes of parts of the body, by Oliver and Schäfer and others, have already been noted. Their observations and other more recent studies, it will be remembered, showed that injected adrenin drove the blood from the abdominal viscera into the organs called upon in emergencies—into the central nervous system, the lungs, the heart, and the active skeletal muscles (see p. 105). The absence of effective vasoconstrictor nerves in the brain and the lungs, and the greater vascular bed in the heart and skeletal muscles during times of increased activity, make the blood supply to these parts dependent on the height of general arterial pressure. In pain and great excitement, as we have already seen, this pressure is likely to be much elevated, and consequently the blood flow through the unconstricted or actually dilated vessels of the body will be all the more abundant.

Adrenin has a well-known stimulating effect on the isolated heart—causing an increase both in the rate and the amplitude of cardiac contraction. This effect accords with the general rule that adrenin simulates the action of sympathetic impulses. It is commonly stated, however, that if the heart holds its normal relations in the body, adrenin causes slowing of the beat.[29] This view is doubtless due to the massive doses that have been employed, which are quite beyond physiological limits and which induce such enormous increases of arterial pressure that the natural influence of adrenin on heart muscle is overcome by mechanical obstacles to quick contractions and by inhibitory impulses from the central nervous system. Hoskins and Lovellette have demonstrated that when the precaution is taken to inject adrenin into a vein in a manner resembling the discharge from the adrenal glands, not only is there increased blood pressure, but generally, also, an acceleration of the pulse.[30]   At the same time, therefore, that a greater amount of work, from increased arterial pressure, is demanded of the heart, blood is delivered to the heart in greater abundance, and the muscle is excited by adrenin and by sympathetic impulses to more rapid and vigorous pulsations.   The augmentation of the heart beat is thus coördinate with the other adaptive functions of the adrenal glands in great emergencies.

That the acceleration of the heart is of primary importance in the doing of muscular work has been shown in an experiment on a dog with a completely denervated heart.   This animal, studied by Campos, Lundin, Walker and myself,[31] had run 167 minutes at 110 meters per minute with an energy output of 20,000 kilogrammeters and with the pulse rising from 96 to 156 beats per minute before showing signs of exhaustion.   On October 11, she ran, under the influence of adrenin, 203 minutes at 148 meters per minute, with an energy output of 33,000 kilogrammeters and with the pulse rising from 84 to 156.   The heart was denervated on November 1.   Thereafter the greatest increase ever observed when the animal was induced to run was 12 beats per minute.   The animal could not be made to run to an extent resulting in signs of being tired.   She would travel for a relatively short time and then would brace all four feet and refuse to move.

Administration of adrenin, however, would raise the heart rate from its basal (96 beats per minute) to 120 and therewith considerably augment the work capacity. For example, on December 1, the animal ran in short periods (two of 13 and 15 minutes, others of 2 or 3 minutes only) for 44 minutes at 129 meters per minute—an energy output of 6,000 kilogrammeters. No further work would the animal perform. The heart rate remained at 96. Four days later (December 4) the animal was given adrenin (0.035 milligrams per kilogram) at the start and twice later. She ran for an hour and a half—the first half hour "steadily"—at 123 meters per minute, putting forth 12,000 kilogrammeters of energy. The heart rate was raised from 96 to 120. These results were typical. They show quite strikingly the great limitation of the ability to run when the heart does not take part in the organic adjustments.

THE VALUE OF AN INCREASED NUMBER OF RED BLOOD CORPUSCLES

An urgent need in struggle or flight is a generous supply of oxygen to burn the metabolites of muscular contraction, and a quick riddance of the resultant carbon dioxide from the body. Both oxygen and carbon dioxide are carried by the red corpuscles of the blood. When the blood pressure is high, from constriction of the splanchnic vessels and from a faster beating of the heart, the blood flows faster through the unconstricted vessels of the brain and spinal cord and through the actually dilated vessels of the active muscles. Thus the regularly available red corpuscles are put to greater use by being forced to make an increased number of trips between the lungs and the laboring organs.

Besides that device for carrying in larger volume the respiratory gases there is a release of extra erythrocytes from concentrated storage in the spleen. As previously shown, brief excitement may increase the percentage of circulating erythrocytes by 20 per cent or more. These extra carriers of oxygen and carbon dioxide are not simply added to the circulation; they are brought out when the heart is beating rapidly and the head of arterial pressure is high. Their service to the organism, therefore, is to be multiplied by the faster rate of movement of the corpuscles in those circumstances. Fatigue is to a great degree dependent on the accumulation of nonvolatile waste products (lactic acid) in the working muscles. The polycythemia induced by excitement would be favorable to prolonged muscular exertion, because it would help to bring more oxygen for the burning of the nonvolatile waste to volatile carbon dioxide and to carry away the carbon dioxide for riddance through the lungs.

THE CHANGES IN RESPIRATORY FUNCTION ARE FAVORABLE TO GREAT EFFORT

When vigorous exercise is begun the breathing at once changes so as to bring about a more thorough ventilation of the lungs. And one of the most characteristic reactions of animals in pain and emotional excitement is deep and rapid respiration. Again the reflex response is precisely what would be most serviceable to the organism in the strenuous efforts of fighting or escape that might accompany or follow distress or fear or rage. It is known that by such forced respirations the carbon dioxide content of the blood can be so much reduced that the need for any breathing whatever may be deferred for as much as a minute or even longer.[32] And Douglas and Haldane [33] have found that moderately forced breathing for three minutes previous to severe muscular exertion results in greatly diminishing the subsequent respiratory distress, as well as lessening the amount of air breathed and the amount of carbon dioxide given off. Furthermore, the heart beats less rapidly after the performance and returns more quickly from its increased rate to normal. The forced respirations in deeply emotional experiences can be interpreted, therefore, as an anticipatory reduction of the carbon dioxide in the blood, a preparation for the augmented discharge of carbon dioxide into the blood as soon as great muscular exertion begins.*

As the air moves to and fro in the lungs with each respiration, it must pass through the fine divisions of

---

* The excessive production of heat in muscular work gives rise to sweating. The evaporation of sweat helps to keep the body temperature from rising unduly from the heat of exertion. Again in strong emotion and in pain the "cold sweat" that appears on the skin may be regarded as a reaction anticipatory of the strenuous muscular movements that are likely to ensue.

the air tubes or bronchioles. The bronchioles are provided with smooth muscle, which, in all probability,
like smooth muscle elsewhere in the body, is normally
held in a state of tonic contraction. When this tonic
contraction is much increased, as in asthma, breathing
becomes difficult, and even with the body at rest unusual effort is then required to maintain the minimal
necessary ventilation of the lungs. During strenuous
exertion, with each breath the air must rush through
the bronchioles in greatly increased volume and speed.
Thus in a well person "winded" with running, for example, the bronchioles might become *relatively* too
small for the stream of air, just as they are too small
in a person ill with asthma. And then some extra
energy would have to be expended to force the air back
and forth with sufficient rapidity to satisfy the bodily
needs. It is probable that even under the most favorable conditions, the labored breathing in hard exercise
involves to some degree the work of accelerating the
tidal flow of the respiratory gases. This extra labor
would obviously be reduced, if the tonic contraction of
the ring-muscles in the wall of the bronchioles was reduced, so that the tubules were enlarged. It has been
shown by a number of investigators, who have used
various methods, that adrenin injected into the blood
stream has as one of its precise actions the dilating of
the bronchioles.[34] The adrenin discharged in emotional
excitement goes to the bronchial arteries on leaving the
heart and is at once delivered to their territory; it may,
therefore, have as its first effect the relaxation of the

smooth muscles of the lungs. This would be another very direct means of rendering the organism more efficient when fierce struggle calls for a bounteous supply of oxygen and a speedy discharge of the carbonaceous waste.

EFFECTS PRODUCED IN ASPHYXIA SIMILAR TO THOSE PRODUCED IN PAIN AND EXCITEMENT

All the bodily responses occurring in pain and emotional excitement have thus far been considered as *anticipatory* of the instinctive acts which naturally follow. And as we have seen, these responses can reasonably be interpreted as preparatory to the great exertions which may be demanded of the organism. This interpretation of the facts is supported by the discovery that a mechanism exists whereby the changes initiated in an anticipatory manner by emotional excitement are continued or perhaps augmented by the exertion itself.

Great exertion, such as might attend flight or conflict, might result in an insufficient supply of necessary oxygen. Then, although respiratory and circulatory changes of emotional origin may have prepared the body for struggle, the emotional provisions for keeping the working parts at a high level of efficiency may not continue to operate, or they may not be adequate. If there is painful gasping for breath in the course of prolonged and vigorous exertion, or for a considerable period after the work has ceased, a condition of partial asphyxia has evidently been induced. This condition, as every one knows, is distinctly unfavorable to further effort. But the asphyxia itself may act as a stimulus.[35]

In our examination of the influence of various conditions on the secretion of the adrenal glands, Hoskins and I [36] tested the effects of asphyxia. By use of the intestinal segment as an indicator we compared the action of blood, taken as nearly simultaneously as possible from the inferior vena cava above the adrenal vessels and from the femoral vein before asphyxia, with blood taken from the same sources after asphyxia had been produced. The femoral venous blood after passing the capillaries of the leg thus acted as a standard for the same blood after receiving the contribution of the adrenal veins. Asphyxia was caused by covering the tracheal cannula until respiration became labored and slow, but capable of recovery when air was admitted. It may be regarded, therefore, as not extreme.

The results of the degree of asphyxia above described are shown by graphic record in Fig. 38. Blood taken from the vena cava and from the femoral vein before asphyxia ("normal") failed to cause inhibition of the contractions. Blood taken from the femoral vein after asphyxia produced almost the same effect as blood from the same vein before; asphyxia, therefore, had wrought no change demonstrable in the general venous flow. Blood taken from the vena cava after asphyxia had, on the contrary, an effect markedly unlike blood from the same region before (compare the record after

1 and after 7, Fig. 38)—it caused the typical inhibition
which indicates the presence of adrenal secretion.*

That the positive result obtained in moderate
asphyxia is not attributable to other agencies in the

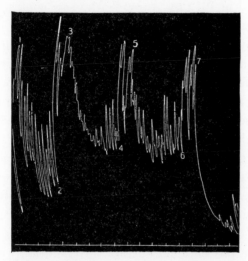

FIG. 38.—Adrenal secretion produced by asphyxia. At *1* normal
    vena-cava blood applied, at *2* removed.   At *3* normal blood
    from femoral vein applied, at *4* removed.   At *5* blood from
    femoral vein after asphyxia applied, at *6* removed.   At *7* blood
    from the vena cava after asphyxia applied.   Time, half-minutes.

blood than adrenin is indicated by the failure of asphyxial femoral blood to cause inhibition, while vena-
cava blood, taken almost simultaneously, brought

* This positive result might suggest that the comparison of both
femoral and vena-cava blood under each condition was unnecessary,
and that a comparison merely of vena-cava blood before and after
asphyxia would be sufficient.   Positive results were indeed thus
secured, but they occurred even when the adrenal glands were carefully removed and extreme asphyxia (i. e., stoppage of respiration)
was induced.   That the blood may contain in extreme asphyxia a
substance or substances capable of causing inhibition of intestinal

about immediate relaxation of the muscle. The conclusion was drawn, therefore, that asphyxia results in increased secretion of the adrenal glands.

These observations and this conclusion were corroborated in 1912 by Anrep [37] who saw contraction of the denervated limb and the denervated kidney attending asphyxia; in 1914 by Gasser and Meek [38] who noted marked acceleration of the denervated heart of the dog when the animal was asphyxiated for 30 seconds; in 1919 by myself [39] and in 1922 by Carrasco-Formiguera and myself [5] with use likewise of the denervated heart. In all these tests the effects disappeared after the adrenal glands were excluded from participation; and in the experiments which Carrasco-Formiguera and I performed, the faster heart beat was alternately present or absent in correspondence with the presence or absence of blood flow from the adrenal glands at the time of asphyxiation. Further corroboration was supplied by Kellaway [40] in 1919 and by Hartman, McCordock and Loder [41] in 1923 experimenting on the denervated iris, by Tournade and Chabrol [42] in 1923 and by Houssay and Molinelli [43] in 1925 testing adrenal secretion by its effects when passed from the adrenal vein of the asphyxiated animal directly into the blood

---

contractions was thus demonstrated. In one instance, after the blood was proved free from adrenin, the aorta and vena cava were tied close below the diaphragm, and the carotids were tied about midway in the neck. Extreme asphyxia was produced (lasting five minutes). Blood now taken from the heart caused marked inhibition of the beating intestinal segment. Probably, therefore, the inhibitory action of blood taken from an animal when *extremely* asphyxiated cannot be due to adrenin alone.

stream of another animal. This mass of positive testimony is confronted by the inability of Stewart and Rogoff [44] to obtain any increased discharge of adrenin as a result of general asphyxia. They are alone in their claim that asphyxia leaves unaffected the secretion of adrenin. Kodama,[45] using Stewart and Rogoff's method, has confirmed our results. The evidence for asphyxial stimulation of the sympathico-adrenal system is overwhelming. Indeed, as Zwemer and Newton [46] have shown, even the nerve supply to the adrenals is not essential—the denervated glands can be made to secrete adrenin, which will accelerate the denervated heart, if only the blood flow to them is completely stopped for as long as ten seconds. It is quite possible, therefore, that asphyxia is effective not only by action on the sympathetic centers in the brain and spinal cord, but also by peripheral action on the adrenal medulla itself.

Asphyxia, like pain and excitement, not only liberates adrenin, but, as might be inferred from that fact, also mobilizes sugar.[47]   And, furthermore, Starkenstein [48] has shown that the asphyxia due to carbon-monoxide poisoning is not accompanied by increased blood sugar if the adrenal glands have been removed.

In case strong emotions are followed by vigorous exertions, therefore, asphyxia is likely to result, and this will act in conjunction with the emotional excitement and pain, or perhaps in continuation of the influences of these states, to bring forth still more adrenal discharge and still further output of sugar from the liver.

And these in turn would serve the laboring muscles in the manner already described. This suggestion harmonizes with Zuntz's statement [49] that the asphyxia of great physical exertion may call out sugar to such a degree that, in spite of the increased use of it in the active muscles, glycosuria may ensue.

The evidence previously adduced that adrenin causes relaxation of the smooth muscle of the bronchioles, taken in conjunction with the evidence that adrenal secretion is liberated in asphyxia, suggests that relief from difficult breathing may thus be automatically provided for in the organism. The well-known phenomenon of "second wind" is characterized by an almost miraculous refreshment and renewal of vigor, after an individual has persisted in violent exertion in spite of being "out of breath." It seems not improbable that this phenomenon, for which many explanations have been offered, is really due to setting in operation the supporting mechanism which, as we have seen, plays so important a rôle in augmenting bodily vigor in emotional excitement. The release of sugar and adrenin, the abundance of blood flow through the muscles—supplying energy and lessening fatigue—and the relaxation of the bronchiolar walls, are all occurrences which may reasonably be regarded as resulting from asphyxia. And when they take place they doubtless do much to abolish the distress itself by which they were occasioned. According to this explanation "second wind" would consist in the establishment of the same group of bodily changes, leading to more efficient physical struggle, that are observed in pain and **excite-ment.**

THE UTILITY OF RAPID COAGULATION IN PREVENTING LOSS OF BLOOD

The increase of blood sugar, the secretion of adrenin, the altered circulation and the polycythemia in pain and emotional excitement have been interpreted in the foregoing discussion as biological adaptations to conditions in wild life which are likely to involve pain and emotional excitement, i. e., the necessities of fighting or flight. The more rapid clotting of blood under these same circumstances may also be regarded as an adaptive process, useful to the organism. The importance of conserving the blood, especially in the struggles of mortal combat, needs no argument. The effect of local injury in favoring the formation of a clot to seal the opened vessels is obviously adaptive in protecting the organism against hemorrhage. The injury that causes opening of blood vessels, however, is, if extensive, likely also to produce pain. And, as already shown, conditions producing pain increase adrenal secretion and hasten coagulation. Thus injury would be made less dangerous as an occasion for serious hemorrhage by two effects which the injury itself produces in the body —the local effect on clotting at the region of injury and the general effect on the speed of clotting wrought by reflex secretion of adrenin.

According to the argument here presented the strong

emotions, as fear and anger, are rightly interpreted as the concomitants of bodily changes which may be of utmost service in subsequent action. These bodily changes are so much like those which occur in pain and fierce struggle that, as early writers on evolution suggested, the emotions may be considered as foreshadowing the suffering and intensity of actual strife. On this general basis, therefore, the bodily alterations attending violent emotional states would, as organic preparations for fighting and possible injury, naturally involve the effects which pain itself would produce. And increased blood sugar, a larger output of adrenin, an adapted circulation, a greater number of red corpuscles and rapid clotting would all be favorable to the preservation of the organism that could best produce them.

SOME CRITICISMS CONSIDERED

The conclusion just drawn has been criticized by Dumas.[50] Some of his points were made with apparent misunderstanding of both the evidence and the inferences therefrom. I shall quote him in substance. "Adrenin favors flight but also struggle"—but adrenin has never been regarded as a differentiator of emotions (see p. 342; as a symbol of the bodily changes in emotional excitement it indicates preparedness and since both flight and struggle involve great muscular effort, the bodily changes in both would favor success in such effort. "Adrenin empties the intestine of blood but does nothing for the brain or the lungs"—but, as was pointed out in 1915 (see p. 106), in precisely these regions, as well as in the active muscles, the circulation becomes more abundant. "There may be pallor in fear and anger, and this is not consistent with peripheral vasodilation"—but, as was explained in 1920 (see p. 105), adrenin causes dilation of skeletal muscles and constriction of cutaneous vessels. "Gley and Quinquaud seem to have shown that adrenin in the general circulation becomes so diluted that it cannot manifest its properties"—but evidence to the contrary has existed for many years and in 1925 Gley [51] admitted the existence of an effective "adrenalinemia." "Stewart and Rogoff have demonstrated that cats with adrenals inactivated present the same reactions of rage and fright as normal cats"—but no claim has been made that the emotional display of animals is dependent on secreted adrenin. "Fear which paralyzes is as much fear as that which gives speed to flight"— true, but not pertinent, for failure to employ organic preparations for action is not a valid argument against their being serviceable when they are employed.

Dumas rightly derides the free use of the imagination in devising elaborate utilitarian explanations of the contracted brow, the dilated nostrils and other trivial facial expressions seen in great emotional excitement. Spencer and Darwin made much of these superficial changes of features; they knew nothing of the profounder internal changes with which we have been concerned. We have not attempted to show that fear and rage are dependent on these changes, as some of the above quotations from Dumas would indicate. We have been confronted by a group of facts and have tried to understand them. The facts at once have significance if considered in relation to the struggle for existence. For ages past this struggle has disciplined and relentlessly selected the most efficient. If fear always paralyzed it would result only in danger of destruction. But fear and aggressive feeling, as anticipatory responses to critical situations, make ready for action and thereby they have had great survival values. And the remarkable system of internal adjustments which attend these emotions and which mobilize the forces of the body are such as to have had great survival values. Thus the bodily changes may reasonably be interpreted. When a more reasonable theory is offered it will be welcomed.

REFERENCES

1. See DARWIN, *Expression of Emotions in Man and Animals* (New York, 1905), pp. 101-117.
2. SPENCER, *Principles of Psychology* (London, 1855).
3. MCDOUGALL, *Introduction to Social Psychology* (London, 1908), pp. 49, 59.
4. CRILE, *Boston Medical and Surgical Journal*, clxiii (1910), p. 893.
5. CANNON and CARRASCO-FORMIGUERA, *American Journal of Physiology*, lxi (1922), p. 215.
6. BRITTON, *ibid.*, lxxxvi (1928), p. 340.
7. NASSE, *Archiv für die gesammte Physiologie*, ii (1869), p. 106; xiv (1877), p. 483.
8. FRENTZEL, *ibid.*, lvi (1894), p. 280.
9. ZUNTZ, *Oppenheimer's Handbuch der Biochemie* (Jena, 1911), iv, first half, p. 841.

10. MANN and MAGATH, *American Journal of Physiology*, lxv (1923), p. 403.

11. KROGH and LINDHARD, *Biochemical Journal*, xiv (1920), p. 290.

12. FURUSAWA, *Proceedings of the Royal Society of London*, Bxcviii(1925), p. 65.

13. CHAUVEAU and KAUFMANN, *Comptes Rendus, Académie des Sciences*, ciii (1886), p. 1062.

14. QUINQUAUD, *Comptes Rendus de la Société de Biologie* xxxviii (1886), p. 410.

15. MORAT and DUFOURT, *Archives de Physiologie*, xxiv (1892), p. 327.

16. PAVY, *The Physiology of the Carbohydrates* (London, 1894), p. 166.

17. MAGNUS-LEVY, v. *Noorden's Handbuch der Pathologie des Stoffwechsels*, i (1906), p. 385.

18. LOCKE and ROSENHEIM, *Journal of Physiology*, xxxvi (1907), p. 211.

19. PATTERSON and STARLING, *ibid.*, xlvii (1913), p. 143.

20. See MACLEOD and PEARCE, *American Journal of Physiology*, xxxii (1913), p. 192. PAVY and SIAU, *Journal of Physiology*, xxix (1903), p. 375. MACLEOD, *American Journal of Physiology*, xxiii (1909), p. 278.

21. LOCKE, *Centralblatt für Physiologie*, xiv (1900), p. 671.

22. SCHUMBERG, *Archiv für Physiologie* (1896), p. 537.

23. FRENTZEL, *ibid.* (1899), Supplement Band, p. 145.

24. LEE and HARROLD, *American Journal of Physiology*, iv (1900), p. ix.

25. WILENKO, *Biochemische Zeitschrift*, xlii (1912), p. 58.

26. LUSK and RICHE, *Archives of Internal Medicine*, xiii (1914), p. 68.

27. TOMPKINS, STURGIS and WEARN, *ibid.*, xxiv (1919), p. 269.

28. SANDIFORD, *American Journal of Physiology*, li (1920), p. 407.

29. See BIEDL, *Die Innere Sekretion*, i (1913), p. 464.

30. HOSKINS and LOVELLETTE, *Journal of the American Medical Association*, lxiii (1914), p. 317.

31. CAMPOS, CANNON, LUNDIN and WALKER, *American Journal of Physiology*, lxxxvii (1929), p. 680.

32. See HALDANE and PRIESTLEY, *Journal of Physiology*, xxxii (1905), p. 255.

33. DOUGLAS and HALDANE, *ibid.*, xxxix (1909), p. 1.

34. See JANUSCHKE and POLLAK, *Archiv für experimentelle Pathologie und Pharmakologie*, lxvi (1911), p. 205. TRENDELENBURG, *Zentralblatt für Physiologie*, xxvi (1912), p. 1. JACKSON, *Journal of Pharmacology and Experimental Therapeutics*, iv (1912), p. 59.

35. Cf. HOSKINS and McCLURE, *Archives of Internal Medicine*, x (1912), p. 355.

36. CANNON and HOSKINS, *American Journal of Physiology*, xxix (1911), p. 275.

37. ANREP, *Journal of Physiology*, xlv (1912), p. 307.

38. GASSER and MEEK, *American Journal of Physiology*, xxxiv (1914), p. 63.

39. CANNON, *ibid.*, 1 (1919), p. 399.

40. KELLAWAY, *Journal of Physiology*, liii (1919), p. 211.

41. HARTMAN, McCORDOCK and LODER, *American Journal of Physiology*, lxiv (1923), p. 1.

42. TOURNADE and CHABROL, *Comptes Rendus de la Société de Biologie*, lxxxviii (1923), p. 1180.

43. HOUSSAY and MOLINELLI, *Revista di la Sociedad Argentina de Biologia*, i (1925), p. 402.

44. STEWART and ROGOFF, *Journal of Pharmacology and Experimental Therapeutics*, x (1917), p. 49.

45. KODAMA, *Tohoku Journal of Experimental Medicine*, v (1924), p. 47.

46. ZWEMER and NEWTON, *American Journal of Physiology*, lxxxv (1928), p. 507.

47. For evidence and for references to this literature, see BANG, *Der Blutzucker* (Wiesbaden, 1913), pp. 104-108.

48. STARKENSTEIN, *op. cit.*, p. 94.

49. ZUNTZ, *op. cit.*, p. 854.

50. DUMAS, *Revue Philosophique*, xciii (1922), p. 68; also *Traité de Psychologie*, i (Paris, 1923), p. 606.

51. GLEY, *Bulletin de la Société de Pathologie Comparée*, xxv (1925), p. 102.

CHAPTER XIII

THE ENERGIZING INFLUENCE OF EMOTIONAL EXCITEMENT

THE close relation between emotion and muscular action has long been perceived. As Sherrington [1] has pointed out, "Emotion 'moves' us, hence the word itself. If developed in intensity, it impels toward vigorous movement. Every vigorous movement of the body . . . involves also the less noticeable coöperation of the viscera, especially of the circulatory and respiratory. The extra demand made upon the muscles that move the frame involves a heightened action of the nutrient organs which supply to the muscles the material for their energy." The researches here reported have revealed a number of unsuspected ways in which muscular action is made more efficient because of emotional disturbances of the viscera. Every one of the visceral changes that have been noted—the cessation of processes in the alimentary canal (thus freeing the energy supply for other parts); the shifting of blood from the abdominal organs to the organs immediately essential to muscular exertion; the increased vigor of contraction of the heart; the discharge of extra blood corpuscles from the spleen; the deeper respiration; the dilation of the bronchioles; the quick abolition of the effects of muscular fatigue; the mobilizing of sugar in the circulation—these changes are *directly service-able in making the organism more effective in the violent display of energy which fear or rage or pain may involve.*

"RESERVOIRS OF POWER"

That the major emotions have an energizing effect has been commonly recognized.* Darwin testified to having heard, "as a proof of the exciting nature of anger, that a man when excessively jaded will sometimes invent imaginary offenses and put himself into a passion, unconsciously, for the sake of reinvigorating himself; and," Darwin [2] continues, "since hearing this remark, I have occasionally recognized its full truth." Under the impulse of fear also, men have been known to achieve extraordinary feats of running and leaping. McDougall [3] cites the instance of an athlete who, when pursued as a boy by a savage animal, leaped over a wall which he could not again "clear" until he attained his full stature and strength. The exploit of John Colter, as reported by a contemporary, exemplifies vividly the reënforcing effects of great excitement. In Montana, in 1808, Colter and a companion were seized by Indians. Colter was stripped naked; his companion, who resisted, was killed and hacked in pieces. The Chief then made signs to Colter to go away across the

---

* Russell (*The Pima Indians,* United States Bureau of Ethnology, 1908, p. 243) relates a tale told by the Indians to their children, in which an injured coyote was chasing some quails. "Finally the quails got tired," according to the story, "but the coyote did not, for he was angry and did not feel fatigue."

prairie. When he had gone a short distance he saw the younger men casting aside everything but their weapons and making ready for a chase. "Now he knew their object. He was to run a race, of which the prize was to be his own life and scalp. Off he started with the speed of the wind. The war whoop immediately arose; and looking back, he saw a large company of young warriors, with spears, in rapid pursuit. He ran with all the speed that nature, excited to the utmost, could give; fear and hope lent a supernatural vigor to his limbs, and the rapidity of his flight astonished himself." After nearly three miles his strength began to wane. He stopped and looked back. Only one of his pursuers was near. The Indian rushed towards him, attempted to cast his spear and fell headlong. Colter seized the spear, killed his enemy and again set out, "with renewed strength, feeling, as he said to me, as if he had not run a mile." [4] The very unusual abilities, both physical and mental, which men have exhibited in times of stress were dealt with from the psychological point of view by William James [5] in one of his last essays. He suggested that in every person there are "reservoirs of power" which are not ordinarily called upon, but which are nevertheless ready to pour forth streams of energy if only the occasion presents itself. These figurative expressions of the psychologist receive definite and concrete exemplification, so far as the physical exhibitions of power are concerned, in the highly serviceable bodily changes which have been described in the foregoing chapters.

It would doubtless be incorrect to attempt to account for all the increased strength and tireless endurance, which may be experienced in periods of great excitement, on the basis of abundant supplies provided then for muscular contraction, and a special secretion for avoiding or abolishing the depressive influences of fatigue. Tremors, muscular twitchings, the assumption of characteristic attitudes, all indicate that there is an immensely augmented activity of the nervous system— an activity that discharges powerfully even into parts not directly concerned in struggle, as, for example, into the muscles of the voice, causing peculiar cries or warning notes; into the muscles of the ears, drawing them back or causing them to stand erect, and into the small muscles about the lips, tightening them and revealing the teeth. The typical appearances of human beings, as well as lower animals, when in the grip of such deeply agitating emotions as fear and rage, are so well recognized as to constitute a primitive and common means of judging the nature of the experience through which the organism is passing. This "pattern" response of the nervous system to an emotion-provoking object or situation is probably capable of bringing into action a much greater number of neurones in the central nervous system than are likely to be concerned in even a supreme act of volition. The nervous impulses delivered to the muscles, furthermore, operate upon organs well supplied with energy-yielding material and well fortified by rapidly circulating blood and by secreted adrenin, against quick loss of power because of accumulating waste. Under such circumstances of excitement the performance of extraordinary feats of strength or endurance is natural enough.*

In connection with the conception that strong emotion has a dynamogenic value, it is of interest to note that on occasions when great demands are likely to be placed on the neuro-muscular system in the doing of unusual labors, emotional excitement is not uncommonly an accompaniment. In order to emphasize points in the argument developed thus far, I propose to cite some examples of the association of emotional excitement with remarkable exhibitions of power or resistance to fatigue.

THE EXCITEMENTS AND ENERGIES OF
COMPETITIVE SPORTS

Already in an earlier account (see p. 74) I have mentioned finding sugar in the urine in approximately fifty per cent of a group of college football players after the most exacting game of the season's play. As is well understood, such games are heralded far and wide, loyal supporters of each college may travel hundreds of miles to attend the contest, enthusiastic meetings of undergraduate students are held in each college to demonstrate their devotion to the team and their confidence in its prowess—indeed, the incitements to victory, the

---

* Since single neurones obey the law of either supreme action or inaction, the "all-or-none law," the only means of securing a graded response is through variation of the *number* of neurones engaged in action—the more, the greater the resulting manifestation of strength.

songs, the cheering, are likely to be so disturbing to the
players, that before an important contest they are not
infrequently removed from college surroundings in
order to avoid being overwrought when the contest
comes.

On the day of the contest the excitement is multiplied manyfold. There is practically a holiday in college and to a large extent in the city as well. The
streets are filled with eager supporters of each team
as the hosts begin to gather at the field. As many as
70,000 spectators may be present, each one tense and
strongly partisan. The student bands lead the singing,
by thousands of voices, of songs which urge to the
utmost effort for the college; and, in anticipation, these
songs also celebrate the victory.

Into the center of that huge, cheering, yelling, singing, flag-waving crowd, the players are welcomed in a
special outburst of these same demonstrations of enthusiasm. Soon the game begins. The position of
every player is known, if not because of previous acquaintance and recognition, because card-diagrams give
the information. Every important play is seen by the
assembled thousands, and the player who makes it is
at once announced to all, and is likely to be honored by
his multitudinous college mates in a special cheer, ending in his name. Any player who, by infraction of the
rules or failure to do his part, loses ground gained by
his team is also known. The man who is "played out"
in efforts to win for his team and college, and consequently has to leave the field, is welcomed to the side

lines by acclamations suited for a great hero. In short, every effort is made, through the powerful incentives of censure and a flaunting recognition, to make each member of the team realize vividly his responsibility, both personal and as one of a group, for the supreme, all-important result—victory for his college.

This responsibility works tremendously on the emotions of the players. In the dressing room before a critical contest I have seen a "gridiron warrior," ready in canvas suit, cleated shoes, and leather helmet, sitting grimly on a bench, his fists clenched, his jaws tight, and his face the grayish color of clay. He performed wonderfully when the game began, and after it was over there was a large percentage of sugar in his urine! Probably no sport requires a more sustained and extreme display of neuro-muscular effort than American football. And from the foregoing description of the conditions that surround the contests it is easy to realize that they conspire to arouse in the players excitements which would bring forth very efficiently the bodily reserves for use in the fierce struggle which the game requires.

What is true of footfall is true, though perhaps to a less degree, of the racing sports, as running and rowing. Again great multitudes attend the events, the contests are followed closely from beginning to end, and as the goal is approached the cheering and cries for victory gather in volume and intensity as if arranged for a thrilling climax. The whole setting is most highly favorable to the dramatic development of an acme of excitement as the moment approaches when the last desperate effort to win is put forth.

FRENZY AND ENDURANCE IN CEREMONIAL AND
OTHER DANCES

Dancing, which formed a significant feature of primitive rituals, has always been accompanied by exciting conditions, and not unusually was an exhibition of remarkable endurance. In the transfer of the Ark to Zion there were processions and sacrifices, and King David "danced before the Lord with all his might." Mooney[6] in his account of dances among the American Indians tells of a young man who in one of the ceremonials danced three days and nights without food, drink or sleep. In such a terrible ordeal the favoring presence of others, who through group action help to stimulate both the excitement and the activities, must be an important element in prolonging the efforts of the individual.

In the history of religious manias[7] there are many instances of large numbers of people becoming frenzied and then showing extraordinary endurance while dancing. In 1374 a mania broke forth in Germany, the Netherlands and France, in which the victims claimed to dance in honor of Saint John. Men and women went about dancing hand in hand, in pairs, or in circles, on the streets, in the churches, at their homes, or wherever they might be, hour after hour without rest. While dancing they sang, uttered cries, and saw visions. Whole companies of these crazy fanatics went dancing along the public roads and into the cities, until they had to be checked.

In 1740 an extraordinary sect, known as the "Jumpers," arose in Wales. According to the description given by Wesley, their exercises were not unlike those of certain frenzied exhibitions among the Indians. "After the preaching was over," Wesley [8] wrote, "any one who pleased gave out a verse of a hymn; and this they sung over and over again, with all their might and main, thirty or forty times, till some of them worked themselves into a sort of drunkenness or madness; they were then violently agitated, and leaped up and down in all manner of postures, frequently for hours together." There were sometimes thousands at a single meeting of the Jumpers, shouting out their excitement and ready to leap for joy.[9] Wesley has also described instances of tremendous emotional outburst at Methodist meetings which he addressed. "Some were torn with a kind of convulsive motion in every part of their bodies, and that so violently that often four or five persons could not hold one of them. I have seen many hysterical or epileptic fits," he wrote, "but none of them were like these in many respects."

Among the dervishes [10] likewise the dance is accompanied by intense excitement and apparently tireless movements.

The cries of "Yâ Allah!" are increased doubly, as also those of "Yâ Hoo!" with frightful howlings shrieked by the dervishes together in the dance. . . . There was no regularity in their dancing, but each seemed to be performing the antics of a madman; now moving his body up and down; the next moment turning round, then using odd gesticulations with his arms, next jumping, and sometimes screaming. . . . At the moment when they would seem to stop from sheer exhaustion the sheikh makes a point of exciting them to new efforts by walking through their midst, making also himself most violent movements. He is next replaced by two elders, who double the quickness of the step and the agitation of the body; they even straighten themselves up from time to time, and excite the envy or emulation of others in their astonishing efforts to continue the dance until their strength is entirely exhausted.

Such is the frenzy thus developed that the performers may be subjected to severe pain, yet only show signs of elation.

In all these dances the two most marked features are the intense excitement of those who engage in them and the very remarkable physical endurance which they manifest. Although there is no direct evidence, such as was obtained in examining the football players, that bodily changes favorable to great neuro-muscular exertion are developed in these furies of fanaticism, it is highly probable that they are so developed, and that the feats of fortitude which are performed are to a large extent explicable on the basis of a "tapping of the reservoirs of power" through the emotional excitement.

THE FIERCE EMOTIONS AND STRUGGLES OF BATTLE

Throughout the discussion of the probable significance of the bodily changes in pain and great emotion, the value of these changes in the struggle of conflict or escape was emphasized. In human beings as well as in lower animals the wildest passions are aroused when the necessities of combat become urgent. One needs only to glance at the history of warfare to observe that when the primitive emotions of anger and hatred are permitted full sway, men who have been considerate and thoughtful of their fellows and their fellows' rights suddenly may turn into infuriated savages, slaughtering innocent women and children, mutilating the wounded, burning, ravaging, and looting, with all the wild fervor of demons. It is in such excesses of emotional turbulence that the most astonishing instances of prolonged exertion and incredible endurance are to be found.

Probably the fiercest struggles between men that are recorded are those which occurred when the wager of battle was a means of determining innocence or guilt. In the corners of the plot selected for the combat a bier was prepared for each participant, as a symbol that the struggle was for life or death. Each was attended by his relatives and followers, and by his father confessor.[11] After each had prayed to God for help in the coming combat, the weapons were selected, the sacrament was administered, and the battle was begun. The principals fought to the end with continuous and brutal ferocity, resembling the desperate encounters of wild beasts. A fairly illustrative example is furnished in an incident which followed the assassination of Charles the Good of Flanders in 1127. One of the accomplices, a knight named Guy, was challenged for complicity by another named Herman. Both were renowned warriors. Herman was speedily unhorsed by

Guy, who with his lance frustrated all Herman's attempts to remount. Then Herman disabled Guy's
horse, and the combat was renewed on foot with swords.
Equally skillful in fence, they continued the struggle
till fatigue compelled them to drop sword and shield,
whereupon they wrestled for the mastery. Guy threw
his antagonist, fell on him, and beat him in the face
with his gauntlets till he seemed to be motionless; but
Herman had quietly slipped his hand below the other's
coat of mail and, grasping the testicles, with a mighty
effort wrenched them away. Immediately Guy fell
over and expired.[12] In such terrific fights as these,
conducted in the extremes of rage and hate, the mechanisms for reënforcing the parts of the body which are
of primary importance in the struggle are brought fully
into action and are of utmost value in securing victory.

THE STIMULATING INFLUENCE OF WITNESSES AND OF MUSIC

It is noteworthy that in all the instances thus far
cited—in the great games, in dancing, and in fighting—
two factors are present that are well known to have an
augmenting effect both in the full development of emotions and in the performance of unusual muscular labors. One of these is the crowd of witnesses or participants, who contribute the "mob spirit" that tends to
carry the actions of the individual far beyond the limits
set by any personal considerations or prudencies. The
other is the influence of music. As Darwin years ago

indicated, music has a wonderful power of recalling in a vague and indefinite manner strong emotions which have been felt by our ancestors in long-past ages. Especially is this true of martial music. For the grim purposes of war the reed and the lute are grotesquely ill-suited; to rouse men to action strident brass and the jarring instruments of percussion are used in full force. The influence of martial music on some persons is so profound as to cause the muscles to tremble and tears to come to the eyes—both indications of the deep stirring of emotional responses in the body. And when deeds of fortitude and fierce exertions are to be performed the effectiveness of such music in rousing the aggressive emotions has long been recognized. The Romans charged their foes amid the blasts of trumpets and horns. The ancient Germans rushed to battle, their forces spurred by the sounds of drums, flutes, cymbals and clarions. There is a tradition that the Hungarian troops are the worst in Europe, until their bands begin to play—then they are the best! The late General Linevitch is quoted as saying: "Music is one of the most vital ammunitions of the Russian army. Without music a Russian soldier would be dull, cowardly, brutal and inefficient. From music he absorbs a magic power of endurance, and forgets the sufferings and mortality. It is a divine dynamite." And Napoleon is said to have testified that the weird and barbaric tunes of the Cossack regiments infuriated them to such rage that they wiped out the cream of his army.[13] A careful consideration of the use of martial music in warfare would perhaps bring further interesting evidence that its function is to reënforce the bodily changes that attend the belligerent emotions.

Only a few instances of the combination of extreme pain, rage, terror or excitement, and tremendous muscular power have been given in the preceding pages. Doubtless in numerous other conditions these two groups of phenomena occur together. In the lives of firemen and the police, in the experiences of escaping prisoners, of shipwrecked sailors, in the struggles between pioneers and their savage enemies, in accounts of forced marches or retreats, search would reveal many examples of such bodily disturbances as have been described in earlier chapters as augmenting the effectiveness of muscular efforts, and such exhibitions of power or endurance as are evidently far beyond the ordinary. There is every reason for believing that, were the conditions favorable to experimental testing, it would be possible to demonstrate and perhaps to measure the addition to the dynamics of bodily action that appears as the accompaniment of violent emotional disturbance.

THE FEELING OF POWER

In this connection it is highly significant that in times of strong excitement there is not infrequent testimony to a sense of overwhelming power that sweeps in like a sudden tide and lifts the person to a new high level of ability.   A friend of mine, whose nature is somewhat choleric, has told me that when he is seized with anger, he is also possessed by an intense conviction that he could crush and utterly destroy the object of his hostility.   And I have heard a football player confess that just before the final game such an access of strength seemed to come to him that he felt able, on the signal, to crouch and with a jump go crashing through any ordinary door.   There is intense satisfaction in these moments of supreme elation, when the body is at its acme of its powers.   And it is altogether probable that the critical dangers of adventure have a fascination because fear is thrilling, and extrication from a predicament, by calling forth all the bodily resources and setting them to meet the challenge of the difficulty, yields many of the joys of conquest.   For these reasons vigorous men go forth to seek dangers and to run large chances of serious injury.   "Danger makes us more alive.   We so love to strive that we come to love the fear that gives us strength for conflict.   Fear is not only something to be escaped from to a place or state of safety, but welcomed as an arsenal of augmented strength." [14]   And thus in the hazardous sports, in mountain climbing, in the hunting of big game, and in the tremendous adventure of war, risks and excitement and the sense of power surge up together, setting free unsuspected energies, and bringing vividly to consciousness memorable fresh revelations of the possibilities of achievement.

REFERENCES

1. SHERRINGTON, *The Integrative Action of the Nervous System* (New York, 1906), p. 265.
2. DARWIN, *The Expression of Emotions in Man and Animals* (New York, 1905), p. 79.
3. McDOUGALL, *Introduction to Social Psychology* (London, 1908), p. 50.
4. JAMES, *Three Years among the Indians,* quoted in VINTON, *John Colter* (New York, 1926).
5. JAMES, "The Energies of Men," p. 227, *Memories and Studies* (New York, 1911).
6. MOONEY, *The Ghost-Dance Religion* (United States Bureau of Ethnology, 1892-3), p. 924.
7. SCHAFF, *Religious Encyclopedia,* iii (New York, 1908), p. 346.
8. SOUTHEY, *Life of Charles Wesley,* ii (New York, 1820), p. 164.
9. SOUTHEY, *op. cit.,* i, p. 240.
10. BROWN, *The Dervishes* (London, 1868), pp. 218-222, 260.
11. MAJER, *Geschichte der Ordalien* (Jena, 1796), pp. 258-261.
12. LEA, *Superstition and Force* (Philadelphia, 1892), p. 178.
13. NARODNY, *Musical America,* xx (1914), No. 14.
14. HALL, *American Journal of Psychology,* xxv (1914), p. 154

CHAPTER XIV

EMOTIONAL DERANGEMENT OF BODILY FUNCTIONS

In the foregoing chapters the facts which have been presented and the interpretations which have been offered have led to an emphasis on the *utility* of the reactions in the powerful emotions of fear and anger. There are psychologists, however, who are more impressed by the disturbances of bodily function produced by these emotions than by their service to the organism. Piéron,[1] for example, has described emotion as "associated with an affective discharge of abnormally intense nervous energy." Although admitting that a part of the energy is applied to useful, adapted reactions—yielding increased strength and greater speed of running in case of need—he declares that a more or less considerable part is expended in useless facial contortions "and even finds its way into the vegetative organs where" he adds, without analysis, "many different reactions are produced, varying accordingly as the excitatory or inhibitory systems are stimulated, and where injurious or even pathogenic processes are aroused." He cites instances of disease and even death in which great emotional stress was antecedent and presumably played an essential rôle in bringing on the event. In view of the tendency of the bodily changes in strong affective states to move "toward the pathological as a limit," Piéron is skeptical of the value of "finalistic" utilitarian interpretations.

At the outset I disavow any fixed idea that the explanation of the phenomena described in the foregoing chapters is in intent finalistic. The possibly temporary character of theories was pointed out at the moment we changed from a study of observed facts to a search for their meaning (see p. 193); and a readiness to welcome a more reasonable account of the facts than that here offered has already been stressed (see p. 222). It is pertinent, furthermore, to repeat that from the beginning we have been concerned with "researches into the function of emotional excitement," i. e., into its physiology and not its pathology. There are many systems in the body which, because of misuse or misfortune, may have their services to the organism as a whole so altered as to be actually harmful. Thus vicious circles of causation become established which may lead to death. The kidneys, for example, rid the body of non-volatile waste. They may fail to function normally and then the accumulation of the waste in the blood injures the body, the kidneys themselves included. The development of pathological functions in a system is quite consistent with its usual performance of normal functions. We are not justified in denying the existence of normal functions because they may become abnormal. The problem is presented of attempting to learn under what circumstances the transformation occurs. And so, in an examination of the bodily changes which characterize the strong emotions, we may admit the common utility of the changes as preparations for action, we may admit also that such changes may become so persistent as to be a menace instead of a benefit, and we may be stimulated by this contrast to attempt to understand how it may arise.

THE CHARACTERISTICS OF THE RAGE RESPONSE AS A TYPE

In making the attempt to understand the pathology of emotional excitement we shall first summarize briefly some points previously considered. From the physiological point of view an emotion is a typical reaction pattern. Let us consider rage as an example. In its extreme form the signs of rage include the crouching body, the moist or frowning brow, the firm lips, the clenched or grinding teeth, the growled threats or imprecations, and the tightened fists or the seized weapon ready for attack. This is a complex attitude which we do not have to learn—its occurrence is a part of our native inheritance. It occurs promptly when the stimulus is appropriate. It is a constant and uniform type of behavior, having features which are common in widely scattered races of men and even in lower animals, so that the nature of the attitude is at once understood without the necessity of words. It is a permanent mode of reaction; throughout an individual's life the characteristic display of the rage response may be suddenly evoked in all its elaborateness and, whether in childhood or old age, it differs only in minor details. Further, it is a response to a fairly definite stimulus—any hampering or checking of activity, or opposition to one or another primary impulse brings it out. Threaten the free motion of a dog or a man and the teeth will be uncovered. Again, the rage response may be interpreted as being useful. In the foregoing chapters we have seen the wide range of bodily adjustments which occur when one is enraged, all of which may properly be regarded as rendering the organism more efficient in struggle, in such struggle as may be required to overwhelm the opposition and to allow the natural impulse to prevail. As we survey the characteristics of the outburst of rage as a typical emotion—the inborn, prompt, constant, uniform, permanent and useful nature of the response to a definite kind of stimulus—we note that these are the *characteristics of a simple reflex*, such as sneezing or coughing. They differ not in quality but in complexity.

Man is superior to the lower animals mainly because of the extensive development of the cerebral hemispheres. Comparative anatomy shows that in the course of evolution these structures have been superposed on a brain stem which differs relatively little in the higher vertebrates. And physiological investigation has proved that whereas the reactions which involve the cerebral cortex may be complicated, delayed, unpredictable, short-lived, and readily modifiable,

those which involve the lower levels of the brain and
spinal cord are like the ordinary reflexes—prompt, uniform and stereotyped. Hence the difference between
the complex behavior of the human being with normal
cerebral hemispheres and the relatively simple behavior of the idiot in whom they are defective. It is of
interest, therefore, to learn where the nervous mechanisms lie which operate the various emotional displays. Do these mechanisms have their seat in the
newly developed cerebral cortex or in the more ancient
parts of the brain?

THE CENTRAL CONTROL OF EMOTIONAL EXPRESSION

In the brain stem are centers which, in the lower
vertebrates, lacking a cerebral cortex, carry on the
primitive functions of maintaining existence, such as
seizing their prey and escaping from their enemies.
These are activities which in man are associated with
attack or with flight from danger and are attended by
the emotions of rage or fear. In higher forms the
centers for these functions, though normally held in
check by the dominant cortex, are capable of energetic
response when conditions require urgent and insistent
action. It seemed reasonable to expect that the centers in the brain stem would manifest their typical
activity if the cerebral cortex were removed. Removal of the cortex would destroy the possibility of
sensation and, therefore, a depressing or disturbing anesthetic could be dispensed with. Accordingly Britton

and I,[2] using cats as subjects, undertook an investigation of some of the immediate effects of cerebral decortication which left intact almost all of the gray masses at the base of the brain. As soon as recovery from anesthesia was complete a remarkable group of activities appeared, such as are usually seen in an infuriated animal—a sort of sham rage. These quasi-emotional phenomena included lashing of the tail, arching of the trunk, thrusting and jerking of the restrained limbs, display of the claws and clawing motions, snarling and attempts to bite. These were all actions due to skeletal muscles. Besides these, and more typical and more permanent, were effects on the viscera, produced by impulses discharged over the sympathetic nerve fibers. They included erection of the tail hairs, sweating of the toe pads, dilation of the pupils, micturition, a high blood pressure, a very rapid heart beat, an abundant outpouring of adrenin, and an increase of blood sugar up to five times the normal concentration.[3] This play of a "pseudaffective" state or sham rage might continue for two or three hours.

As stated above, Britton and I left untouched almost all of the basal gray matter of the anterior brain stem. Where among these basal ganglia does the neurone pattern for the rage response reside? The answer to this question was obtained by Bard[4] who, after removing under ether the cerebral cortex and various amounts of the brain stem, studied the behavior of the preparation. He found that typical sham rage, accompanied by vigorous discharge of sympathetic im-

pulses, occurs when both hemispheres, the corpora stri-
ata and the anterior half of the diencephalon have
been completely isolated (i. e., the crosshatched parts,
C H and part of D, in Fig. 39). The additional ex-
tirpation of the posterior half of the diencephalon
promptly abolishes the spontaneous activity. Further
tests proved that the center lies in a small brain mass
in the ventral part of this region.

Here is a fundamental fact which I wish to emphasize—that the nervous organization for the display
of rage, both in bodily attitudes and in visceral
changes, is located in an ancient portion of the brain,
the optic thalamus, which is a part of the diencephalon.
This region is not like the cerebral cortex where new
adjustments with the outer world are constantly being

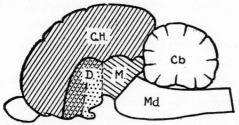

Fig. 39.—Median section of the brain. *CH*, cerebral hemispheres;
D, diencephalon (indicated by dots); *M*, mesencephalon; *Cb*,
cerebellum; *Md*, medulla. The crosshatching, from right downward to left, marks the portion of the brain which can be
removed without interfering with the emotional expression of
rage.

made or modified. Instead, it is like the spinal cord,
a place where the simpler mechanisms for orderly motions reside and where stimulation evokes fixed and
uniform reflex responses. The typical postures and

visceral changes which result from action of the thalamus are more complicated than the knee jerk or
other spinal reflexes, but they are not essentially different.

I have laid stress on the locus of the physiological
mechanism for the reflex figure of rage because it may
serve as a model for other primitive emotional responses. The expressions of fear, joy and grief are
similar to it in character. In their essential features
they are not learned (i. e., they are inborn) and they
are prompt, constant, uniform and permanently established patterns of reaction to appropriate stimuli. In
other words they are like the simple reflexes and not
like the complicated adjustments managed by the cortex. There is good evidence that the central control
for the expression of these emotions, like that for
rage, lies in the thalamic region. For example, Bechterev [5] has reported that in an animal freshly deprived
of its cerebral hemispheres, petting may call forth
signs of pleasure, e. g., purring in the cat and tail
wagging in the dog.

The evidence which I have adduced to show that
the neural arrangement for emotional display is near
the optic thalamus has been based wholly on experiments on lower animals. That evidence, however, is
consistent with indications that in man also emotional
expression is controlled by parts of the brain below
the cortex and specifically by centers in or near the
optic thalamus. Indeed, the common features of emotional responses in man and lower animals, which Dar-

win so well demonstrated, are common, in spite of wide divergence of development, because the responses are organized in a part of the brain which is similar in

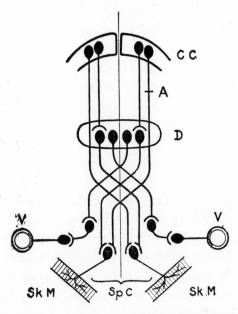

Fig. 40.—Diagram of possible relations of some neurones of the cerebral cortex (*C C*) and of the thalamic portion of the diencephalon (*D*) to the viscera (*V*) and to skeletal muscles (*Sk M*). *Sp C* = spinal cord. The cortico-thalamic tract is regarded as inhibitory. Sensory fibers are not represented. Damage to the cortico-spinal tract at *A* interrupts cortical control of certain skeletal muscles on one side, but it does not prevent control of these muscles on both sides by the centers in the diencephalon. Unilateral injury of centers in the diencephalon may leave bilateral control from the cortex.

man and lower animals, viz., the brain stem, and not in a part which is very dissimilar, viz., the cerebral hemispheres. The detailed evidence that the neural arrangements for the display of emotion in man are

established in the thalamus will be presented later
(see p. 363). For present purposes it is sufficient to
state that in certain forms of one-sided paralysis (hemiplegia) patients are incapable of moving the face on
the paralyzed side; but if an emotional (i. e., a sorrowful or joyous) situation develops, the muscles
which were unresponsive to voluntary control (i. e.,
control from the cerebral cortex) flash into action
and give *both* sides of the face the expression of sadness or gayety.[6] These are cases of subcortical interruption of the motor tract (e. g., at A, Fig. 40), and
presence of an intact optic thalamus. The converse
of this condition is seen in unilateral injury of the
thalamic neurones (Fig. 40); then the patient moves
symmetrically both sides of the face at will, but when
he laughs or weeps the emotional expression is unilateral. Many other observations on human beings,
consistently point to the optic thalamus as the region
in which resides the neural organization for the different emotional expressions.

DIFFERENCE BETWEEN CORTICAL AND THALAMIC CON-
TROL OF SKELETAL MUSCLES AND VISCERA

We have reviewed the evidence that the neurones
of the thalamic region discharge outward and downward to muscles and viscera to produce the typical
bodily changes of emotional excitement. We shall consider later the evidence that they discharge upward
to the cortex to add richness and warmth to the simple

sensations. Two other important points I wish now to elaborate.

The first of these is concerned with the relations of the cortical and the thalamic control of bodily processes. It is clear that certainly some *skeletal muscles are governed at both levels, cortical and thalamic* (see Fig. 40); for example, we may laugh spontaneously because of a ludicrous situation (thalamic laughter) or we may laugh as a voluntary act (cortical laughter). It is quite as clear that the *viscera,* on the other hand, *are only under thalamic government;* we cannot by direct act of will increase the blood sugar, accelerate the heart, or stop digestion. When there is double control the cortical neurones, to be sure, are ordinarily dominant and may not release the excited neurones of the thalamus (though we sometimes cry or laugh "in spite of ourselves"). Then there is conflict between the higher and lower controls of the bodily functions—there are opposing influences with accompanying confusion. *The cortex, however, can check only those bodily functions which are normally under voluntary control.* That point I would emphasize. Just as the cortex cannot cause, so likewise it cannot prevent those stormy processes of the thalamus that increase the blood sugar, accelerate the heart, stop digestion, or produce the other disturbances characteristic of great excitement. When an emotion is repressed, therefore, it is repressed only in its external manifestations. There is evidence, to be sure, that when the external manifestations are maximal,

the internal turmoil is also maximal;[2] and it is probable that cortical control of the outward display of
excitement results in less internal disturbance than
would accompany free expression. Nevertheless in a
conflict between the cortical government and the activities of the thalamic centers the ungovernable internal manifestations might be intense.

The second point is related to evidence that states
of consciousness are associated only with the cortical
neurones. Certainly we are unaware of the numerous
and complicated reflexes which determine bodily posture or the size of the pupil, for example, although
these reflexes are regulated in the brain stem. It follows that the neural mechanisms for the primitive
emotions, active in the basal ganglia, are likewise probably not directly associated with consciousness. This
consideration explains, I conceive, some of the most
characteristic features of emotional experience. The
disturbance in extra-conscious parts boils up into the
realm of the conscious. Therefore, we have emotional
"seizures"; we may laugh, weep or rage "uncontrollably"; we feel as if "possessed"; what we do in the
stress of excitement is "surprising" or "shocking"—
something "surges up within us" and our actions seem
no longer our own. These common bywords are explicable in terms of a sudden and powerful dominance
of the bodily forces by subcortical neurones, i. e.,
neurones whose activity is not immediately attended
by conscious states. Under favoring circumstances,
with only a momentary lifting of the normal inhibi-

tory check, these lower neurones capture the machinery of action and drive it violently into one or another of its variegated patterns.

ILLUSTRATIONS OF THE DERANGING EFFECTS OF EMOTIONS

We have seen that the thalamic region, when freed from cortical control, is capable of elaborate independent activity of a stereotyped character, and that when it acts it produces the typical reaction patterns in posture, expression and visceral responses that characterize various strong emotions. Now the question arises, how are these considerations related to pathological states? How do the processes going on deep down in the old part of the brain affect the workings of the body? To show how events in the thalamus can profoundly disarrange the nice adjustments of the normal organism, I shall cite some illustrative cases.

First, with regard to digestive functions. In an earlier chapter I have described instances of total stoppage not only of the mechanical action of the canal, but also of the work of the digestive glands, in consequence of emotional stresses. The whole digestive process, which is subject to check by the sympathetic system, may be profoundly deranged by anxiety and distress—the minor aspects of fear. McLester [7] has estimated that one-third of the patients with disorders of the alimentary tract are suffering because of lack of emotional balance. Alvarez [8] cites a case of per-

sistent vomiting which started when an income tax
collector threatened punishment if a discrepancy in
the tax statement was not explained, and which ceased
as soon as Alvarez himself went to the collector, as
a therapeutic measure, and straightened out the difficulty.   The natural processes of the alimentary canal
are fundamental to all other functions of the body.
Any disturbance of normal peristalsis, segmentation,
and secretion of the digestive fluids may have widespread ill effects in the organism.   Cabot [9] has recorded
an instance of fracture of the leg which failed to unite.
Investigation showed that the patient was fearful lest
his family was suffering while he was absent at the
hospital, i. e., the anxiety resulted in loss of desire
for food (absence of hunger contractions of the stomach), that resulted in impaired nutrition, and that in
turn led to such impairment of the reparative processes that the bone fragments were not welded together.
Assurance that his family was well and happy, and
being cared for, quickly altered the patient's condition;
he ceased worrying, thereupon began to eat heartily
and gain in nutrition, and then his broken bones began
to knit.

The cardiovascular system, like the digestive system,
is under the influence of the sympathetic nerves, but
instead of being depressed or inhibited, it is stimulated
by them.   The excitement which stops gastric digestion makes the heart beat more rapidly and raises
blood pressure by contracting the blood vessels.   During the War there appeared not infrequently cases

of "disorderly action of the heart" or, as it was sometimes called, "soldier's heart." The slightest excitement or perturbation would send the pulse bounding
at a high rate (130 to 150 beats per minute). The
general physical and nervous condition of the victims
of this disturbance—their anxious faces, their troubled
eyes, the drawn lines about the mouth, their trembling—was such as to make reasonable the view that
the stresses of the war had become intolerable and
had resulted in such sensitizing of the sympathetic
control of the heart that even mild stimulation produced extreme effects.[10] The mechanism by which
emotion may bring about such sensitizing is illustrated
in a case reported by Foster [11]:

A wife, who was free from any cardiac disorder, saw her
husband walking arm in arm with a strange woman and acting
in such a way as to rouse jealousy and suspicion. Profoundly
stirred by the incident the wife hastened home and remained
there several days. She then began to fear going out lest she
might meet her husband with her rival. After days of wretched-
ness she was persuaded by a friend to venture forth, "probably
in a state of abject terror," as Foster remarks, but she had not
gone far when she ran back to her home. Then she noted that
her heart was thumping hard, that she had a sense of oppression
in her chest and a choking sensation. Later attempts to go out-
doors produced the same alarming symptoms. She began to feel
that she might die on the street if she went out. There was no
organic disease of the heart, and yet slight effort as she moved
from her home brought on acute distress.

The influence of excitement on arterial blood pressure has already been noted (see p. 93). The pressure
is produced by the energy of the inflow of blood into
the arteries and the resistance to the outflow from

them. The sympathetic impulses, by speeding the heart rate and constricting the arterioles, raise the pressure by affecting positively both factors. It is clear that patients suffering from hypertension and senile impairment of the circulatory system should avoid conditions and obligations which are likely to cause excitement. Indeed, the instances of sudden death that are attributed to intense emotion are probably explicable as the result of acute strain on damaged heart or blood vessels.

There is evidence that violent emotional disturbance can produce profound effects on the organism through influences on the thyroid gland. Marañon [12] has collected an extensive series of cases of hyperthyroidism brought on by stressful experiences during the Great War. Recently Emerson [13] has reported some striking instances of hyperthyroidism which followed intensely affective scenes in the lives of the patients.

One was a married woman who had had two illegitimate children and whose husband committed suicide in her presence as a rebuke to her manner of living. Thereupon she dropped to the floor and exhausted herself in shrieking. At once she had a sense of constriction of her throat and was troubled with difficulty in swallowing; the thyroid gland enlarged and six weeks after the incident she had a metabolism 65 per cent above normal. Later troubles of an exacting character were associated with the development of high blood sugar and a high arterial pressure.

Another case. A man of twenty years had a quarrel with his fiancée. She, pretending to commit suicide, had in his presence swallowed some pills and fallen down screaming. The man departed hastily. Within a week he was suffering from swelling of the neck and nervousness. When he appeared at the hospital four months later he had lost weight, he presented a large goitre over which a definite thrill could be felt, and his basal metabolism was up 24 per cent above the normal level.

A third case was that of a married woman who had seen her husband kill his two brothers. The husband bitterly reproached her for not coming to his defense at the trial. A week after the trial a goitre became evident and reached a large size in seven days. When she came to the hospital a few months later, the goitre was huge, it pulsated visibly, had a palpable thrill and was causing an oppressive sense of suffocation. There was pronounced exophthalmus with marked tremor and restlessness. *stop* The basal metabolism varied from plus 40 to plus 117 per cent.

There are other emotional disturbances of bodily functions which might be mentioned, such as disorders of menstruation,[14] emptying of the bladder,[15] secretion of milk,[16] and others. Enough instances have been given, however, to show that there are effects wrought on the organs innervated by the sympathetic nervous system—glands both of external and internal secretion and parts supplied with smooth muscle—that are just as real as the effects which are produced when the biceps is used to lift a weight. A remarkable difference lies in the level of the nervous control of these two effects. Whereas the biceps is usually managed from the cortex, the viscera are managed from the diencephalon. Whereas the biceps is under "voluntary" control, the viscera are not under that control, but are influenced favorably or unfavorably by processes associated with feelings and emotions. Although the neural center for emotional expression is subcortical—indeed, is low in the brain stem—yet cortical processes are involved in the total reaction to a situation which evokes strong feelings. We might be frightened by a real bear, but not by a stuffed bear. The discrimination between the two is made by the cortex. How may this relation between cortex and thalamus be interpreted in physiological terms?

AN EXPLANATION OF EMOTIONAL DERANGEMENT OF BODILY PROCESSES

Earlier I have pointed out that an emotional reaction has many of the characteristics of a reflex response. To evoke a reflex an appropriate stimulus must be applied; an irritant in the larynx produces coughing, food in the mouth calls forth a flow of saliva. Similarly with the emotional expressions. Watson [17] has studied new-born babies and has found that from the beginning loud sounds and also indications of loss of support are the natural stimuli for the reaction of fear. Limitation or hampering of the freedom of bodily movement is from the beginning the natural stimulus for rage.

It is clear that persistence of an adequate stimulus for a reflex action is sufficient cause for persistence of the action. If an irritant affects the eye the tears flow; if the tears wash away the irritant they cease flowing; if they fail to wash it away they continue. The conditions appear to be similar in the more complex reflex responses associated with intense emotional experiences. They are very potent incentives to vigorous effort. When they are effective they may result in such victory or defeat, in such escape from danger or such failure to achieve that the effective stimulus ceases to operate. The outcome is prompt and decisive, and other stimuli soon control behavior. This effect would illustrate the *physiological* workings of an emotional incident. On the other hand, the adequate stimulus may persist, as in the account of the man with the broken leg who was fearful lest his family was suffering; a pathological state resulted from his continued anxiety which only ceased when the continuing occasion for it was removed.

Again, powerful affective stimuli may persist because there is no avoiding their persistence. The woman, mentioned above, whose husband committed suicide in her presence as a rebuke to her, the man whose fiancée had supposedly committed suicide in his presence, the wife who saw her husband kill his two brothers, had all suffered profound emotional shocks. *Nothing could be done. The acts were final. They could not be forgotten. Many associations recalled them.* And every remembrance of them was the occasion for a renewal of the original stimulus, which, even though diminished in intensity, acted on a sensitized set of responding neurones.

Furthermore, agents other than the natural stimuli can easily be made to set a reflex in action if only they are closely associated with the natural stimuli. Thus if a red light is flashed repeatedly at the same time that food is placed in the mouth, the red light will itself, alone, become as effective as the food in causing a salivary discharge. The indifferent stimulus, the red light, is then called the conditioned stimulus and the reflex salivary secretion, under the circumstances, a conditioned reflex. All sorts of ordinarily indifferent external agents—not only a light, but a sound, a shape, a contact, an odor, indeed *anything* that will influence a sense organ—may be made into an effective stimulus by close association in time with the normally effective stimulus. Thus objects and events in the world about us are constantly acquiring new significance for our reactions. All the processes of conditioning are carried on in the cerebral cortex. These facts, which have been studied in great detail and most instructively by Pavlov,[18] have pertinence for the explanation of emotional behavior.

Our emotional reflexes, like the salivary reflex, become complicated by the conditioning of indifferent stimuli. A white rat shown to a baby causes the baby to reach for it and to play with it; there is no fear. Then the rat is presented repeatedly but at the same time a loud sound is made by striking a steel bar. The rat thus becomes a conditioned stimulus for the fear reaction produced by the loud sound, and thereafter, when the rat is shown, the baby cries and turns away. He is now afraid of the rat not because it is a rat but because it has become the signal and symbol of something fearful—the loud sound. In such ways as this the indifferent circumstances of an emotional disturbance become conditioned stimuli or signals for renewal of the disturbance. The wife who saw her husband paying attention to a strange woman on the street had an intense emotional experience which was renewed, not by seeing again the errant husband and his distressing companion, but by going into the street! Thus by extended associations emotional responses become subjected to more and more involved conditioned stimuli, until great complexity and intricacy of affective behavior result.

To sum up, then, the persistent derangement of bodily functions in strong emotional reactions can be interpreted as due to persistence of the stimuli which evoke the reactions. They may persist because not naturally eliminated by completion of the emotional impulse, or because completion of the impulse is made impossible by circumstances (recurrences of the original stimuli [memories], with emotional attachments [terror, remorse], then keep the reactions alive), or because they become associated with a common object which, repeatedly encountered, is a repeated conditioned stimulus.

REASONS FOR A PHYSIOLOGICAL EMPHASIS IN EXPLAINING EMOTIONAL DISTURBANCES

In the foregoing discussion I have purposely emphasized the physiological mechanisms of emotional disturbances, and for two main reasons. First, I wished to show that these remarkable perturbations could be described in terms of neurone processes. And again, I wished to show that these interesting phenomena need not be set aside as mystical events occurring in the realm of the "psyche." It seemed possible that by emphasis on physiological features attention could be drawn to two important reasons for the slighting of emotional troubles, especially by physicians.

Although physicians have not infrequent occasions to observe instances of functional disturbance due to emotional causes, there is an inclination to minimize or to slight that influence, or even to deny that it is part of a physician's service to his patient to concern himself with such troubles. Let the patient go to the clergyman for comfort and consolation and for the resolution of his deep anxieties. A too common unwillingness among physicians to regard seriously the emotional elements in disease is due perhaps to the subtle influence of two extreme attitudes and disciplines. On the one hand is the powerful impress of morphological pathology, the study of diseased organs as seen after death. So triumphantly and so generally have the structural alterations which accompany altered functions been demonstrated under the microscope, that any state which has no distinct "pathology" appears to be unreal or of minor significance. Fears, worries and states of rage and resentment leave no clear traces in the brain. What, then, have physicians to do with them? On the other hand, these mysterious and dominant feelings which surge up within us from unknown sources—are they not pure perturbations of the "psyche"? In that case, what, again, have physicians to do with them? If physicians show this indifference, however, is it surprising that men and women, beset by emotional stresses, turn from them and go for help to faith healers and to others who recognize the reality of these disturbing states?

An escape from the insistent demands of the pathologist for structural evidence of disease, and also from the vagueness and mysticism of the psychological healers, can be found in an understanding of the physiological processes, which accompany deep emotional disturbances. The physiologist has the reasonable right to consider what goes on in the nerve paths of the brain as not associated with any demonstrable structural change. Indeed, very pronounced and disastrous consequences may result in the organism because of habit reactions, which may be regarded as not different in quality from any of our ordinary ways of behaving. Also the physiologist has the reasonable right to regard suddenly altered functions of organs innervated from the central nervous system as occurring in consequence of nerve impulses discharged from that system. Using the physiological point of view, therefore, I have considered emotions in terms of nerve impulses, much as I might have considered the nerve impulses from the "motor area" of the cerebral cortex as they govern the movements of skeletal muscles.

SOME PRACTICAL SUGGESTIONS

In what has been presented above there are physiological implications which have practical bearings on the care of persons who have been or are being deeply disturbed by emotional experience.

First, there is the importance of early treatment. We are all acquainted with the readiness with which habits are established in the nervous system by frequently repeating an act. Every time the nerve impulses traverse a given course they make easier the passage of later impulses. Thus habitual emotional impressions, both in the facies and in the viscera, may become fixed and deep-set in the neural organization, just as the complicated adjustments of swimming, skating or bicycle riding become inwrought during our later years by repeated practice. It is clear that so far as possible emotional habit-reactions should be prevented by prompt treatment.

As we have seen, the cortex has no direct control over the functions of the viscera. It is useless, therefore, to try to check a racing heart or to lower a high blood pressure, or to renew the activities of an inhibited digestive system by a coldly reasoned demand for different behavior. The man whose broken bone failed to knit because he was fearful about his family's welfare could not be *argued* out of his fear; the fear left him when he learned that his family was actually comfortable. The cortex, which is concerned with analysis of the outer world, should not, therefore, be the sole means by which treatment is attempted; the *occasion* for worries, anxieties, conflicts, hatreds, resentments, and other forms of fear and anger, which affect the thalamic centers, must be removed. In short, the factors in the whole situation which are the source of strong feeling must be discovered and either explained away or eliminated.

Although the cortex has no direct control over the viscera, it has indirect control—we can walk into danger and have a thrill, though we cannot have a thrill by merely resolving to have one. Similarly we can often avoid the circumstances which rouse fear or rage or disgust and their attendant visceral turmoil—we need not go near the agitating spot.

It is known that conditioned stimuli can be inhibited, so that they do not exercise their usual effects, if strange or unusual stimuli intervene. The new stimuli start other responses (the "investigatory behavior" described by Pavlov). Thus, in psychological terms, the attention is diverted. This method is commonly used to interrupt the continuity of conditions which are maintaining a harmful emotional state.

Again, when the reason for the perturbation is not clear, it can sometimes be found by careful inquiry or analysis. It is an interesting fact that a full explanation of the way in which the trouble has been caused will not infrequently suffice to remove the trouble, promptly and completely.

Finally, a word of warning may not be out of place. If an objective cause for a complaint is not found, nothing is easier than to attribute the difficulty to nervous factors. There is danger, when one emphasizes the importance of nervous factors as disturbers of the bodily peace, that one may be understood as minimizing the need of search for a demonstrable pathology. Nothing could be farther from my intention. The assumption that emotional agencies are causing mischief in the organism should be a last resort—an explanation which is offered only after every effort has been made to find another explanation. And even when the cause is ascribed to fear or rage or some other strong feeling, proof for that conclusion should be carefully sought both at the source of the trouble and in the effect of appropriate treatment. Nor should the possibility be overlooked that along with profound emotional disturbance there will be discovered an organic lesion. The two conditions, the altered structure of some organ and the altered function of the nervous system, may be causally related, and may have to be treated as a single disorder. Certain it is that only when they are both regarded as the perturbations of a single unity, the organism, will they be properly conceived and effectively treated.

REFERENCES

1. Piéron, *Wittenberg Symposium on Feelings and Emotions* (Worcester, 1928), p. 289.
2. Cannon and Britton, *American Journal of Physiology*, lxxii (1925), p. 283.
3. Bulatao and Cannon, *ibid.*, p. 295.
4. Bard, *ibid.*, lxxxiv (1928), p. 490.
5. Bechterev, *Virchow's Archiv*, cx (1887), p. 345.
6. Roussy, *La Couche Optique* (Paris, 1907), p. 31
7. McLester, *Journal of the American Medical Association*, lxxxix (1927), p. 1019.
8. Alvarez, Personal communication.
9. Cabot, *Harvard Alumni Bulletin*, xxviii (1925), p. 384.

10. COHN, *American Journal of the Medical Sciences,* clviii
    (1919), p. 453.
11. FOSTER, *Journal of the American Medical Association,*
    lxxxix (1927), p. 1018.
12. MARANON, *Annales de Médicine,* ix (1921), p. 81.
13. EMERSON, *Transactions of the Association of American Phy-
    sicians,* xlii (1927), p. 346.
14. MAYER, *Schwarz's Psychogenese und Psychotherapie körper-
    licher Symptome* (Vienna, 1925), p. 298.
15. SCHWARZ, *ibid.,* p. 273.
16. GREVING, *Müller's Die Lebensnerven* (Berlin, 1924), p. 226.
17. WATSON, *Lectures on Behaviorism* (New York, 1925), p. 114.
18. PAVLOV, *Conditioned Reflexes* (Oxford), 1927.

CHAPTER XV

THE NATURE OF HUNGER

On the same plane with pain and the dominant emotions of fear and anger, as agencies which determine the action of organisms, is the sensation of hunger. It is a sensation so peremptory, so disagreeable, so tormenting, that men have committed crimes in order to assuage it. It has led to cannibalism, even among the civilized. It has resulted in suicide. And it has defeated armies—for the aggressive spirit becomes detached from larger loyalties and turns personal and selfish as hunger pangs increase in vigor and insistence.

In 1905, while observing in myself the rhythmic sounds produced by the activities of the alimentary tract, I had occasion to note that the sensation of hunger was not constant but recurrent, and that the moment of its disappearance was often associated with a rather loud gurgling sound as heard through the stethoscope. This and other evidence, indicative of a source of the hunger sensations in the contractions of the digestive canal, I reported in 1911.[1] That same year, with the help of one of my students, A. L. Washburn, I obtained final proof for this inference.

APPETITE AND HUNGER

The sensations of appetite and hunger are so complex and so intimately interrelated that any discussion of either sensation is sure to go astray unless at the start there is clear understanding of the meanings of the terms. The view has been propounded that appetite is the first degree of hunger, the mild and pleasant stage, agreeable in character; and that hunger itself is a more advanced condition, disagreeable and even painful—the unpleasant result of not satisfying the appetite.[2] On this basis appetite and hunger would differ only quantitatively. Another view, which seems more justifiable, is that the two experiences are fundamentally different.

Careful observation indicates that appetite is related to previous sensations of taste and smell of food. Delightful or disgusting tastes and odors, associated with this or that edible substance, determine the appetite. It has, therefore, important psychic elements in its composition. Thus, by taking thought, we can anticipate the odor of a delicious beefsteak or the taste of peaches and cream, and in that imagination we can find pleasure. In the realization, direct effects in the senses of taste and smell give still further delight. As already noted in the first chapter, observations on experimental animals and on human beings have shown that the pleasures of both anticipation and realization, by stimulating the flow of saliva and gastric juice, play a highly significant rôle in the initiation of digestive processes.

Among prosperous people, supplied with abundance of food, the appetite seems sufficient to insure for bodily needs a proper supply of nutriment. We eat because dinner is announced, because by eating we avoid unpleasant consequences, and because food is placed before us in delectable form and with tempting tastes and odors. Under less easy circumstances, however, the body needs are supplied through the much stronger and more insistent demands of hunger.

The sensation of hunger is difficult to describe, but almost every one from childhood has felt at times that dull ache or gnawing pain referred to the lower mid-chest region and the epigastrium, which may take imperious control of human actions. As Sternberg has pointed out, hunger may be sufficiently insistent to force the taking of food which is so distasteful that it not only fails to rouse appetite, but may even produce nausea. The hungry being gulps his food with a rush. The pleasures of appetite are not for him—he wants quantity rather than quality, and he wants it at once.

Hunger and appetite are, therefore, widely different —in physiological basis, in localization and in psychic elements. Hunger may be satisfied while the appetite still calls. Who is still hungry when the tempting dessert is served, and yet are there any who refuse it, on the plea that they no longer need it? On the other hand, appetite may be in abeyance while hunger is goading.[3] What ravenous boy is critical of his food? Do we not all know that "hunger is the best sauce"? Although the two sensations may thus exist separately, they nevertheless have the same function of leading to the intake of food, and they usually appear together. Indeed, the coöperation of hunger and appetite is probably the reason for their being so frequently confused.

THE SENSATION OF HUNGER

Hunger may be described as having a central core and certain more or less variable accessories. The peculiar dull ache of hungriness, referred to the epigastrium, is usually the organism's first strong demand for food; and when the initial order is not obeyed, the sensation is likely to grow into a highly uncomfortable pang or gnawing, less definitely localized as it becomes more intense. This may be regarded as the essential feature of hunger. Besides the dull ache, however, lassitude and drowsiness may appear, or faintness, or violent headache, or irritability and restlessness such that continuous effort in ordinary affairs becomes increasingly difficult. That these states differ much with individuals—headache in one and faintness in another, for example—indicates that they do not constitute the central fact of hunger, but are more or less inconstant accompaniments. The "feeling of emptiness," which has been mentioned as an important element of the experience,[4] is an inference rather than a distinct datum of consciousness, and can likewise be eliminated from further consideration. The dull pressing sensation is left, therefore, as the constant characteristic, the central fact, to be examined in detail.

Hunger can evidently be regarded from the psychological point of view, and discussed solely on the basis of introspection; or it can be studied with reference to its antecedents and to the physiological conditions which accompany it—a consideration which requires the use of both objective methods and subjective observation. This psycho-physiological treatment of the subject will be deferred till the last. Certain theories which have been advanced with regard to hunger, and which have been given more or less credit, must first be examined.

Two main theories have been advocated. The first is supported by contentions that hunger is a general sensation, arising at no special region of the body, but having a local reference. This theory has been more widely credited by physiologists and psychologists than the other. The other is supported by evidence that hunger has a local source and therefore a local reference. In the course of our examination of these views we shall have opportunity to consider some pertinent new observations.

THE THEORY THAT HUNGER IS A GENERAL SENSATION

The conception that hunger arises from a general condition of the body rests in turn on the notion that, as the body uses up material, the blood becomes impoverished. Schiff [5] advocated this notion, and suggested that poverty of the blood in food substance affects the tissues in such manner that they demand a new supply. The nerve cells of the brain share in this general shortage of provisions, he said, and because of internal changes, give rise to the sensation. Thus is hunger explained as being dependent on the body as a whole.

Three classes of evidence are cited in support of this view:

1. "Hunger increases as time passes"—a partial statement. The development of hunger as time passes is a common observation which quite accords with the assumption that the condition of the body and the state of the blood are becoming constantly worse, so long as the need, once established, is not satisfied.

While it is true that with the lapse of time hunger increases as the supply of body nutriment decreases, this concomitance is not proof that the sensation arises directly from a serious encroachment on the store of food materials. If this argument were valid we should expect hunger to become more and more distressing until death follows from starvation. There is abundant evidence that the sensation is not thus intensified; on the contrary, during continued fasting, hunger, at least in some persons, wholly disappears after the first few days. Luciani,[6] who carefully recorded the experience of the faster Succi, states that after a certain time the hunger feelings vanish and do not return.

And he tells of two dogs that showed no signs of hunger after the third or fourth day of fasting; thereafter they remained quite passive in the presence of food. Tigerstedt,[7] who also has studied the metabolism of starvation, declares that although the desire to eat is very great during the first day of the ordeal, the unpleasant sensations disappear early, and that at the end of the fast the subject may have to force himself to take nourishment. The subject, "J. A.," studied by Tigerstedt and his co-workers,[8] reported that after the fourth day of fasting, he had no disagreeable feelings.

Carrington,[9] after examining many persons who, to better their health, abstained from eating for different periods, records that "habit-hunger" usually lasts only two or three days and, if plenty of water is drunk, does not last longer than three days. Viterbi,[10] a Corsican lawyer condemned to death for political causes, determined to escape execution by depriving his body of food and drink. During the eighteen days that he lived he kept careful notes. On the third day the sensation of hunger departed, and although thereafter thirst came and went, hunger never returned. Still further evidence of the same character could be cited, but enough has already been given to show that after the first few days of fasting the hunger feelings may wholly cease. On the theory that hunger is a manifestation of bodily need, are we to suppose that, in the course of starvation, the body is mysteriously not in need after the third day, and that therefore the sensation of hunger disappears? The absurdity of such a view is obvious.

2. "Hunger may be felt though the stomach be full" —a selected alternative. Instances of duodenal fistula in man have been carefully studied, which have shown that a modified sensation of hunger may be felt when the stomach is full. A famous case described by Busch [11] has been repeatedly used as evidence. His patient, who lost nutriment through a duodenal fistula, was hungry soon after eating, and felt satisfied only when the chyme was restored to the intestine through the distal fistulous opening. As food is absorbed mainly through the intestinal wall, the inference is direct that the general bodily state, and not the local conditions of the alimentary canal, must account for the patient's feelings.

A full consideration of the evidence from cases of duodenal fistula cannot so effectively be presented now as later. That in Busch's case hunger disappeared while food was being taken is, as we shall see, quite significant. It may be that the restoration of chyme to the intestine quieted hunger, not because nutriment was thus introduced into the body, but because the presence of material altered the nature of gastro-intestinal activity. The basis for this suggestion will be given in due course.

3. "Animals may eat eagerly after section of their vagus and splanchnic nerves"—a fallacious argument. The third support for the view that hunger has a general origin in the body is derived from observations on

experimental animals. By severance of the vagus and splanchnic nerves, the lower esophagus, the stomach and the small intestine can be wholly separated from the central nervous system. Animals thus operated upon nevertheless eat food placed before them, and may indeed manifest some eagerness for it.[12] How is this behavior to be accounted for—when the possibility of local stimulation has been eliminated— save by assuming a central origin of the impulse to eat?

The fallacy of this evidence, though repeatedly overlooked, is easily shown. We have already seen that appetite as well as hunger may lead to the taking of food. Indeed, the animal with all gastro-intestinal nerves cut may have the same incentive to eat that a well-fed man may have, who delights in the pleasurable taste and smell of food and knows nothing of hunger pangs. Even when the nerves of taste are cut, as they were in Longet's experiments,[13] sensations of smell are still possible, as well as agreeable associations which can be roused by sight. More than seventy years ago Ludwig [14] pointed out that, even if all the nerves were severed, psychic reasons could be given for the taking of food, and yet because animals eat after one or another set of nerves is eliminated, the conclusion has been drawn by various writers that the nerves in question are thereby proved to be not concerned in the sensation of hunger. Evidently, since hunger is not required for eating, the act of eating is no testimony whatever that the animal is hungry, and, after the nerves have been severed, is no proof that hunger is of central origin.

WEAKNESS OF THE ASSUMPTIONS UNDERLYING THE THEORY THAT HUNGER IS A GENERAL SENSATION

The evidence thus far examined has been shown to afford only shaky support for the theory that hunger is a general sensation. The theory, furthermore, is weak in its fundamental assumptions. There is no clear indication, for example, that the blood undergoes or has undergone any marked change, chemical or physical, when the first stages of hunger appear. There is no evidence of any direct chemical stimulation of the gray matter of the cerebral cortex. Indeed, attempts to excite the gray matter artificially by chemical agents have been without results; [15] and even electrical stimulation, which is effective, must, in order to produce movements, be so powerful that the movements have been attributed to excitation of underlying white matter rather than cells in the gray. This insensitivity of cortical cells to direct stimulation is not at all favorable to the notion that they are sentinels set to warn against too great diminution of bodily supplies.

BODY NEED MAY EXIST WITHOUT HUNGER

Still further evidence opposed to the theory that hunger results directly from the using up of organic stores is found in patients suffering from fever. Metabolism in fever patients is augmented, body substance is destroyed, to such a degree that the weight of the patient may be greatly reduced, and yet the sensation of hunger under these conditions of increased need is wholly lacking.

Again, if a person is hungry and takes food, the sensation is suppressed soon afterwards, long before any considerable amount of nutriment could be digested and absorbed, and therefore long before the blood and the general bodily condition, if previously altered, could be restored to normal.

Furthermore, persons exposed to privation have testified that hunger can be temporarily suppressed by swallowing indigestible materials. Certainly scraps of leather and bits of moss, not to mention clay eaten by the Otomacs, would not materially compensate for large organic losses. In rebuttal to this argument the comment has been made that central states as a rule can be readily overwhelmed by peripheral stimulation, and just as sleep, for example, can be abolished by bathing the temples, so hunger can be abolished by irritating the gastric walls.[16] This comment is beside the point, for it meets the issue by merely assuming as true the condition under discussion. The absence of hunger during the ravages of fever, and its quick abolition after food or even indigestible stuff is swallowed, still further weakens the argument, therefore, that the sensation arises directly from lack of nutriment in the body.

THE THEORY THAT HUNGER IS OF GENERAL ORIGIN DOES NOT EXPLAIN THE QUICK ONSET AND THE PERIODICITY OF THE SENSATION

Many persons have noted that hunger has a sharp onset. A person may be tramping in the woods or working in the fields, where fixed attention is not demanded, and without premonition may feel the abrupt arrival of the characteristic ache. The expression "grub-struck" is a picturesque description of this experience. If this sudden arrival of the sensation corresponds to the general bodily state, the change in the general bodily state must occur with like suddenness or have a critical point at which the sensation is instantly precipitated. There is no evidence whatever that either of these conditions occurs in the course of metabolism.

Another peculiarity of hunger, which I have already mentioned, is its intermittency. It may come and go several times in the course of a few hours. Furthermore, while the sensation is prevailing, its intensity is not uniform, but marked by ups and downs. In some instances the ups and downs change to a periodic presence and absence without change of rate. In my own experience the hunger pangs came and went on one occasion as follows:

Came	*Went*
12—37—20	12—38—30
40—45	41—10
41—45	42—25
43—20	43—35
44—40	45—55
46—15	46—30

And so on, for ten minutes longer. Again in this relation, the intermittent and periodic character of hunger would require, on the theory under examination, that the bodily supplies be intermittently and periodically insufficient. During one moment the absence of hunger would imply an abundance of nutriment in the organism, ten seconds later the presence of hunger would imply that the stores had been suddenly reduced, ten seconds later still the absence of hunger would imply a sudden renewal of plenty. Such zig-zag shiftings of the general bodily state may not be impossible, but from all that is known of the course of metabolism, such quick changes are highly improbable. The periodicity of hunger, therefore, is further evidence against the theory that the sensation has a general basis in the body.

THE THEORY THAT HUNGER IS OF GENERAL ORIGIN DOES NOT EXPLAIN THE LOCAL REFERENCE

The last objection to this theory is that it does not account for the most common feature of hunger— namely, the reference of the sensation to the region of the stomach. Schiff and others [17] who have supported the theory have met this objection by two contentions. First they have pointed out that the sensation is not always referred to the stomach. Schiff interrogated ignorant soldiers regarding the local reference; several indicated the neck or chest, twenty-three the sternum, four were uncertain of any region, and two only designated the stomach. In other words, the stomach region was most rarely mentioned.

The second contention against the importance of local reference is that such evidence is fallacious. An armless man may feel tinglings which seem to arise in fingers which have long since ceased to be a portion of his body. The fact that he experiences such tinglings and ascribes them to dissevered parts, does not prove that the sensation originates in those parts. And similarly the assignment of the ache of hunger to any special region of the body does not demonstrate that the ache arises from that region. Such are the arguments against a local origin of hunger.

Concerning these arguments we may recall, first, Schiff's admission that the soldiers he questioned were too few to give conclusive evidence. Further, the testimony of most of them that hunger seemed to originate in the chest or the region of the sternum cannot be claimed as unfavorable to a peripheral source of the sensation. The description of feelings which develop from disturbances within the body is almost always indefinite. As Head [18] and others have shown, conditions in a viscus which give rise to sensation are likely not to be attributed to the viscus, but to related skin areas. Under such circumstances we do not dismiss the testimony as worthless merely because it may not point precisely to the source of the trouble. On the contrary, we use such testimony constantly as a basis for judging internal disorders.

With regard to the contention that reference to the

periphery is not proof of the peripheral origin of a sensation, we may answer that the force of that contention depends on the amount of accessory evidence which is available. Thus if we see an object come into contact with a finger, we are justified in assuming that the simultaneous sensation of touch which we refer to that finger has resulted from the contact, and is not a purely central experience accidentally attributed to an outlying member. Similarly in the case of hunger— all that we need as support for the peripheral reference of the sensation is proof that conditions occur there, simultaneously with hunger pangs, which might reasonably be regarded as giving rise to those pangs.

With the requirement in mind that peripheral conditions be adequate, let us examine the state of the fasting stomach to see whether, indeed, conditions may be present in times of hunger which would sustain the theory that hunger has a local outlying source.

HUNGER NOT DUE TO EMPTINESS OF THE STOMACH

Among the suggestions which have been offered to account for a peripheral origin of the sensation is that of attributing it to emptiness of the stomach. By use of the stomach tube Nicolai [19] found that when his subjects had their first intimation of hunger the stomach was quite empty. But, in other instances, after lavage of the stomach, the sensation did not appear for intervals varying between one and a half and three and a half hours. During these intervals the stomach must have been empty, and yet no sensation was experienced. The same testimony was given long before by Beaumont,[20] who, from his observations on Alexis St. Martin, declared that hunger arises some time after the stomach is normally evacuated. Mere emptiness of the organ, therefore, does not explain the phenomenon.

HUNGER NOT DUE TO HYDROCHLORIC ACID IN THE EMPTY STOMACH

A second theory, apparently suggested by observations on cases of hyperacidity, is that the ache or pang is due to the natural hydrochloric acid of the stomach but secreted while the organ is empty. Again the facts are hostile. Nicolai [21] reported that the gastric washwater from his hungry subjects was neutral or only slightly acid. This testimony confirms Beaumont's statement, and is in complete agreement with the results of gastric examination of fasting animals reported by numerous experimenters. There is no secretion into the empty stomach during the first days of starvation. Furthermore, persons suffering from absence of hydrochloric acid (achylia gastrica) declare that they have normal feelings of hunger. Hydrochloric acid cannot, therefore, he called upon to account for the sensation.

HUNGER NOT DUE TO TURGESCENCE OF THE GASTRIC MUCOUS MEMBRANE

Another theory, which was first advanced by Beaumont,[22] is that hunger arises from turgescence of the

gastric glands. The disappearance of the pangs as fasting continues has been accounted for by supposing that
the gastric glands share in the general depletion of the
body, and that thus the turgescence is relieved.* This
turgescence theory has commended itself to several recent investigators. Luciani [23] has accepted it, and by
adding the idea that nerves distributed to the mucosa
are specially sensitive to deprivation of food he accounts for the hunger pangs. Also Valenti [24] declared
a few years ago that the turgescence theory of
Beaumont is the only one with a semblance of truth
in it.

The experimental work reported by these two investigators, however, does not necessarily sustain the turgescence theory. Luciani severed the previously exposed
vagi after cocainizing them, and Valenti merely cocainized the nerves; the fasting dogs, eager to eat a
few minutes previous to this operation, now ran about
as before, but when offered food, licked and smelled it,
but did not take it. This total neglect of the food
lasted varying periods up to two hours. The vagus
nerves seem, indeed, to convey impulses which affect
the procedure of eating, but there is no clear evidence
that those impulses arise from distention of the gland
cells. The turgescence theory, moreover, does not explain the effect of taking indigestible material into the
stomach. According to Pavlov, and to others who have

---

* A better explanation perhaps is afforded by Boldireff's discovery
that at the end of two or three days the stomachs of fasting dogs
begin to secrete gastric juice and continue the secretion indefinitely.
(Boldireff, *Archives Biologiques de St. Petersburg*, xi, 1905, p. 98.)

observed human beings, the chewing and swallowing
of unappetizing stuff does not cause any secretion of
gastric juice (see p. 7). Yet such stuff when swallowed
will cause the disappearance of hunger, and Nicolai
found that the sensation could be abolished by simply
introducing a stomach sound. It is highly improbable
that the turgescence of the gastric glands can be reduced by either of these procedures. The turgescence
theory, furthermore, does not explain the quick onset
of hunger, or its intermittent and periodic character.
That the cells are repeatedly swollen and contracted
within periods a few seconds in duration is almost in-
conceivable. For these reasons, therefore, the theory
that hunger results from turgescence of the gastric
mucosa can reasonably be rejected.

HUNGER THE RESULT OF CONTRACTIONS

There remain to be considered, as a possible cause of
hunger-pangs, contractions of the stomach and other
parts of the alimentary canal. This suggestion is not
new. Many years ago (in 1846) Weber [25] declared his
belief that "strong contraction of the muscle fibers of
the wholly empty stomach, whereby its cavity disappears, makes a part of the sensation which we call hunger." Vierordt [26] drew the same inference twenty-five
years later (in 1871), and since then Ewald, Knapp,
and Hertz have declared their adherence to this view.
These writers have not brought forward any direct evidence for their conclusion, though Hertz has cited

Boldireff's observations on fasting dogs as probably accounting for what he terms "the gastric constituent of the sensation."

THE EMPTY STOMACH AND INTESTINE CONTRACT

The argument commonly used against the gastric contraction theory is that the stomach is not energetically active when empty. Thus Schiff [27] stated, "The movements of the empty stomach are rare and much less energetic than during digestion." Luciani [28] expressed his disbelief by asserting that gastric movements are much more active during gastric digestion than at other times, and cease almost entirely when the stomach has discharged its contents. And Valenti [29] stated (1910), "We know very well that gastric movements are exaggerated while digestion is proceeding in the stomach, but when the organ is empty they are more rare and much less pronounced," and, therefore, they cannot account for hunger.

Evidence opposed to these suppositions has been in existence for many years. In 1899 Bettmann [30] called attention to the contracted condition of the stomach after several days' fast. In 1902 Wolff [31] reported that after forty-eight hours without food the stomach of the cat may be so small as to look like a slightly enlarged duodenum. In a similar circumstance I have noticed the same extraordinary smallness of the organ, especially in the pyloric half. The anatomist His [32] also recorded his observation of the phenomenon. In 1905

Boldireff [33] demonstrated that the whole gastro-intestinal tract has a periodic activity while not digesting.
Each period of activity lasts from twenty to thirty minutes, and is characterized in the stomach by rhythmic
contractions ten to twenty in number. These contractions, Boldireff reports, may be stronger than during
digestion, and his published records clearly support this
statement. The intervals of repose between periodic
recurrences of the contractions lasted from one and a
half to two and a half hours. Especially noteworthy is
Boldireff's observation that if fasting is continued for
two or three days, the groups of contractions appear at
gradually longer intervals and last for gradually shorter
periods, and thereupon, as the gastric glands begin continuous secretion, all movements cease.

OBSERVATIONS SUGGESTING THAT CONTRACTIONS
CAUSE HUNGER

The research of 1905, already mentioned, on the
rhythmic sounds produced by the digestive process, I
was engaged in when Boldireff's paper was published.
That contractions of the alimentary canal on a gaseous
content might explain the hunger pangs which I had
noticed seemed probable at that time, especially in the
light of Boldireff's observations. Indeed, Boldireff [34]
himself had considered hunger in relation to the activities he described, but solely with the idea that hunger
might *provoke* them; and since the activities dwindled
in force and frequency as time passed, whereas, in his

belief, they should have become more pronounced, he abandoned the notion of any relation between the phenomena. Did not Boldireff misinterpret his own observations? When he was considering whether hunger might cause the contractions, did he not overlook the possibility that the contractions might cause hunger? A number of experiences have led to the conviction that Boldireff did, indeed, fail to perceive part of the significance of his results. For example, I have noticed the disappearance of a hunger pang as gas was heard gurgling upward through the cardia. That the gas was rising rather than being forced downward was proved by its regurgitation immediately after the sound was heard. In all probability the pressure that forced the gas from the stomach was the cause of the preceding sensation of hunger. Again the sensation can be momentarily abolished a few seconds after swallowing a small accumulation of saliva or a teaspoonful of water. If the stomach is in strong contraction in hunger, this result can be accounted for, in accordance with the observations of Lieb and myself,[35] as due to the inhibition of the contraction by swallowing. Thus also could be explained the prompt vanishing of the ache soon after we begin to eat, for repeated swallowing results in continued inhibition.* Furthermore, Ducceschi's discovery [36] that hydrochloric acid diminishes the tonus of the pyloric portion of the stomach may have its application here; the acid would be secreted

---

* The absence of hunger in Busch's patient while food was being eaten (see p. 275) can also be accounted for in this manner.

as food is taken and would then cause relaxation of the
very region which is most strongly contracted.

THE CONCOMITANCE OF CONTRACTIONS AND HUNGER
IN MAN

Although the evidence above outlined had led me
to the conviction that hunger results from contractions
of the alimentary canal, direct proof was still lacking.
In order to learn whether such proof might be secured,
Washburn determined to become accustomed to the
presence of a rubber tube in the esophagus.* Almost
every day for several weeks Washburn introduced as
far as the stomach a small tube, to the lower end of
which was attached a soft-rubber balloon about 8 centimeters in diameter. The tube was thus carried about
each time for two or three hours. After this preliminary experience the introduction of the tube and
its presence in the gullet and stomach were not at all
disturbing. When a record was to be taken, the balloon, placed just within the stomach, was moderately
distended with air, and was connected with a water
manometer ending in a cylindrical chamber 3.5 centimeters wide. A float recorder resting on the water in
the chamber permitted registering any contractions of
the fundus of the stomach. On the days of observation
Washburn would abstain from breakfast, or eat spar-

---

* Nicolai (op. cit.) reported that although the introduction of a
stomach tube at first abolished hunger in his subjects, with repeated
use the effects became insignificant.

ingly; and without taking any luncheon would appear in the laboratory about two o'clock. The recording apparatus was arranged as above described. In order to avoid any error that might arise from artificial pressure on the balloon, a pneumograph, fastened below the ribs, was made to record the movements of the abdominal wall. Uniformity of these movements would show that no special contractions of the abdominal muscles were made. Between the records of gastric pressure and abdominal movement, time was marked in minutes, and an electromagnetic signal traced a line which could be altered by pressing a key. All these recording arrangements were out of Washburn's sight; he sat with one hand at the key, ready whenever the sensation of hunger was experienced to make the current which moved the signal.

Sometimes the observations were started before any hunger was noted; at other times the sensation, after running a course, gave way to a feeling of fatigue. Under either of these circumstances there were no contractions of the stomach. When Washburn stated that he was hungry, however, powerful contractions of the stomach were invariably being registered. As in my own earlier experience, the sensations were characterized by periodic recurrences with free intervals, or by periodic accesses of an uninterrupted ache. The record of Washburn's introspection of his hunger pangs agreed closely with the record of his gastric contractions. Almost invariably, however, the contraction nearly

reached its maximum before the record of the sensation was started (see Fig. 41).

This fact may be regarded as evidence that the contraction precedes the sensation, and not *vice versa,* as
Boldireff considered it. The contractions were about a
half-minute in duration, and the intervals between
varied from thirty to ninety seconds, with an average

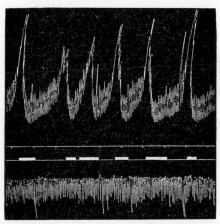

FIG. 41.—One-half the original size. The top record represents
intragastric pressure (the small oscillations due to respiration,
the large to contractions of the stomach); the second record is
time in minutes (ten minutes); the third record is W's report
of hunger pangs; the lowest record is respiration registered by
means of a pneumograph about the abdomen.

of about one minute. The augmentations of intragastric pressure in Washburn ranged between eleven
and thirteen in twenty minutes; I had previously
counted in myself eleven hunger pangs in the same
time. The rate in each of us was, therefore, approximately the same. This rate is slightly slower than
that found in dogs by Boldireff; the difference is per-

haps correlated with the slower rhythm of gastric peristalsis in man compared with that in the dog.[37]

Before hunger was experienced by Washburn the recording apparatus revealed no signs of gastric activity. Sometimes a rather tedious period of waiting had to be endured before contractions occurred. And after they began they continued for a while, then ceased (see Fig. 42). The feeling of hunger, which was reported while

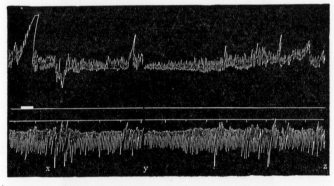

Fig. 42.—One-half the original size. The same conditions as in Fig. 41. (Fifteen minutes.) There was a long wait for hunger to disappear. After x, W. reported himself "tired but not hungry." The record from y to z was the continuance, on a second drum, of x to y.

the contractions were recurring, disappeared as the waves stopped. The inability of the subject to control the contractions eliminated the possibility of their being artifacts, perhaps induced by suggestion. The close concomitance of the contractions with hunger pangs, therefore, clearly indicates that they are the real source of those pangs.

This study of hunger, reported by Washburn and

myself in 1912, has since been taken up by Carlson of Chicago, and in observations on a man with a permanent gastric fistula, as well as on himself and his collaborators, he has fully confirmed our evidence as to the relation between contractions of the alimentary canal and the hunger sensation. In a series of more than a score of interesting papers, Carlson and his students [38] have greatly amplified our knowledge of the physiology of the "empty" stomach. Not only are there the contractions observed by Washburn and myself, but at times these may fuse into a continuous cramp of the gastric muscle. The characteristic contractions, furthermore, continue after the vagus nerve supply to the stomach has been destroyed, and, therefore, are not dependent on the reception of impulses by way of the cranial autonomic fibers. Rogers and Martin [39] have examined the stomach with the X-rays and have found that the essential activity underlying the hunger pang is a strong contraction of the encircling muscles of the lower third of the stomach.

The hunger contractions occur during sleep. They are stopped by chewing and temporarily by swallowing. They cease during intense emotional states such as joy, fear and anger. They are weakened and may be completely abolished by smoking, the effects apparently varying with the "strength" of the tobacco. They may be banished for ten or fifteen minutes by pulling a belt tightly about the waist. Very vigorous muscular exercise inhibits the contractions, but after the exercise they may be more intense than before.

The conditions for the occurrence of hunger contractions are not yet clearly understood. When the normal sugar concentration in the circulating blood is reduced about 25 per cent, hunger contractions increase. If the blood sugar is then raised, they cease.[40] They may be related, therefore, to need for the most generally useful energy-yielding material in the body, viz., glucose.

With these demonstrations that contractions are the immediate cause of hunger, most of the difficulties confronting other explanations are readily obviated. Thus the sudden onset of hunger and its peculiar periodicity —phenomena which no other explanation of hunger can account for—are at once explained.

In fever, when bodily material is being most rapidly used, hunger is absent. Its absence is understood from an observation made by F. T. Murphy and myself,[41] that infection, with systemic involvement, is accompanied by a total cessation of all movements of the alimentary canal. Boldireff observed that when his dogs were fatigued the rhythmic contractions failed to appear. Being "too tired to eat" is thereby given a rational explanation.

A pathological form of the sensation—the inordinate hunger (bulimia) of certain neurotics—is in accordance with the well-known disturbances of the tonic innervation of the alimentary canal in such individuals.

There is evidence that the intestines originate vague sensations by their contractions. The final banishment of the modified hunger sensation in the patient with duodenal fistula, described by Busch, may have been due to the lessened activity of the intestines when chyme was injected into them.

The observations recorded in this chapter have, as already noted, numerous points of similarity to Boldireff's observations [42] on the periodic activity of the alimentary canal in fasting dogs. Each period of activity, he found, comprised not only widespread contractions of the digestive canal, but also the pouring out of bile, and of pancreatic and intestinal juices rich in ferments. Gastric juice was not secreted at these times; when it was secreted and reached the intestine the periodic activity ceased. What is the significance of this extensive disturbance? I have elsewhere reported evidence [43] that gastric peristalsis is dependent on the stretching of gastric muscle when tonically contracted. The evidence that the stomach is in fact strongly contracted in hunger—i. e., in a state of high tonus—has been presented above.* Thus the very condition which causes hunger and leads to the taking of food is the condition, when the swallowed food stretches the shortened muscles, for immediate starting of gastric peristalsis. In this connection the observations of Haudek and Stigler [44] are probably significant. They found that the stomach discharges its contents more rapidly if food is eaten in hunger than if not so

---

* The "empty" stomach and esophagus contain gas (see Hertz, *Quarterly Journal of Medicine,* iii, 1910, p. 378; Mikulicz, *Mittheilungen aus den Grenzgebieten der Medicin und Chirurgie,* xii, 1903, p. 596). They would naturally manifest rhythmic contractions on shortening tonically on their content.

eaten. Hunger, in other words, is normally the signal that the stomach is contracted for action; the unpleasantness of hunger leads to eating; eating starts gastric digestion, and abolishes the sensation. Meanwhile the pancreatic and intestinal juices, as well as bile, have been prepared in the duodenum to receive the oncoming chyme. The periodic activity of the alimentary canal in fasting, therefore, is not solely the source of hunger pangs, but is at the same time an exhibition in the digestive organs of readiness for prompt attack on the food swallowed by the hungry animal.

REFERENCES

1. CANNON, *The Mechanical Factors of Digestion* (London and New York, 1911), p. 204.
2. BARDIER, *Richet's Dictionnaire de Physiologie,* article "Faim," vi (1904), p. 1. See also, HOWELL, *Text book of Physiology* (4th edition, Philadelphia and London, 1911), p. 285.
3. See STERNBERG, *Zentralblatt für Physiologie,* xxii (1909), p. 653. Similar views were expressed by BAYLE in a thesis presented to the Faculty of Medicine in Paris in 1816.
4. See HERTZ, *The Sensibility of the Alimentary Canal* (London, 1911), p. 38.
5. SCHIFF, *Physiologie de la Digestion* (Florence and Turin, 1867), p. 40.
6. LUCIANI, *Das Hungern* (Hamburg and Leipzig, 1890), p. 113.
7. TIGERSTEDT, *Nagel's Handbuch der Physiologie,* i (Berlin, 1909), p. 376.
8. JOHANSON, LANDERGREN, SONDEN and TIGERSTEDT, *Skandinavisches Archiv für Physiologie,* vii (1897), p. 33.
9. CARRINGTON, *Vitality, Fasting and Nutrition* (New York, 1908), p. 555.
10. VITERBI, quoted by BARDIER, *op. cit.,* p. 7.
11. BUSCH, *Archiv für pathologische Anatomie und Physiologie und für klinische Medicin,* xiv (1858), p. 147.

12. See SCHIFF, *op. cit.*, p. 37; also DUCCESCHI, *Archivio di Fisiologia*, viii (1910), p. 579.

13. LONGET, *Traité de Physiologie*, i (Paris, 1868), p. 23.

14. LUDWIG, *Lehrbuch der Physiologie des Menschen*, ii (Leipzig and Heidelberg, 1858), p. 584.

15. MAXWELL, *Journal of Biological Chemistry*, ii (1906-7), p. 194.

16. See SCHIFF, *op. cit.*, p. 49.

17. See SCHIFF, *op. cit.*, p. 31; BARDIER, *op. cit.*, p. 16.

18. HEAD, *Brain*, xvi (1893), p. 1; xxiv (1901), p. 345.

19. NICOLAI, *Ueber die Entstehung des Hungergefühls* (Inaugural Dissertation, Berlin, 1892), p. 17.

20. BEAUMONT, *The Physiology of Digestion* (2nd edition, Burlington, 1847), p. 51.

21. NICOLAI, *op. cit.*, p. 15.

22. BEAUMONT, *op. cit.*, p. 55.

23. LUCIANI, *Archivio di Fisiologia*, iii (1906), p. 54. TIEDEMANN long ago suggested that gastric nerves become increasingly sensitive as fasting progresses. (*Physiologie des Menschen*, Darmstadt, 1836, iii, p. 22.)

24. VALENTI, *Archives Italiennes de Biologie*, liii (1910), p. 94.

25. WEBER, *Wagner's Handwörterbuch der Physiologie*, iii [2] (1846), p. 580.

26. VIERORDT, *Grundriss der Physiologie* (Tübingen, 1871), p. 433.

27. SCHIFF, *op. cit.*, p. 33.

28. LUCIANI, *op. cit.*, p. 542.

29. VALENTI, *op. cit.*, p. 95.

30. BETTMANN, *Philadelphia Monthly Medical Journal*, i (1899), p. 133.

31. WOLFF, *Dissertation* (Giessen, 1902), p. 9.

32. HIS, *Archiv für Anatomie* (1903), p. 345.

33. BOLDIREFF, *op. cit.*, p. 1.

34. BOLDIREFF, *op. cit.*, p. 96.

35. See CANNON and LIEB, *American Journal of Physiology*, xxix (1911), p. 267.

36. DUCCESCHI, *Archivio per le Scienze Mediche*, xxi (1897), p. 154.

37. See CANNON, *American Journal of Physiology*, viii (1903), p. xxi; xiv (1905), p. 344.

38. See *American Journal of Physiology*, 1913, 1914.

39. ROGERS and MARTIN, *ibid.*, lxxvi (1926), p. 349.

40. BULATAO and CARLSON, *ibid.*, lxix (1924), p. 107.
41. CANNON and MURPHY, *Journal of the American Medical Association,* xlix (1907), p. 840.
42. BOLDIREFF, *op. cit.*, pp. 108-111.
43. CANNON, *American Journal of Physiology.* xxix (1911), p. 250.
44. HAUDEK and STIGLER, *Archiv für die gesammte Physiologie,* cxxxiii (1910), p. 159.

CHAPTER XVI

THE PHYSIOLOGICAL BASIS OF THIRST

IN regarding the human body as a self-regulating organization we observe that, so far as mere existence is concerned, it depends on three necessary supplies from the outer world,—on food, to provide for growth and repair and to yield energy for internal activities and the maintenance of body heat; on oxygen, to serve the oxidative processes essential to life; and on water, as the medium in which occur all the chemical changes of the body. These three supplies are of different orders of urgency. Thus a man may live for thirty or forty days without taking food, as professional fasters have demonstrated [1] and suffer no apparent permanent injury to his bodily structure or functions. On the other hand, lack of oxygen for only a brief period may result in unconsciousness and death. Indeed, certain nerve cells in the cerebral cortex cannot withstand total deprivation of oxygen for more than eight or nine minutes without undergoing such fundamental changes that they do not again become normal when they receive their proper supply.[2] Intermediate between the long survival without food and the very brief survival without oxygen is the period of existence which is possible without water. Records of men who have missed their way in desert regions and who, with no water to drink, have wandered in the scorching heat have proved that they rarely live under these circumstances of struggle and torrid atmosphere for more than three days, and many die within 36 hours. An exceptional instance has been reported, of a Mexican, who, lost in the dry plains of the southwestern part of the United States, walked, or crept on his hands and knees, between 100 and 150 miles, repeatedly drinking his own excretions, and succeeded, after nearly seven days wholly without water, in reaching a habitation.[3] This is a record which, for its conditions, has no parallel. If the thirsting man is not subjected to heat or exertion his life may continue much longer than seven days. Viterbi, the Italian political prisoner who committed suicide by refusing food and drink, died on the eighteenth day of his voluntary privation. As already noted, the pangs of hunger ceased after the third day, but, until almost the last, thirst was always more insistent and tormenting. He records again and again his parched mouth and throat, his burning thirst, his ardent and continual thirst, his thirst constant and ever more intolerable.[4] Thus though the period of survival varies, death is sure to come whether food, or oxygen, or water is withheld.

Normally these three supplies—food, oxygen, and water—are maintained in more or less constant adjustment to the bodily needs. Food material is being continually utilized in building body structure, and in providing energy for bodily activities, but it is periodically restored. Oxygen is continually combining with carbon and hydrogen and leaving the body in carbon-dioxide and water, but the loss is compensated for with every breath. And water, likewise, is always being discharged in expired air, in secretion from the kidneys, and in the sweat. So great is the escape by way of the lungs and skin alone that it is estimated that approximately 25 per cent of the heat loss from the body is due to evaporation from these surfaces.[5] This continuous lessening of the water content must be checked by a new supply, or important functions will begin to show signs of need.

THE IMPORTANCE OF WATER FOR THE BODY

The evidence for the absolute necessity of water in our physiological processes requires no elaboration. Water is a universal and essential ingredient of all forms of organisms. Without it life disappears or is latent—the dry seed awakens only on becoming moist. Because we may have it at almost any moment we are likely to overlook its absolute necessity in our lives. Among inhabitants of desert regions, however, water is the central nucleus of thought about which all other ideas revolve; it is an ultimate standard of things, incomparably more stable and more exalted than the gold of civilized commerce, the constantly remembered basis of existence.[6] In our bodies the presence of water as the main constituent of the digestive secretions, its rôle in the chemical changes of digestion, its service as a vehicle of absorption, its importance in the composition of blood and lymph, its use, together with other substances, in body fluids as a lubricant, its action in regulating body temperature—these functions need merely to be mentioned to illustrate how water influences every activity which living beings display.

Because water is a fundamental essential to life, and is continually escaping from the body, and because there is consequent need for repeated replenishment of the store, an inquiry into the mechanism of the replenishment is a matter of interest.

That such a mechanism exists is indicated by the fact that all our essential functions, leading to preservation of the individual and of the race, are controlled not through memory and volition, but by insistent sensations and desires. The unpleasant sensation of thirst causes us to drink. Not towards the subjective aspect of these automatic arrangements, however, is the special attention of the physiologist directed. He is primarily concerned with the bodily states which give rise to the sensation. Only when these states and their relations to the needs of the organism are known is the automatic control explained.

THE SENSATION OF THIRST

Even more imperious than hunger as an insistent and tormenting sensation, accompanied by a dominant impulse which determines our behavior, is thirst. Indeed, these two experiences—hunger and thirst—are such impelling motives in directing our conduct that from early times they have been used as supreme examples of a strong desire. The ancient prophet spoke of a "hunger and thirst after righteousness" to express the eagerness of his yearning. And the common acquaintance of mankind with the potent demands of hunger and thirst for satisfaction renders these similes easily understood.

In undertaking a discussion of thirst it is necessary at the start to distinguish clearly between the primitive sensation itself and appetite. Just as in the case of food, an appetite for this or that peculiar potable substance develops from former experience and from established associations of an agreeable character. We drink not only because we are thirsty, but also because we relish a certain aroma or bouquet, or a peculiar taste, and wish to enjoy it again. In respect to appetite the taking of fluid differs from the taking of food in that fluid, which leaves the stomach rapidly, may not occasion a sense of satiety as does food, which accumulates in the stomach. In this possibility of continuing pleasurable sensations associated with drinking lie the dangers that arise from the excessive use of beverages. Under normal conditions, however, it is through the satisfaction of appetite for a particular drink, e. g., for tea, or coffee, or light alcoholic beverages, that the body may be supplied with sufficient water for its needs before thirst has had occasion to manifest itself. As there is provided, however, back of the appetite for food, in readiness to become imperious if necessary, the sensation of hunger, so likewise, as a final defense against a too great depletion of the water content of the body, there may appear the urgent and distressing sensation of thirst.

There is a general agreement that thirst is a sensation referred to the mucous lining of the mouth and pharynx, and especially to the root of the tongue and to the palate. McGee, an American geologist of large experience in desert regions, who made numerous observations on sufferers from extreme thirst, has distinguished five stages through which men pass on their way to death from lack of water.[3] In the first stage there is a feeling of dryness in the mouth and throat, accompanied by a craving for liquid. This is the common experience of normal thirst. The condition may be alleviated, as everyday practice demonstrates, by a moderate quantity of water, or through exciting a flow of saliva by taking into the mouth fruit acids such as lemon or tomato juice, or by chewing insoluble substances. In the second stage the saliva and mucus in the mouth and throat become scant and sticky. There is a feeling of dry deadness of the mucous membranes. The inbreathed air feels hot. The tongue clings to the teeth or cleaves to the roof of the mouth. A lump seems to rise in the throat, and starts endless swallowing motions to dislodge it. Water and wetness are then exalted as the end of all excellence. Even in this stage the distress can be alleviated by repeatedly sipping and sniffing a few drops of water at a time. "Many prospectors," McGee states, "become artists in mouth moistening, and carry canteens only for this purpose, depending on draughts in camp to supply the general needs of the system." The last three stages described by McGee, in which the eyelids stiffen over eyeballs set in a sightless stare, the tongue-tip hardens to a dull weight, and the wretched victim has illusions of lakes and running streams, are too pathological for our present interest.

The fact I wish to emphasize is the persistent dryness of the mouth and throat in thirst. Direct testimony is given by King, a medical officer in a United States Cavalry troop, which for three and one-half days was lost without water in the torrid "Llando Estacado" of Texas. He records that, on the third day, salivary and mucous secretions had long been absent, and that mouths and throats were so parched that food, on being chewed, gathered about the teeth and in the palate, and could not be swallowed. "Sugar would not dissolve in the mouth." [7]

Further evidence of the relation between local dryness of the mouth and throat and the sensation of thirst is found in some of the conditions which bring on the sensation. Breathing hot air free from moisture, prolonged speaking or singing, the repeated chewing of desiccated food, the inhibitory influence of fear and anxiety on salivary secretion, have all been observed to result in dryness of the buccal and pharyngeal mucous membrane and in attendant thirst. On the other hand, conditions arising in regions remote from the mouth and involving a reduction of the general fluid content of the body, such as profuse sweating, the excessive diarrhea of cholera, the diuresis of diabetes, as well as such losses as occur in hemorrhage and lactation, are well recognized causes of the same sensation. There appear to be, therefore, both local and general origins of thirst. In correspondence with these observations, two groups of theories have arisen, just as in the case of hunger— one explaining thirst as a local sensation, the other explaining it as a general and diffuse sensation. These theories require examination.

THE THEORY THAT THIRST IS OF LOCAL ORIGIN

The view that thirst is a sensation of local origin has had few advocates, and the evidence in its favor is meager. In 1885 Lepidi-Chioti and Fubini [8] reported observations on a boy of 17, who, suffering from polyuria, passed from 13 to 15 litres of urine daily. When prevented from drinking for several hours, this youth was tormented by a most distressing thirst, which he referred to the back of the mouth, and at times to the epigastrium. The observers tried the effect of brushing the back of the mouth with a weak solution of cocaine. Scarcely was the application completed before the troublesome' sensation wholly ceased, and the patient remained comfortable from 15 to 35 minutes. If, instead of cocaine, water was used to brush over the mucous membranes, thirst was relieved for only two minutes. The temporary abolition of a persistent thirst by use of a local anesthetic, in a human being who could testify regarding his experience, is suggestive support for the local origin of the sensation. The evidence adduced by Valenti is also suggestive. He cocainized the back of the mouth and the upper esophagus of dogs which had been deprived of water for several days, and noted that they then refused to drink.[9] One might suppose that the refusal to take water was due to inhibition of the swallowing reflex by anesthetization of the pharyngeal mucosa, as reported by Wassilief.[10] But Valenti states that his animals are quite capable of swallowing.[11]

Though these observations are indicative of a local source of the thirst sensation, they leave unexplained the manner in which the sensation arises. Valenti has put forward the idea that all the afferent nerves of the upper part of the digestive tube are excitable to stimuli of thirst, but that suggestion does not advance our knowledge so long as we are left unenlightened as to what these stimuli are. A similar criticism may be offered to Luciani's theory that the sensory nerves of the buccal and pharyngeal mucosa are especially sensitive to a diminution of the water-content of the circulating fluid of the body; indeed, that these nerves are advance sentinels, like the skin nerves for pain, warning the body of danger.[12] No special features of the nerves of this region, however, are known. No special end-organs are known. The intimation that these nerves are peculiarly related to a general bodily need is pure hypothesis. That they mediate the sensation of thirst is unquestioned. But the problem again is presented, How are they stimulated?

THE THEORY THAT THIRST IS OF GENERAL ORIGIN

The view that thirst is a general sensation was well stated by Schiff. It arises, he declared, from a lessened water-content of the body, a condition from which the whole body suffers. The local reference to the pharynx, like the local reference of hunger to the stomach, is due to association of experiences. Thus the feeling of dryness in the throat, though it accompanies thirst, has only the value of a secondary phenomenon, and bears no deeper relation to the general sensation than heaviness of the eyelids bear to the general sensation of sleepiness.[13] The conception of thirst, as a general sensation, is commonly accepted, and is supported by considerable experimental evidence. The interpretation of this evidence, however, is open to question, and should be examined critically.

First among the experiments cited are those of Dupuytren and the later similar experiments of Orfila.[14] These observers abolished thirst in dogs by injecting water and other liquids into the dogs' veins. And Schiff quotes Magendie as having treated successfully by the same procedure the thirst of a patient suffering from hydrophobia. In these instances the treatment was no doubt general, in that it affected the body as a whole. But the assumption that thirst is thus proved to be a general sensation is unwarranted, for the injection of fluid into the circulation may have changed local conditions in the mouth and pharynx, so that the local sensation no longer arose.

A classic experiment repeatedly cited in the literature of thirst was one performed by Claude Bernard. He opened a gastric fistula which he had made in a dog, and allowed the water which the animal drank to pass out. As the animal became thirsty, it would drink until "fatigued," as the report states, and when "rested" it would begin again. But after the fistula was closed, drinking quickly assuaged the desire for water. The inference was drawn that thirst must be a general sensation, for the passage of water through the mouth and pharynx wet those surfaces, and yet the animal was not satisfied until the water was permitted to enter the intestine and be absorbed by the body.[15] This evidence appears conclusive. The expressions "fatigued" and "rested," however, are interpretations of the observer, and not the testimony of the dog. Indeed, we may with equal reasonableness assume that the animal stopped drinking because he was not thirsty, and started again when he became thirsty. The only assumptions necessary for such an interpretation of the animal's behavior are that appreciable time is required to moisten the buccal and pharyngeal mucosa sufficiently to extinguish thirst —a point made by Voit [16]— and that these regions become dried rapidly when there is absence of an adequate water-content in the body. This interpretation is consistent with the view that thirst is a sensation having a local source. Furthermore, this interpretation is not contradicted by the satisfaction manifested by the dog after the fistula was closed, for the water which is absorbed, like that injected into veins, may quench thirst by altering local conditions. We cannot admit, therefore, that Bernard's experiment is proof that thirst is a general sensation.

Another set of observations cited as favorable to the theory of the diffused character of the origin of thirst are those of Longet. After severing the glosso-pharyngeal, the lingual and the vagus nerves on both sides in dogs, he observed that they drank as usual after eating.[17] If thirst has a local origin in the mouth and pharynx, why should the animals in which the nerves to these regions were cut still take water? Two answers to this question may be given. First, as Voit has pointed out,[18] Longet did not cut all branches of the vagi and trigemini to the mouth and pharynx, and consequently some sensation persisted. And second, even if all nerves were cut, the fact that the animals drank would not prove that thirst exists as a general feeling, for one may drink from the sight of fluid, or from custom, without the stimulation of a dry mouth, just as one may eat from the sight of food without the stimulus of hunger. In other words, the element of appetite, previously considered, may enter, and as a matter of habit and associated experience determine present reactions.

BLOOD CHANGES INTERPRETED AS SHOWING THAT THIRST IS A GENERAL SENSATION

The remaining evidence in favor of the diffused origin of thirst is found in studies of blood changes.

These changes, by altering the "milieu intérieur" of the body cells, must affect them all. In 1900, Mayer published reports on the increase of osmotic pressure of the blood, as determined by depression of the freezing point of the serum, which he noted in conditions naturally accompanied by thirst. Dogs deprived of water for several days had a blood serum in which the osmotic pressure was increased, and rabbits kept in a specially warmed chamber showed the same change. Thus, conditions in which the water supply to the body was stopped, or the loss of water from the body by sweating or pulmonary evaporation was increased, either of which is known to cause thirst, were associated with a rise of osmotic pressure. And Mayer argued that all other circumstances in which thirst appears—in diabetes with increased blood sugar, in renal disease with accumulation of waste material in the body fluids, in acute rabies with total deprivation of water, in cholera with excessive outpouring of water into the intestine—the osmotic pressure of the blood would be augmented. Moreover, when a thirsty dog drinks, the hypertonicity of his serum disappears, his normal condition is restored, and he stops drinking.

By these observations Mayer was led to the conclusion that whenever the osmotic pressure of the blood rises above normal, thirst appears; whenever it returns to normal, thirst vanishes; and as the pressure varies, thirst also varies. Since intravenous injections of hypertonic salt solution cause, by stimulation of the bulbar centers, according to Mayer, a rise of arterial pressure and renal and intestinal vasodilation—both operating to lower the abnormally high osmotic pressure of the blood—he infers that other agencies are present in the organism besides the desire for water, which tend to keep the blood normal. Thirst, he declares, is the last of a series of mechanisms acting to protect the organism against hypertonicity of its fluids.

In summary, then, the thirsty individual has a blood with high osmotic pressure. This condition affects all the cells of the body. It disturbs the cells of the central nervous system, and thus leads both to protective circulatory reactions and, in case these fail, to malaise and irritability, and a reference of unpleasantness to the region of the pharynx. Accompanying this, there is the impulse to drink, and when that is satisfied, the water taken in restores the normal state.[18]

Mayer's observations were soon confirmed, but his inferences were challenged. In 1901, Wettendorff, working in Brussels, reported that if dogs are deprived of water their blood does, indeed, develop a hypertonicity, as Mayer had found, but that this is a phenomenon which does not occur to any marked degree in the first days of the deprivation. In one instance there was no change in the freezing point of the serum during three days of thirst. Serious alteration of the osmotic pressure of the blood, therefore, is comparatively tardy in its appearance. Since the organism is continually losing water, and nevertheless the blood remains for a day or two unchanged, Wettendorff concluded that the consistency of the blood is preserved as long as possible by withdrawal of water from the extravascular fluids and the tissues. Further, thirst is clearly demonstrable long before any considerable change in the blood is evident. One animal in which the freezing point of the serum had been lowered only 0.01° C. by four days' deprivation of water, drank 200 cubic centimeters of physiological salt solution, a liquid which to the dog in normal condition is quite repugnant. Again, when the blood has become slightly hypertonic, a dog may drink normal salt solution without lowering his osmotic pressure and afterwards, by refusing further drink, act quite as if he had slaked his thirst. But if an animal with a very hypertonic blood is placed before hypertonic salt solution he takes it again and again—an action which may be explained by a draining of water from the tissues with increasing intensity, and a consequent increasing thirst.

From all these observations Wettendorff concluded that the origin of thirst does not reside in alterations of the blood itself, but in the act of withdrawing water from the tissues. The liquids bathing the cells, therefore, would be first to concentrate as water is lost from the organism. And since the conditions of cellular life would thus be modified in all the tissues, the peculiar state would develop which occasions the sensation of thirst. This effect is generally diffused, and is independent of any peculiar influence of the process of dehydration on the nervous system itself.

In accounting for the localizing of the sensation in

the mouth and throat Wettendorff distinguished between a "true thirst" and a "false thirst." "True
thirst," he declared, is dependent on an actual bodily
need, and is persistent until the need is satisfied.
"False thirst" is only a dryness of the mouth and
pharynx. Dryness in this region occurs, to be sure,
in true thirst, but it is then an expression of the general dehydration of the tissues, exaggerated perhaps
by contact with the outer air. Through experience the
two conditions—buccal dryness and general dehydration—have become associated. Even in true thirst
we may temporarily abolish the sensation by moistening the pharyngeal mucous membrane, but the result
is only a "false satisfaction," a self-deception, made
possible because long and pleasant experience has
proved that moistening this region by drink leads to
the satisfaction of an instinctive need.[19]

THE CENTRAL FACT OF THIRST

The foregoing review of observations and theories
has revealed that the attitude of physiologists with
reference to thirst has been much as it was with reference to hunger. In each condition a general bodily
need has arisen from a lack of essential bodily material and is signaled by a well-defined sensation. In
each the testimony of ingenuous persons regarding
their feelings has been carefully set down, and then
explained away. Thus in the case of thirst the primary sensation is described universally as an experi-

ence of dryness and stickiness in the mouth and throat.[20] Instead of attempting to account for the experience as such, however, attention has been paid to the bodily need which accompanies it; apparently, since the need is a general one, the sensation has been supposed to be general, and the thirst which everybody experiences and knows about has been classed as an associated secondary phenomenon or the peripheral reference of a central change. The really doubtful feature in this view of thirst, just as in the older conception of hunger, is the "general sensation." That even the early stages of a need of water may be accompanied by increased irritability, and a vague sense of weakness and limpness, is not denied. But the thirsty man does not complain of these general conditions. He is tormented by a parched and burning throat, and any explanation of the physiological mechanism for maintaining the water content of the body must take into account this prominent fact.

In looking for a mechanism which would automatically keep up the water supply of our bodily economy, we may follow two clues; first, that there may be a peripheral arrangement which in the presence of a general bodily need for water would lead to dryness of the mouth and throat; and second, that a peripheral arrangement of this nature should be especially characteristic of animals which are constantly and rapidly losing water and require repeated renewal of the supply. These two clues offer a biological approach to the explanation of thirst which I wish to utilize.

THIRST A SENSATION OF LAND ANIMALS

In one sense all animals are constantly losing water, for even in the simplest forms waste material is excreted in solution. With 'respect to water loss, however, we should expect to find a marked difference between animals living in water itself and those living in air. Indeed, it is difficult to conceive of an animal living in water as experiencing thirst. The entire body surface and the mouth and throat are throughout active life continuously bathed in a moving flow. The food is taken wet from a wet medium. Probably renal activity and the secretion of the digestive glands are the only important ways for water to leave the economy; and the digestive secretions are soon largely re-absorbed. In contrast, the land animals—mammals, for example—lose moisture not only in these ways but also by the moistening of dry food, by evaporation from the extensive surface of the lungs, and by the action of innumerable sweat glands. It is because of the possibility of great and rapid loss of water from its body that the land animal has special need for an assurance of adequate supply.

In the water inhabitant the skin, and the mouth and gullet, are all kept wet by the medium in which he lives and moves. In the process of evolution, however, as organisms changed their habitat from water to air, the skin became dry and scaly. Of the parts which in marine animals were constantly bathed by water, only the mouth and throat continue to be

moist. These regions are now exposed to air, however, instead of being flushed by a flowing stream,
and consequently they tend to dry. The structural
lining of these parts probably renders them especially
liable to desiccation in the presence of dry air, for
the mucosa of the mouth and also of the pharynx,
below the level of the floor of the nasal chambers,
is composed of squamous epithelium. Some scattered
mucous glands are present, but they are not capable
of keeping the surfaces satisfactorily wet, as any one
can readily prove by breathing through the mouth for
only a few minutes. When air passes to and fro by way
of this watercourse, as in prolonged speaking or singing,
and in smoking, it is to be expected that feelings of dryness and stickiness, which we call thirst, should arise.

Contrast this condition of the mouth with the condition of the respiratory tract, in which the lining
membrane consists of columnar epithelium and is
richly provided, particularly in the nose, with multitudes of mucous glands. Through this tract air moves
to and fro constantly with no sign of inducing desiccation except in extreme and prolonged deprivation of
water. But there is one portion of this normal path-
way for the air which, in the absence of sufficient moisture, is peculiarly liable to become dried. It is the
pharynx, where the respiratory tract crosses the digestive tract—i. e., where the inbreathed air, which
may be insufficiently moistened in the nose, passes
over surfaces of the ancient watercourse. Here, even
with nasal respiration, unpleasant feelings may be

excited, if the water-content of the body is reduced, and, in cases of marked thirst, the dryness of this region may stimulate tireless swallowing motions.

BUCCAL GLANDS A CHARACTERISTIC OF LAND ANIMALS

The central questions now appear: Why do not the mouth and pharynx feel dry and uncomfortable under normal conditions? And why do they feel so when the body stands in need of water? Again, a comparison of conditions in the water inhabitants, in which the buccal and pharyngeal regions are kept moistened by the surrounding medium, with conditions in the air inhabitants, in which these regions tend to be dried by the surrounding medium, will offer pertinent suggestions. A characteristic difference between these two animal groups is the possession, by the air inhabitants, of special buccal glands. They are not present in fishes, but are found in the rest of the vertebrate series from the amphibia onwards. At first little differentiated, they develop in mammals into the three pairs of salivary glands—the parotid, submaxillary, and sub-lingual. For the purpose of considering thirst in man, we may deal solely with this salivary group. The action of these organs is to secrete a fluid which is normally more than 97 per cent, and may be more than 99 per cent, water.[21] The theory of thirst, on which I wish to offer evidence, may now be stated. In brief, it is that the salivary glands have, among their functions, that of keeping moist the ancient watercourse; that they, like other tissues, suffer when water is lacking in the body—a lack especially important for them, however, because their secretion is almost wholly water, and that, when these glands fail to provide sufficient fluid to moisten the mouth and throat, the local discomfort and unpleasantness which result constitute the feeling of thirst.

That one of the uses of buccal glands is to keep wet the surfaces over which their secretion is distributed is indicated by the fact that these structures first appear in air-inhabiting vertebrates. This indication receives support from the conditions seen in the cetacea, the mammalian forms which have returned to an aquatic existence, and in which both the water-loss from the body and the need for wetting the mouth and throat are greatly reduced. It is a remarkable fact that in these animals the salivary glands are either lacking or are very rudimentary. The appearance and disappearance of the buccal glands in large animal groups, in correspondence with the exposure or non-exposure of the mouth and throat to desiccating air, point to these glands as protectors of the buccal mucosa against drying.

THE FUNCTION OF THE SALIVARY GLANDS IN RELATION TO THIRST

Experimental evidence as to the protective function of the salivary secretions was provided incidentally many years ago by Bidder and Schmidt. They were interested in studying any fluid secretion which might appear in the mouth apart from saliva. To this end they tied in dogs all the salivary ducts. The first effect was such a striking diminution of the fluid layer over the buccal mucosa that only when the mouth was held closed was the surface kept moist, and, when the animal breathed through the mouth, a real drying of the surface was hardly prevented. The eagerness for water, they state, was enormously increased, so that the animal was always ready to drink.[22]

Related to this service of saliva in moistening and lubricating the mouth parts is the presence of a special reflex for salivary secretion when the buccal mucosa is exposed to conditions which tend to dry it. As Pavlov's [23] researches have demonstrated, with dry food in the mouth, much more saliva is secreted than with moist food. And Zebrowski [24] found in the course of observations on patients with a parotid fistula, that, whereas no saliva flowed with the mouth closed, as much as 0.25 cubic centimeters in five minutes came from the duct when the mouth was opened. This reflex is readily demonstrable. If one closes the nostrils and breathes through the mouth for five minutes, usually nothing happens during the first minute. The mucosa then begins to feel dry, and at once the saliva starts flowing, and continues for the rest of the period. I have thus collected as much as 4.7 cubic centimeters in four minutes. Chewing motions, with the mouth empty, yielded in five minutes only about 1 cubic centimeter. In these observations precautions were taken against any psychic effect due to interest, by adding long columns of figures during the test. It seems clear, therefore, that if the mouth tends to become dry, the salivary glands are normally stimulated to action, and, if there is sufficient outflow from them, the affected surfaces are moistened. The act of swallowing favors the process, for the fluid is thereby spread backwards on the tongue and wiped down the back wall of the pharynx.

The question whether there is a relation between the existence of water-need in the body and diminished flow of saliva I have examined in two ways—by going without fluid for a considerable period and by profuse sweating, combined with measurements of salivary secretion under uniform stimulation. The method of determining salivary output was that of chewing for five minutes and at a uniform rate a tasteless gum, collecting the saliva which flowed during this period, and measuring its volume. All these observations are best made when one is inactive, and in my experience more nearly uniform results are obtained if one lies quiet during the tests.

The influence on salivary flow of going without fluid for some time may be illustrated by an example. The chewing to evoke salivary action was started at 7 o'clock in the morning, and repeated each hour until 8 o'clock in the evening. A breakfast consisting of a dry cereal preparation was taken between 8 and 9 o'clock, and a luncheon of dry bread between 12 and 1 o'clock. Nothing had been drunk since the previous evening. From the first test at 7 o'clock until 11 there was little change in the output of saliva; the average amount secreted in 5 minutes was 14.1 cubic centimeters, with variations between 13 and 16.4 cubic centimeters. Then the output began to fall, and at 2 o'clock only 6.4 cubic centimeters was secreted. The average amount for the two observations at 2 and 3 o'clock was 7.7 cubic centimeters—only little more than half that poured out in the morning. Between 3 and 4 o'clock a liter of water was drunk. The effect was soon apparent. At 4 o'clock the output was 15.6 cubic centimeters, and during the next 4 hours, in which more water was taken, and a supper with thin soup and other fluid was consumed, the average amount secreted was 14.6 cubic centimeters, a figure closely corresponding to the 14.1 cubic centimeters of the morning hours. These results are illustrated graphically in Fig. 43. Other tests of this character gave similar results, though there was variation in the rate of decrease in the amounts of saliva secreted.

A similar diminution of the salivary secretion occurs after the loss of water from the body by sweating. In one instance, the loss in about one hour of approximately 500 cubic centimeters of body fluid as sweat was accompanied by a reduction in the salivary output of almost 50 per cent.

Corresponding to the diminution of the salivary output as the result of chewing was a diminution in the reflex flow as a consequence of letting the mouth become dry. The reflex flow has fallen, in my experience, from 3 or 4 cubic centimeters in five minutes under normal conditions to a little more than 1 cubic centimeter during thirst.

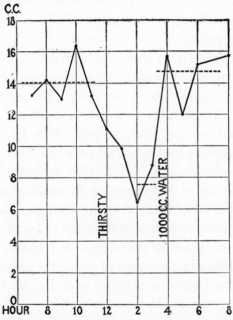

FIG. 43.—Chart showing saliva secreted each hour from 7 A.M. until 8 P.M. in consequence of chewing a tasteless gum five minutes. No fluid was drunk between 7 o'clock the previous evening and 3 o'clock P.M. For further description, see text.

The relation between the decrease of salivary flow in these experiments and the sensation of thirst was quite definite. In the experiment illustrated in Fig. 43, for example, the feeling of being "thirsty" was absent until the secretion of saliva began to decline,

after 11 o'clock. From that time onward the back of
the throat began to feel dry; there was frequent swallowing, and both the movements of the tongue and
the act of deglutition were associated with a sense
of "stickiness," a lack of adequate lubrication of the
parts. All of this unpleasantness and discomfort disappeared after the restoration of the saliva flow by
drinking water.

The increased spontaneous activity of the tongue
and the repeated swallowing motions as "thirst" became more marked are noteworthy. These movements
are a slight stimulus to salivary secretion, and they
have, furthermore, the obvious effect of spreading
about any fluid that might be present. In the absence
of sufficient fluid, however, they augment the dis-
agreeableness of the condition by making prominent
the friction due to lack of lubrication. The "lump
in the throat," which is complained of by persons who
suffer from extreme thirst, can be explained as due
to the difficulty encountered when the epiglottis and
root of the tongue are rubbed over the dry back wall
of the pharynx in attempts to swallow.

The only statement that I am aware of, which is
contradictory to the evidence just presented, is that
made by one of a group of psychologists, reported by
Boring.[25] This one observer testified that when he
was beginning to be thirsty the saliva flow was still
copious. The eight other observers of the group speak
of thirst as being characterized by dryness of the roof
of the mouth, dryness of the lips, the sensation of

having a "dry sore throat," feelings of stickiness, and uncomfortable "puckery" pressure localized in the middle and back of the tongue and in the palate— in other words, as one of them summed up his experience, "dryness expresses the complex as a whole." This body of testimony agrees closely with that presented earlier.

Other evidence on the relation between absence of saliva and the presence of thirst as a sensation was obtained through checking salivary secretion by atropine. Before the injection the amount secreted during 5 minutes by chewing averaged 13.5 cubic centimeters. After the full effect of the drug was manifest, the amount fell to 1 cubic centimeter. All the feelings that were noted in ordinary thirst—the sense of dry surfaces, the stickiness of the moving parts, the difficulties of speaking and swallowing—all were present. These disagreeable experiences, constituting the thirst sensation, disappeared as soon as the mouth and throat were washed out with a weak novocaine solution. The immediate effect in these circumstances was doubtless due to the water in the solution, but since the relief lasted much longer than when water was used, the anesthetic was also a factor. This experience agrees with that of Lipidi-Chioti and Fubini, mentioned earlier. No water was drunk by me during the period of atropine effect, and yet when that effect disappeared, and the saliva flow was reëstablished, thirst also was abolished. The relation between thirst and such drug action has been noted before, but so strong has been the theory that thirst is a "general" sensation, that the drug has been supposed to produce its effect not by local action but by central changes and by alteration of the blood.[26]

Similar in character to the thirst which results from the action of atropine is that which accompanies anxiety and fright. The effect of such emotional states in causing inhibition of salivary secretion is well known. It was the basis of the ancient "ordeal of rice," already described, as a means of detecting the guilty one in a group of suspected persons. It is illustrated by Hoche's report of the effects of air raids on the people of Freiburg-in-Baden, in whom the signs of great fear—chattering of the teeth, pallor, and diarrhea—were attended by intense thirst.[27] The unquenchable nature of the thirst which results from terror is a large part of the torment suffered by the novice in public speaking.

EXPLANATION OF THIRST AS DUE TO DISTURBED FUNCTION OF THE SALIVARY GLANDS

On the basis of the foregoing evidence I would explain thirst as due directly to what it seems to be due to—a relative drying of the mucosa of the mouth and pharynx. This may result either from excessive use of this passage for breathing, as in prolonged speaking or singing, or it may result from deficient salivary secretion. In the latter case "true thirst" exists, but it is not to be distinguished, so far as sensation is concerned, from "false thirst." True thirst is dependent on the fact that the salivary glands, which keep the buccal and pharyngeal mucosa moist, require water for their action. According to the observations and inferences of Wettendorff, the osmotic pressure of the blood is maintained, in spite of deprivation of water, by the withdrawal of water from the tissues. The salivary glands are included under "tissues," and they appear to suffer in a way which would support Wettendorff's view, for in the presence of a general need for water in the body, they fail to maintain the normal amount and quality * of secretion. The same is doubtless true of other glands. The importance of this failure of action of the salivary glands, however, to the mechanism of the water supply of the body, lies in the strategic position of these glands in relation to a surface which tends to become dry by the passage of air over it. If this surface is not kept moist, discomfort arises and with it an impulse to seek well tried means of relief. Thus the diminishing activity of the salivary glands becomes a delicate indicator of the bodily demand for fluid.

The foregoing explanation is in agreement with the suggestions which have been offered to account for thirst as having a local origin. But it does not require specialized nerves, or peculiar sensitiveness of the first portion of the digestive tract, which have been as-

---

* There is evidence that, as the quantity of saliva diminishes, its water content is less; i. e., it is more viscous (see Tezner, *Archives Internationales de Physiologie,* ii, 1904-5, p. 153).

sumed to be present by the upholders of this theory.
And by calling attention to the arrangement by which
the salivary glands are made to serve as indicators of
the general bodily need for water, it presents a reasonable account of the manner in which a wide-spread
condition of the organism may exhibit itself locally.

The experiments which have long been the chief
support of the theory that thirst is a general sensation
can also be explained by the evidence above adduced.
The abolition of thirst by injecting fluid into the veins
of thirsty animals would be expected, for, as shown
in the experiment illustrated in Fig. 43, by providing
an adequate water supply the saliva flow is promptly
reëstablished, and the parched mouth and throat are
again continuously moistened. In the classic experiment of Claude Bernard the animal with an open
gastric fistula continued to drink until the fistula
was closed. This was not because there was a general
demand for water throughout the body, so long as the
fistula remained open, but because only when escape
through the fistula was stopped did the body receive
the water needed to provide the output of saliva
which prevented local drying. And the dogs with
salivary ducts tied, described by Bidder and Schmidt,
were always ready to drink, just as are persons who
are terrified or who have been given atropine, because
of thirst—because there is local drying of the mouth
—from lack of saliva, though the body as a whole
may not be in any need of water. The application of
cocaine to the mucous surfaces of the mouth abolishes

the torment of thirst, not by any central effect, and clearly not by satisfying any general bodily requirement for water, but by rendering the surfaces anesthetic. The miraculous virtues of coca leaves, as a balm for the distress of the thirsty, a fact long ago observed, is explicable on these grounds. The thirst of those who suffer from loss of fluid from the body—the diabetic patient, the victim of cholera, the subject of hemorrhage, the perspiring laborer, and the nursing mother—can be accounted for by the reduction of salivary flow as the water-content of the body is lowered, and by the consequent discomfort arising from the sticky buccal mucosa.

Support for this theory has been given in experiments by Pack [28] who withheld food and water from rabbits for seven days and, after inducing salivary secretion in some of them by means of the drug pilocarpine, allowed all of them to drink. The animals salivating from pilocarpine either refused to drink or, as in two cases, drank 15 and 25 cubic centimeters of water within an hour, whereas the others drank from 62 to 137 cubic centimeters within a half-hour. The difference was interpreted as due to the quenching of their thirst by the first group by drinking their own body fluids, i. e., the thirst was of local origin. Some experiments performed by Crisler [29] can also be interpreted as confirming this theory. By withholding water and extracting already incorporated water by intragastric administration of hypertonic salt solution, or by simply withholding water, he "dehydrated" dogs that had a salivary fistula. He had developed in the dogs a typical conditioned salivary reflex by means of morphine—i. e., when placed in a stand where they had previously had injections of morphine, they had an abundant secretion of saliva without any injection. During the period of dehydration the amount of the conditioned secretion promptly and continuously fell until, after 3 to 5 days, it practically disappeared. The unconditioned reflex secretion resulting from the action of morphine itself went through a similar depression though it was not so profound. Because the action of pilocarpine (which has a peripheral effect on the salivary glands) was not greatly affected, Crisler attributed the depression largely to effects of the dehydration in the central control of the glands. The mode of operation of pilocarpine on glands, however, is not clearly understood, and furthermore the results of drug action may be quite artificial when compared with natural physiological processes. Furthermore, even though dehydration does have central effects in addition to effects on the salivary glands themselves, the observations of Crisler clearly support the idea that by their depressed activity the salivary glands faithfully signal the diminished water content of the body. And the experiments of Pack, just mentioned, show that it is not a central state resulting from deprivation of water that induces drinking, but a dryness of the mouth which can be obviated by the peripheral drug action of pilocarpine.

I am aware that many questions arising from the views which I have just developed remain to be solved —questions as to the effects which other glandular activity, removing fluid from the body, may exercise on the functions of the salivary glands; the alteration of properties of the blood and lymph other than osmotic pressure as affecting secretion; the relation between the so-called "free water" of the body fluids and salivary secretion when water is withheld; the influence of strong alcoholic beverages in producing thirst; and the nature of pathological states in which thirst seems to disappear. From the evidence presented, however, it seems to me that we are now in a position to understand the mechanisms by which all three of the essential supplies from the outer world are provided for in our bodily economy. The oxygen supply is arranged for by the control which changes in the blood, brought about mainly by variations in the carbon dioxide content, exert on the center for respiration. The proper food supply ultimately is assured, because we avoid, or check, by taking food, the distressing pangs of hunger which powerful contractions of the empty stomach induce unless food is taken. And the water supply is maintained because we avoid, or abolish, by taking water or aqueous fluid, the disagreeable sensations which arise and torment us with increasing torment if the salivary glands, because of a lowering of the water-content of the body, lack the water they need to function, and fail therefore to pour out their watery secretion in sufficient amount and in proper quality to keep moist the mouth and pharynx.

REFERENCES

1. LUCIANI, *Das Hungern* (Leipzig, 1890).
2. See GOMEZ and PIKE, *Journal of Experimental Medicine*, xi (1909), p. 262.
3. McGEE, *Interstate Medical Journal*, xiii (1906), p. 279.
4. VITERBI, quoted by BARDIER, *Richet's Dictionnaire de Physiologie*, vi (1904), p. 7.
5. GEPHART and DU BOIS, *Archives of Internal Medicine*, xvii (1916), p. 902.
6. McGEE, *17th Annual Report of the Bureau of American Ethnology*, p. 181.
7. KING, *American Journal of the Medical Sciences*, lxxv (1878), p. 404.
8. LEPIDI-CHIOTI and FUBINI, *Giornale della reale Accademia di Medicina di Torino*, xlviii (1885), p. 905.
9. VALENTI, *Archives Italiennes de Biologie*, liii (1910), p. 94.
10. WASSILIEF, *Zeitschrift für Biologie*, xxiv (1888), p. 40.
11. VALENTI, *Centralblatt für Physiologie*, xx (1906), p. 450.
12. LUCIANI, *Archivio di Fisiologia*, iii (1906), p. 541.
13. SCHIFF, *Physiologie de la Digestion* (Florence and Turin, 1867), i, p. 41.
14. ORFILA, *Dictionnaire des Sciences Médicales*, lxi (1821), p. 469.
15. BERNARD, *Physiologie Experimentale* (Paris, 1856), ii, p. 49.
16. VOIT, *Hermann's Handbuch der Physiologie* (Leipzig, 1881), vi, p. 566.
17. LONGET, *Traité de Physiologie* (Paris, 1868), i, p. 35.
18. MAYER, *Comptes Rendus de la Société de Biologie*, lii (1900), pp. 154, 389, 522; also *Essai sur la Soif*, Laboratory of Experimental Pathology, Faculty of Medicine, Paris (1900).
19. WETTENDORF, *Travaux du Laboratoire de l'Institut Solvay* (Brussels, 1901), iv, pp. 353-484.
20. FOSTER, *Textbook of Physiology* (London, 1891), p. 1423; LUDWIG, *Lehrbuch der Physiologie des Menschen* (Leipzig and Heidelberg, 1858), ii, p. 586; VOIT, *Hermann's Handbuch der Physiologie* (Leipzig, 1881), vi, p. 566.

21. BECKER and LUDWIG, *Zeitschrift für Rationelle Medizin*, i (1851), p. 278.
22. BIDDER and SCHMIDT, *Verdauungssäfte und Stoffwechsel* (Leipzig, 1852), p. 3.
23. PAVLOV, *The Work of the Digestive Glands* (2nd edition, London, 1910), pp. 70, 82.
24. ZEBROWSKI, *Archiv für die gesammte Physiologie*, cx (1905), p. 105.
25. BORING, *The Psychological Review*, xxii (1915), p. 307.
26. SHERRINGTON, *Schäfer's Textbook of Physiology* (London 1900), ii, p. 991.
27. HOCHE, *Medizinische Klinik*, xiii (1917), p. 906.
28. PACK, *American Journal of Physiology*, lxv (1923), p. 346.
29. CRISLER, *ibid.*, lxxxv (1928), p. 324.

CHAPTER XVII

THE INTERRELATIONS OF EMOTIONS

Emotions gain expression through discharges along the neurones of the autonomic nervous system. The reader will recall that this system has three divisions —the cranial and sacral, separated by the sympathetic —and that when the neurones of the mid-division meet in any organ the neurones of either of the end divisions, the influence of the two sets is antagonistic. As previously stated (p. 33), there is evidence that arrangements exist in the central nervous system for reciprocal innervation of these antagonistic divisions, just as there is reciprocal innervation of antagonistic skeletal muscles. The characteristic affective states manifested in the working of these three divisions have been described. Undoubtedly these states have correspondents—activities and inhibitions—in the central neurones. The question now arises, are the states which appear in opposed divisions also in opposition?

ANTAGONISM BETWEEN EMOTIONS EXPRESSED IN THE SYMPATHETIC AND IN THE CRANIAL DIVISIONS OF THE AUTONOMIC SYSTEM

The cranial autonomic, as already shown, is concerned with the quiet service of building up reserves and fortifying the body against times of stress. Accompanying these functions are the relatively mild pleasures of sight and taste and smell of food. The possibility of existence of these gentle delights of eating and drinking and also of their physiological consequences is instantly abolished in the presence of emotions which activate the sympathetic division. The secretion of saliva, gastric juice, pancreatic juice and bile is stopped, and the motions of the stomach and intestines cease at once, both in man and in the lower animals, whenever pain, fear, rage, or other strong excitement is present in the organism.

All these disturbances of digestion seem mere interruptions of the "normal" course of events unless the part they may play in adaptive reactions is considered. In discussing the operations of the sympathetic division, I pointed out that all the bodily changes which occur in the intense emotional states —such as fear and fury—occur as results of activity in this division, and are in the highest degree serviceable in the struggle for existence likely to be precipitated when these emotions are aroused. From this point of view these perturbations, which so readily seize and dominate the organs that in quiet times are commonly controlled by the cranial autonomic, are bodily reactions which may be of the utmost importance to life. Thus are the body's reserves—the concentrated erythrocytes, the stored adrenin and the accumulated sugar—called forth for instant service; thus is the blood shifted to nerves and muscles that may have to bear the brunt of struggle; thus is the heart set rapidly beating to speed the circulation; and thus, also, are the activities of the digestive organs for the time abolished. Just as in war between nations the arts and industries which have brought wealth and contentment must suffer serious neglect or be wholly set aside both by the attacker and the attacked, and all the supplies and energies developed in the period of peace must be devoted to the present conflict; so, likewise, the functions which in quiet times establish and support the bodily reserves, are, in times of stress, instantly checked or completely stopped, and these reserves lavishly drawn upon to increase power in the attack and in the defense or flight.*

It is, therefore, the natural opposition between these two processes in the body—between saving and expenditure, between preparation and use, between anabolism and catabolism—and the correlated opposition of central innervations, that underlie the antipathy between the emotional states which normally accompany the processes. The desire for food and drink, the relish of taking them, all the pleasures of the table, are naught in the presence of anger or great anxiety. And of the two sorts of emotional states, those which manifest themselves in the dominant di-

---

* One who permits fears, worries and anxieties to disturb the digestive processes when there is nothing to be done, is evidently allowing the body to go onto what we may regard as a "war footing," when there is no "war" to be waged, no fighting or struggle to be engaged in.

vision of the autonomic hold the field also in consciousness.

ANTAGONISM BETWEEN EMOTIONS EXPRESSED IN THE SYMPATHETIC AND IN THE SACRAL DIVISIONS OF THE AUTONOMIC SYSTEM

The nervi erigentes are the part of the sacral autonomic in which the peculiar excitements of sex are expressed. As previously stated, these nerves are opposed by branches from the sympathetic division—the division which is operated characteristically in the major emotions.

The opposition in normal individuals between the emotional states which appear in these two antagonistic divisions is most striking. Even in animals as low in the scale as birds, copulation is not performed "until every condition of circumstance and sentiment is fulfilled, until time, place and partner all are fit."[1] And among men the effect of fear or momentary anxiety or any intense emotional interest in causing inhibition of the act can be supported by cases in the experience of any physician with extensive practice. Indeed, as Prince[2] has stated, "the suppression of the sexual instinct by conflict is one of the most notorious experiences of this kind in everyday life. This instinct cannot be excited during an attack of fear or anger, and even during moments of its excitation, if there is an invasion of another strong emotion the sexual instinct at once is repressed. Under these conditions, as with other instincts, even habitual excitants can no longer initiate the instinctive process."

When the acme of excitement is approaching it is probable that the sympathetic division is also called into activity; indeed, the completion of the process —the contractions of the seminal vesicles and the prostate, and the subsidence of engorged tissues, all innervated by sympathetic filaments (see pp. 30, 31)— may be due to the overwhelming of sacral by sympathetic nervous discharges. As soon as this stage is reached the original feeling likewise has been dissipated.

The other parts of the sacral division which supply the bladder and rectum are so nearly free from any emotional tone in their normal reflex functioning that it is unnecessary to consider them further with reference to emotional antagonisms. Mild affective states, such as worry and anxiety, can, to be sure, check the activity of the colon and thus cause constipation.[3] But the augmented activity of these parts (contraction of the bladder and rectum) in very intense periods of emotional stress, when the sympathetic division is strongly innervated, presents a problem of some difficulty. Possibly in such conditions the orderliness of the central arrangements is upset, just as it is after tetanus toxin or strychnine poisoning, and opposed innervations no longer discharge reciprocally, but simultaneously, and then the stronger member of the pair prevails. Only on such a basis, at present, can I offer any explanation for the activity and the supremacy of the sacral innervation of the bladder and distal colon when the sympathetic innervation is aroused, as, for example, in great fright.

THE FUNCTIONS OF HUNGER AND THIRST

A summary in few words of the chief functions typically performed or supported by each division of the autonomic would designate the cranial division as the upbuilder and restorer of the organic reserves, the sacral as the servant of racial continuity, and the sympathetic as the preserver of the individual. Self-preservation is primary and essential; on that depends racial continuity, and for that all the resources of the organism are called forth. Analogously the sympathetic innervations, when they meet in organs innervated also by the cranial and sacral divisions, almost without exception predominate over their opponents. And analogously, also, the emotional states which are manifested in the sympathetic division and are characteristically much more intense than those manifested in the other divisions, readily assume ascendancy also in consciousness.

It is obvious that extended action of the sympathetic division, abolishing those influences of the cranial division which are favorable to proper digestion and nutrition, might defeat its own ends. Interruption of the nutritional process for the sake of self-preservation through defense or attack can be only temporary; if the interruption were prolonged, there might be serious danger to the vigor of the organism from failure to replenish the exhausted stores. The body does not have to depend on the return of a banished appetite, however, before its need for restoration is attended to. There is a secondary and very insistent manner in which the requirement of food and water is expressed, and that is through the demands of hunger and thirst.

Unlike many other sensations, hunger and thirst are not such that one becomes accustomed to them and neglects them because of their monotony. During a period of confinement in the citadel of Magdeburg, the celebrated political adventurer Baron von Trenck [4] was allowed only a pound and a half of ammunition bread and a jug of water as his daily ration. He quotes in his memoirs:

It is impossible for me to describe to my reader the excess of tortures that during eleven months I endured from ravenous hunger. I could easily have devoured six pounds of bread every day; and every twenty-four hours, after having received and swallowed my small portion, I continued as hungry as before I began, yet I was obliged to wait another twenty-four hours for a new morsel. . . . My tortures prevented sleep, and looking into futurity, the cruelty of my fate seemed to me, if possible, to increase, for I imagined that the prolongation of pangs like these was insupportable. God preserve every honest man from sufferings like mine! They were not to be endured by the most obdurate villain. Many have fasted three days, many have suffered want for a week or more, but certainly no one besides myself ever endured it in the same excess for eleven months; some have supposed that to eat little might become habitual, but I have experienced the contrary. My hunger increased every day, and of all the trials of fortitude my whole life has afforded, this eleven months was the most bitter.*

_____

* This continued experience of hunger pangs may have been due

The similar testimony of Viterbi regarding the torments of thirst have already been mentioned (see p. 300).

Thus, although the taking of food and drink may be set in abeyance at times of great excitement, and the bodily reserves fully mobilized, that phase of the organism's self-protecting adjustment is limited, and then hunger and thirst assert themselves as agencies imperiously demanding restoration of the depleted stores.

THE RELATIONS OF FEAR AND RAGE TO OTHER AFFECTIVE STATES

The dominant emotions which we have been considering as characteristically expressed in the sympathetic division of the autonomic system are fear and rage. These two emotions are not unlike. As James [5] has indicated, "Fear is a reaction aroused by the same objects that arouse ferocity. . . . We both fear and wish to kill anything that may kill us; and the question which of the two impulses we shall follow is usually decided by some one of those *collateral circumstances* of the particular case, to be moved by which is the mark of superior mental natures." The cornering of an animal when in the headlong flight of fear may suddenly turn the fear to fury and the flight

---

to the repeated eating of amounts of food too small to satisfy the bodily demand. Persons who for some time take no food report that the disagreeable feelings are less intense or disappear after the third or fourth day (see p. 273).

to a fighting in which all the strength of desperation is displayed.

Furthermore, these dominant emotions are states into which many other commonly milder affective states may be suddenly transformed. As McDougall [6] has pointed out, all instinctive impulses when met with opposition or obstruction give place to, or are complicated by, the pugnacious or combative impulse directed against the source of the obstruction. A dog will bristle at any attempt to take away his food, males will fight furiously when provoked by interference with the satisfaction of the sexual impulse, a man will forget the conventions and turn hot for combat when there is imputation against his honor, and a mother all gentle with maternal devotion is stung to quick resentment and will make a fierce display of her combative resources, if any one intentionally injures her child. In these instances of thwarted or disturbed instinctive acts the emotional accompaniments—such as the satisfaction of food and of sexual affection, the feeling of self-pride, and the tender love of a parent—are whirled suddenly into anger. And anger in one is likely to provoke anger or fear in the other who for the moment is the object of the strong feeling of antagonism. Anger is the emotion preëminently serviceable for the display of power, and fear is often its counterpart.

The visceral changes which accompany fear and rage are the result of discharges by way of sympathetic neurones. It will be recalled that these neurones are arranged for diffuse rather than for narrowly directed effects. So far as these two quite different emotions are concerned, present physiological evidence indicates that differences in visceral accompaniments * are not noteworthy—for example, either fear or rage stops gastric secretion (see pp. 9, 10). There is, indeed, obvious reason why the visceral changes in fear and rage should *not be different,* but rather, why they should *be alike.* As already pointed out, these emotions accompany organic preparations for action, and just because the conditions which evoke them are likely to result in flight or conflict (either one requiring perhaps the utmost struggle), the bodily needs in either response are precisely the same.

In discussing the functioning of the sympathetic division I pointed out that it was roused to activity not only in fear and rage, but also in pain. The machinery of this division likewise is operated wholly or partially in emotions which are usually mild—such as joy and sorrow and disgust—*when they become sufficiently intense.* Thus, for instance, the normal course of digestion may be stopped or quite reversed in a variety of these emotional states.

---

* Obvious vascular differences, as pallor or flushing of the face, are of little significance. With increase of blood pressure from vasoconstriction, pallor might result from action of the constrictors in the face, or flushing might result because constrictors elsewhere, as, for example, in the abdomen, raised the pressure so high that facial constrictors are overcome. Such, apparently, is the effect of adrenin already described (see p. 104). Or the flushing might occur from local vasodilation. That very different emotional states may have the same vascular accompaniments was noted by Darwin

Darwin [7] reports the case of a young man who on hearing that a fortune had just been left him, became pale, then exhilarated, and after various expressions of joyous feeling vomited the half-digested contents of his stomach. Müller [8] has described the case of a young woman whose lover had broken the engagement of marriage. She wept in bitter sorrow for several days, and during that time vomited whatever food she took. And Burton,[9] in his *Anatomy of Melancholy*, gives the following instance of the effect of disgust:

A gentlewoman of the same city saw a fat hog cut up, when the entrails were opened, and a noisome savor offended her nose, she much misliked, and would not longer abide; a physician in presence told her, as that hog, so was she, full of filthy excrements, and aggravated the matter by some other loathsome instances, insomuch this nice gentlewoman apprehended it so deeply that she fell forthwith a vomiting, was so mightily distempered in mind and body, that with all his art and persuasion, for some months after, he could not restore her to herself again, she could not forget or remove the object out of her sight.

In these three cases, of intense joy, intense sorrow and intense disgust, the influence of the cranial division of the autonomic has been overcome, digestion has ceased, and the stagnant gastric contents by reflexes in striated muscles have been violently discharged. The extent to which under such circumstances other effects of sympathetic impulses may be manifested, has not, so far as I know, been ascertained.

From the evidence just given it appears that any high

(*The Expression of Emotions in Man and Animals,* New York, 1905), who mentioned the pallor of rage (p. 74) and also of terror (p. 77).

degree of excitement in the central nervous system, whether felt as anger, terror, pain, anxiety, joy, grief or deep disgust, is likely to break over the threshold of the sympathetic division and disturb the functions of all the organs which that division innervates. It may be that there is advantage in the readiness with which these widely different emotional conditions can express themselves in this one division, for, as has been shown (see p. 342), occasions may arise when these milder emotions are suddenly transmuted into the naturally intense types (as fright and fury) which normally activate this division; and if the less intense can also influence it, the physiological aspect of the transmutation is already partially accomplished.

REFERENCES

1. JAMES, *Principles of Psychology* (New York, 1905), i, p. 22.
2. PRINCE, *The Unconscious* (New York, 1914), p. 456.
3. HERTZ, *Constipation and Allied Intestinal Disorders* (London, 1909), p. 81.
4. v. TRENCK, *Merkwürdige Lebensgeschichte* (Berlin, 1787), p. 195.
5. JAMES, *op. cit.*, p. 415.
6. McDOUGALL, *Introduction to Social Psychology* (London, 1908), p. 72.
7. DARWIN, *op. cit.*, p. 76.
8. MÜLLER, *Deutsches Archiv für klinische Medicin*, lxxxix (1907), p. 434.
9. BURTON, *The Anatomy of Melancholy* (first published in 1621; London, 1886), p. 443.

CHAPTER XVIII

A CRITICAL EXAMINATION OF THE JAMES-LANGE
THEORY OF EMOTIONS

THE famous theory of emotions associated with the
names of James and Lange was propounded by them
independently. James first presented his view in 1884,
Lange's monograph appeared in Danish in 1885. The
cardinal points in their respective ideas of the nature
of emotions are so well known that for purposes of
comment only brief references need be made to them.
James' theory may be summarized, in nearly his own
terms, as follows.[1] An object stimulates one or more
sense organs; afferent impulses pass to the cortex and
the object is perceived; thereupon currents run down
to muscles and viscera and alter them in complex
ways; afferent impulses from these disturbed organs
course back to the cortex and when there perceived
transform the "object-simply-apprehended" to the
"object-emotionally-felt." In other words, "the feeling of the bodily changes as they occur is the emotion
—the common sensational, associational and motor
elements explain all." The main evidence cited for
the theory is that we are aware of the tensions, throbs,
flushes, pangs, suffocations—we feel them, indeed, the
moment they occur—and that if we should take away
from the picture of a fancied emotion these bodily
symptoms, nothing would be left.

346

According to Lange [1] stimulation of the vasomotor center is "the root of the causes of the affections, however else they may be constituted." "We owe all the emotional side of our mental life," he wrote, "our joys and sorrows, our happy and unhappy hours, to our vasomotor system. If the impressions which fall upon our senses did not possess the power of stimulating it, we would wander through life unsympathetic and passionless, all impressions of the outer world would only enrich our experience, increase our knowledge, but would arouse neither joy nor anger, would give us neither care nor fear." Since we are unable to differentiate subjectively between feelings of a central and peripheral origin, subjective evidence is unreliable. But because wine, certain mushrooms, hashish, opium, a cold shower, and other agencies cause physiological effects which are accompanied by altered states of feeling, and because abstraction of the bodily manifestations from a frightened individual leaves nothing of his fear, the emotion is only a perception of changes in the body. It is clear that Lange had the same conception as James, but elaborated it on a much narrower basis—on changes in the circulatory system alone.

The backflow of impulses from the periphery, on which James relied to account for the richness and variety of emotional feeling, was assumed to arise from all parts of the organism, from the muscles and skin as well as the viscera. To the latter, however, he inclined to attribute the major rôle—on "the visceral and organic part of the expression," he wrote, "it is probable that the chief part of the felt emotion depends." We may distinguish, therefore, his two sources of the afferent stream. We shall now consider critically the visceral source. In connection therewith we shall comment on Lange's idea that the vasomotor center holds the explanation of emotional experience.

TOTAL SEPARATION OF THE VISCERA FROM THE CENTRAL NERVOUS SYSTEM DOES NOT ALTER EMOTIONAL BEHAVIOR

Sherrington [2] transected the spinal cord and the vagus nerves of dogs so as to destroy any connection of the brain with the heart, the lungs, the stomach and the bowels, the spleen, the liver and other abdominal organs—indeed, to isolate all the structures in which formerly feelings were supposed to reside. Recently Lewis and Britton and I [3] have succeeded in keeping cats in a healthy state for many months after removal of the entire sympathetic division of the autonomic system, the division which operates in great excitement. Thus all vascular reactions controlled by the vasomotor center were abolished; secretion from the adrenal medulla could no longer be evoked; the action of the stomach and intestines could not be inhibited, the hairs could not be erected, and the liver could not be called upon to liberate sugar into the blood stream. These extensively disturbing operations had little if any effect on the emotional responses of the animals. In one of Sherrington's dogs, having a

"markedly emotional temperament," the surgical reduction of the sensory field caused no obvious change
in her emotional behavior; "her anger, her joy, her
disgust, and when provocation arose, her fear, remained as evident as ever." And in the sympathecto-
mized cats all superficial signs of rage were manifested
in the presence of a barking dog—hissing, growling,
retraction of the ears, showing of the teeth, lifting
of the paw to strike—*except* erection of the hairs.
Both sets of animals behaved with full emotional expression in all the organs still connected with the
brain; the only failure was in organs disconnected.
The absence of reverberation from the viscera did not
alter in any respect the appropriate emotional display;
its only abbreviation was surgical.

As Sherrington has remarked, with reference to his
head-and-shoulder dogs, it is difficult to think that the
perception initiating the wrathful expression should
bring in sequel angry conduct and yet have been im-
potent to produce "angry feeling."

At this point interpretations differ. Angell [4] has
argued that Sherrington's experiments afford no evidence that visceral sensation plays no part in the emotional psychosis, and further that they do not prove
that the psychic state, "emotion," precedes its "expression." And Perry [5] has declared that whether, in
the absence of sensations from the organs surgically
isolated, the emotion is *felt* remains quite undecided.

It must be admitted, of course, that we have no
real basis for either affirming or denying the presence

of "felt emotion" in these reduced animals. We have a basis, however, for judging their relation to the James-Lange theory. James attributed the chief part of the felt emotion to sensations from the viscera, Lange attributed it wholly to sensations from the circulatory system. Both affirmed that if these organic sensations are removed *imaginatively* from an emotional experience nothing is left. Sherrington and the Harvard group varied this procedure by removing the sensations *surgically*. In their animals all visceral disturbances through sympathetic channels—the channels for nervous discharge in great excitement—were abolished. The possibility of return impulses by these channels, and in Sherrington's animals by vagus channels as well, were likewise abolished. According to James's statement of the theory the felt emotion should have very largely disappeared, and according to Lange's statement it should have wholly disappeared (without stimulation of our vasomotor system, it will be recalled, impressions of the outer world "would arouse neither joy nor anger, would give us neither care nor fear"). The animals *acted*, however, insofar as nervous connections permitted, with no lessening of the intensity of emotional display. In other words, operations which, in terms of the theory, largely or completely destroy emotional feeling, nevertheless leave the animals behaving as angrily, as joyfully, as fearfully as ever.

The preganglionic fibers of the sympathetic division
of the autonomic system are so related to the outlying
neurones, as we have seen, that the resulting innervation of smooth muscles and glands throughout the
body is not particular but diffuse. At the same time
with the diffuse emission of sympathetic impulses
adrenin is poured into the blood. Since it is thereby
generally distributed to all parts and has the same
effects as the sympathetic impulses wherever it acts,
the humoral and the neural agents coöperate in producing diffuse effects. In consequence of these arrangements the sympathetic system goes into action
as a unit—there may be minor variations as, for example, the presence or absence of sweating, but in the
main features integration is characteristic.

The visceral changes wrought by sympathetic stimulation may be listed as follows: acceleration of the
heart, contraction of arterioles, dilation of bronchioles, increase of blood sugar, inhibition of activity of
the digestive glands, inhibition of gastro-intestinal peristalsis, sweating, discharge of adrenin, widening of the
pupils and erection of hairs. These changes are seen
in great excitement under any circumstances. They
occur in such readily distinguishable emotional states
as fear and rage. Fever [6] and also exposure to cold [7]
are known to induce most of the changes—certainly

a faster heart rate, vasoconstriction, increased blood sugar, discharge of adrenin and erection of the hairs. Asphyxia at the stimulating stage evokes all the changes enumerated above, with the possible exception of sweating. A too great reduction of blood sugar by insulin provokes the "hypoglycemic reaction"— characterized by pallor, rapid heart, dilated pupils, discharge of adrenin, increase of blood sugar and profuse sweating.[8]

In this group of conditions which bring about in the viscera changes which are typical of sympathetic discharge are such intense and distinct emotions as fear and rage, such relatively mild affective states as those attending chilliness, hypoglycemia and difficult respiration, and such a markedly different experience as that attending the onset of fever. The responses in the viscera seem too uniform to offer a satisfactory means of distinguishing emotions which are very different in subjective quality. Furthermore, if the emotions were due to afferent impulses from the viscera, we should expect not only that fear and rage would feel alike but that chilliness, hypoglycemia, asphyxia, and fever should feel like them. Such is not the case.

In commenting on this criticism of the James-Lange theory Angell[4] admits that there may be a considerable matrix of substantially identical visceral excitement for some emotions, but urges that the differential features may be found in the extra-visceral disturbances, particularly in the differences of tone in skeletal muscles. Perry[5] likewise falls back on the conformation of the proprioceptive patterns, on the "motor set" of the expression, to provide the distinctive elements of the various affective states. The possible contribution of skeletal muscles to the genesis of the felt emotion will be considered later. At present the fact may be emphasized that Lange derived no part of the emotional psychosis from that source; and James attributed to it a minor rôle—the chief part of the felt emotion depended on the visceral and organic part of the expression.

THE VISCERA ARE RELATIVELY INSENSITIVE STRUCTURES

There is a common belief that the more deeply the body is penetrated the more sensitive does it become. Such is not the fact. Whereas in a spinal nerve trunk the sensory nerve fibers are probably always more numerous than the motor, in the nerves distributed to the viscera the afferent (sensory) fibers may be only one-tenth as numerous as the efferent.[9] We are unaware of the contractions and relaxations of the stomach and intestines during digestion, of the rubbing of the stomach against the diaphragm, of the squeezing motions of the spleen, of the processes in the liver—only after long search have we learned what is occurring in these organs. Surgeons have found that the alimentary tract can be cut, torn, crushed or burned in operations on the unanesthetized human subject without evoking any feeling of discomfort. We can feel the thumping of the heart because it presses against the chest wall, we can also feel the throbbing of blood vessels because they pass through tissues well supplied with sensory nerves, and we may have abdominal pains but apparently because there are pulls on the parietal peritoneum.[10] Normally the visceral processes are extraordinarily undemonstrative. And even when the most marked changes are induced in them, as when adrenalin acts, the results, as we shall see, are sensations mainly attributable to effects on the cardiovascular system.

VISCERAL CHANGES ARE TOO SLOW TO BE A SOURCE OF EMOTIONAL FEELING

The viscera are composed of smooth muscle and glands—except the heart, which is modified striate muscle. The motions of the body with which we are familiar result from quick-acting striate muscle, having a true latent period of less than 0.001 second. Notions of the speed of bodily processes acquired by observing the action of skeletal muscle we should not apply to other structures. Smooth muscle and glands respond with relative sluggishness. Although Stewart[11] found that the latent period of smooth muscle of the cat was about 0.25 second, Sertoli[12] observed that it lasted for 0.85 second in the dog and 0.8 second in the horse. Langley[13] reported a latent period of 2 to 4 seconds on stimulating the *chorda tympani* nerve supply to the submaxillary salivary gland; and Pavlov[14] a latent period of about 6 *minutes* on stimulating the vagus, the secretory nerve of the gastric glands. Again, Wells and Forbes [15] noted that the latent period of the psychogalvanic reflex (in man), which appears to be a phenomenon due to sweat glands, was about 3 seconds.

In contrast to these long delays before peripheral action in visceral structures barely starts are the observations of Wells; [16] he found that the latent period of affective reactions to pictures of men and women ended not uncommonly within 0.8 second. More recent studies with odors as stimuli have yielded a similar figure (personal communication). According to the James-Lange theory, however, these affective reactions result from reverberations from the viscera. But how is that possible? To the long latent periods of smooth muscles and glands, cited above, there must be added the time required for the nerve impulses to pass from the brain to the periphery and thence back to the brain again. It is clear that the organic changes could not occur soon enough to be the occasion for the appearance of affective states, certainly not the affective states studied by Wells.

ARTIFICIAL INDUCTION OF THE VISCERAL CHANGES TYPICAL OF STRONG EMOTIONS DOES NOT PRODUCE THEM

That adrenin acts in the body so as to mimic the action of sympathetic nerve impulses has repeatedly been mentioned. When injected directly into the blood stream or under the skin it induces dilation of the bronchioles, constriction of blood vessels, liberation of sugar from the liver, stoppage of gastro-intestinal functions, and other changes such as are characteristic of intense emotions. If the emotions are the consequence of the visceral changes we should reasonably expect them, in accordance with the postulates of the James-Lange theory, to follow these changes in all cases. Incidental observations on students who received injections of adrenalin sufficiently large to produce general bodily effects have brought out the fact that no specific emotion was experienced by them —a few who had been in athletic competitions testified to feeling "on edge," "keyed up," just as before a race.[17] In a careful study of the effects of adrenin on a large number of normal and abnormal persons Marañon [18] has reported that the subjective experiences included sensations of precardial or epigastric palpitation, of diffuse arterial throbbing, of oppression in the chest and tightness in the throat, of trembling, of chilliness, of dryness of the mouth, of nervousness, malaise and weakness. Associated with these sensations there was *in certain cases* an indefinite affective state coldly appreciated, and without real emotion. The subjects remarked, "I feel as if afraid," "as if awaiting a great joy," "as if moved," "as if I were going to weep without knowing why," "as if I had a great fright yet am calm," "as if they are about to do something to me." In other words, as Marañon remarks, a clear distinction is drawn "between the perception of the peripheral phenomena of vegetative emotion (i. e..

the bodily changes) and the psychical emotion proper, which does not exist and which permits the subjects to report on the vegetative syndrome with serenity, without true feeling." In a smaller number of the affected cases a real emotion developed, usually that of sorrow, with tears, sobs and sighings. This occurs, however, "only when the emotional predisposition of the patient is very marked," notably in hyperthyroid cases. In some instances Marañon found that this state supervened only when the adrenin was injected after a talk with the patients concerning their sick children or their dead parents. In short, only when an emotional mood already exists does adrenalin have a supporting effect.

From the evidence adduced by Marañon we may conclude that adrenin induces in human beings typical bodily changes which are reported as sensations, that in some cases these sensations are reminiscent of previous emotional experiences but do not renew or revive those experiences, that in exceptional cases of preparatory emotional sensitization the bodily changes may tip the scales towards a true affective disturbance. These last cases are exceptional, however, and are not the usual phenomena as James and Lange supposed. In normal conditions the bodily changes, though well marked, do not provoke emotion.

The numerous events occurring in the viscera in consequence of great excitement, as detailed in earlier chapters, have been interpreted as supporting the James-Lange theory.[19] From the evidence just presented it should be clear that that interpretation is unwarranted. Since visceral processes are fortunately not a considerable source of sensation, since even extreme disturbances in them yield no noteworthy emotional experience, we can further understand now why these disturbances cannot serve as a means for discriminating between such pronounced emotions as fear and rage, why chilliness, asphyxia, hyperglycemia and fever, though attended by these disturbances, are not attended by emotion, and also why total exclusion of visceral factors from emotional expression makes no difference in emotional behavior. It is because the returns from the thoracic and abdominal "sounding-board," to use James's word, are very faint indeed, that they play such a minor rôle in the affective complex. The processes going on in the thoracic and abdominal organs in consequence of sympathetic activity are truly remarkable and various; their value to the organism, however, is not to add richness and flavor to experience, but rather to adapt the internal economy so that in spite of shifts of outer circumstance the even tenor of the inner life will not be profoundly disturbed.

REFERENCES

1. JAMES and LANGE, *The Emotions* (Baltimore, 1922).
2. SHERRINGTON, *Proceedings of the Royal Society of London,* lxvi (1900), p. 397.
3. CANNON, LEWIS and BRITTON, *Boston Medical and Surgical Journal,* cxcvii (1927), p. 514.
4. ANGELL, *The Psychological Review,* xxiii (1916), p. 259.
5. PERRY, *General Theory of Value* (New York, 1926), p. 298.

6. CANNON and PEREIRA, *Proceedings of the National Academy of Sciences*, x (1924), p. 247.

7. CANNON, QUERIDO, BRITTON and BRIGHT, *American Journal of Physiology*, lxxix (1927), p. 466.

8. CANNON, MCIVER and BLISS, *ibid.*, lxix (1924), p. 46.

9. LANGLEY and ANDERSON, *Journal of Physiology*, xvii (1894), p. 185.

10. LENNANDER, *et al.*, *Journal of the American Medical Association*, xlix (1907), p. 836; see also p. 1015.

11. STEWART, *American Journal of Physiology*, iv (1900), p. 192.

12. SERTOLI, *Archives Italiennes de Biologie*, iii (1883), p. 86.

13. LANGLEY, *Journal of Physiology*, x (1889), p. 300.

14. PAVLOV and SCHUMOWA-SIMANOWSKAJA, *Archiv für Physiologie* (1895), p. 66.

15. WELLS and FORBES, *Archives of Psychology*, ii (1911), p. 8.

16. WELLS, *Journal of Experimental Psychology*, viii (1925), p. 64.

17. PEABODY, STURGIS, TOMPKINS and WEARN, *The American Journal of the Medical Sciences*, clxi (1921), p. 508; also personal communication from J. T. WEARN.

18. MARANON, *Revue Française d'Endocrinologie*, ii (1924), p. 301.

19. HUMPHREY, *The Story of Man's Mind* (Boston, 1923), p. 211.

CHAPTER XIX

EMOTION AS A FUNCTION OF THE OPTIC THALAMUS

In his discussion of the cerebral processes accompanying emotion, James argued that either there were special centers for them or they occurred in the ordinary motor and sensory centers of the cerebral cortex. And if in the ordinary centers, according to his postulate, the processes would resemble the ordinary processes attending sensation. Only that and full representation of each part of the body in the cortex would be needed to provide a scheme capable of representing the *modus operandi* of the emotions. Object —sense organ—cortical excitation—perception—reflexes to muscle, skin and viscus—disturbances in them —cortical excitation by these disturbances—perceptions of them added to the original perceptions; such are the occurrences which result in the "object-emotionally-felt." The strict alternative, however, of cortical processes *or* special centers we need not accept. There may be cortical processes *and* special centers. Whether such is the arrangement we may now consider.

EMOTIONAL EXPRESSION RESULTS FROM ACTION OF SUBCORTICAL CENTERS

In a paper published in 1887 Bechterev [1] argued that emotional expression must be independent of the cortex because at times the expression cannot be inhibited (e. g., laughing from tickle, grinding the teeth and crying from pain), because visceral changes occur which are beyond control, and because it is seen just after birth before cortical management is important. Furthermore, he reported that after removing the cerebral hemispheres from various kinds of animals appropriate stimulations would evoke corresponding responses of an affective character. Noxious stimuli would cause the hemisphereless cats to snarl, the dogs to whine, to show their teeth and to bark; gentle stimuli (stroking the back) would cause the cats to purr and the dogs to wag their tails. Since these effects disappeared when the optic thalamus was removed, he drew the conclusion that it plays a predominant rôle in emotional expression.

In 1904 Woodworth and Sherrington [2] proved that some of the physiological phenomena of great excitement would appear in cats from which the thalamus had been wholly removed by section of the brain stem at the mesencephalon. *Strong stimulation* of an afferent nerve was required to evoke the "pseudaffective" responses. Although these observations tended to lessen the importance of the thalamus as a center, recent experiments have again emphasized its dominance. In 1925, as previously stated, Britton and I [3] described a pseudaffective preparation—a cat decorticated under ether anesthesia—which on recovery displayed *spontaneously* the complete picture of intense fury. Further study by Bard [4] showed that this sham rage continued after ablation of all the brain anterior to the diencephalon. Only when the lower posterior portion of the thalamic region (the clear, dotted area, Fig. 39, p. 247) was removed did the extraordinary activities of the preparation subside. These results clearly point to the thalamus as a region from which, in the absence of cortical government, impulses are discharged which evoke an extreme degree of "emotional" activity, both muscular and visceral.

The evidence just cited is confirmed by observations on human beings. As has been pointed out elsewhere [5] when the cortical processes are abolished by anesthesia, emotional display may be most remarkable. During the early (excitement) stage of ether anesthesia, for example, there may be sobbing as in grief, or laughter as in joy, or lively and energetic aggressive actions as in rage. The surgeon may open the chest or perform other operations of equal gravity, while the patient is pushing, pulling, shouting and muttering; a few minutes later the conscious patient will testify that he has been wholly unaware of what has happened. It is when "laughing gas" has set aside the cortical functions that the subjects laugh and weep. Similar release of the mechanisms for emotional expression is indicated in the depression of cortical activity during acute alcoholism. In all these conditions the drug acts first as a depressant on the highly sensitive cells of the cortex, and thus lessens or temporarily destroys their control of lower centers; only when the drug becomes more concentrated does it depress also the lower centers; but before that stage is reached the lower centers, released from the cortical dominance as in the surgically decorticated animals, show forth their functions in free play.

Consistent with the experimental and pharmacological evidence is the evidence derived from pathological cases. In certain forms of hemiplegia, as noted earlier, the patients may be incapable of moving the face on the paralyzed side; if suddenly they are affected by a sorrowful or joyous emotion, however, the muscles, unresponsive to voluntary control, spring into action and give both sides of the face the expression of sadness or gayety.[6] These cases occur when the motor tract is interrupted subcortically and the thalamus is left intact (see Fig. 40). The opposite of this condition is seen in unilateral injury of the thalamus. A patient described by Kirilzev [7] moved symmetrically both sides of his face at will, but when he laughed in fun or made a grimace in pain the right side remained motionless; at autopsy a tumor was found in the center of the left optic thalamus. Similar cases have been described by Wilson.[8] This localization of the central neural apparatus for the expressions of pleasure and pain has interesting relations to emotive phenomena commonly seen in so-called "pseudo-bulbar palsy."

In such cases there is usually a bilateral facial paralysis, with one side slightly more involved than the
other. Voluntary pursing of the lips as in whistling,
or wrinkling of the forehead, or making a grimace
may be impossible. The intractable facial muscles,
however, function normally in laughing or crying,
scowling or frowning. These well-executed expressions come in fits and are uncontrollable and prolonged.
One patient is described who started laughing at ten
o'clock in the morning and continued with few pauses
until two in the afternoon. Tilney and Morrison,[9]
who have reported on 173 recorded cases of the disease,
found such fits of crying and laughing in 17 per cent
of the cases, crying alone in 16 per cent, and laughing
alone in 15 per cent. The fits appear as a rule without
any of the usual provocations and most frequently are
inopportune. The patient may have all the appearances of being convulsed with laughter, yet may not
experience any of the feeling which the motions of
face and body indicate. Such cases are attributed by
Brissaud [10] to lesions of a special part of the cortico-
thalamic tract which free a portion of the thalamus
from the cortical check. It seems probable, as later
evidence will suggest, that afferent thalamo-cortical
tracts are also defective.

All these observations, experimental and clinical,
consistently point to the optic thalamus as a region
in which resides the neural organization for the different emotional expressions. The section in James'
discussion, headed "No Special Brain Centres for Emo-

tion" must be modified in the light of this accumulated information.   The cortex at one end of the nerve paths as a reflex surface and the peripheral organs at the other end as a source of return impulses make too simple an arrangement.   Between the cortex and the periphery lies the diencephalon, an integrating organ on the emotive level, a receiving and discharging station, that on proper stimulation is capable of establishing in stereotyped forms the facies and bodily postures typical of the various affective states.   That all afferent nerve paths leading towards the cortex have relays in the diencephalon is a fact of great significance in explaining the nature of emotions.

THALAMIC PROCESSES ARE A SOURCE OF AFFECTIVE EXPERIENCE

The relaying of all sensory neurones in some part of the optic thalamus has been stressed by Head [11] in his important clinical studies.   He and Holmes [12] attributed to this region a sort of consciousness, an "awareness."   The effect of anesthesia in abolishing consciousness while leaving emotional expression (thalamic in origin) undisturbed would seem to contradict this view.   But even if consciousness is associated only with events in cortical neurones, the important part played by thalamic processes is little disturbed thereby.   The relays of sensory channels in the thalamus and the evidence that disturbances in that region are the occasion for intensely affective sensations are all that we need for understanding its relation to the nature of emotions.

Head [13] has cited numerous cases of unilateral lesions in the thalamic region in which there is a marked tendency to react excessively to affective stimuli; pin pricks, painful pressure, excessive heat or cold, all produce more distress on the damaged than on the normal side of the body. Agreeable stimuli also are felt keenly on the damaged side; warmth stimuli may evoke intense pleasure, attended by signs of enjoyment on the face and exclamations of delight. Again, affective stimuli, such as the playing of music and the singing of hymns, may arouse such increased emotional feeling on the damaged side that they may be intolerable. Affective conscious states have an influence on the damaged side similar to stimuli from the surface receptors. This extravagant influence of affective stimuli, whether from above or below, Head attributed to release of the thalamus from cortical inhibition. It is not an irritative effect, he argued, because it persists for long periods, well after all the disturbances due to the injury have subsided. And since the affective states are increased when the thalamus is freed from cortical control, Head's conclusion is that the essential thalamic center is mainly occupied with the affective side of sensation.

We are now in a position to consider the evidence that the positions and tensions of skeletal muscle make the differentia of emotion. It will be recalled that, although James belittled this element in his theory, his supporters have stressed it, especially since the visceral element proved inadequate (see p. 352). The thalamic cases provide a means of testing the contribution from skeletal muscles, for the feeling-tone of a sensation is a product of thalamic activity, and the fact that a sensation is devoid of feeling-tone shows that the impulses which underlie its production make no thalamic appeal.

Head found that his patients reported marked differences in the feeling-tone of different sensations. A tuning fork may have no effect, whereas patriotic music is felt intensely on the damaged side. All thermal stimuli make a double appeal, to the cortex and to the thalamus. Unselected tactile stimuli act similarly. On the other hand, *sensations which underlie the appreciation of posture are entirely lacking in feeling-tone.* Precisely those afferent impulses from muscles and joints which James and his supporters have relied upon to provide the extra-visceral part of the felt-emotion are the impulses which lack the necessary quality to serve the purpose! This evidence is supported by human cases in which movement of the facial muscles is made impossible by organic disease. Such patients may be acutely conscious of a particular emotion in spite of lack of expression in the face. In an instance of complete absence of expressional movement because of bilateral facial paralysis the patient testified that "his greatest misfortune was being forced to be joyful or sad without making any demonstration of his feelings to his fellow creatures."

And in another similar instance the patient "retained her good humor and sometimes laughed heartily . . . as if behind a mask, her face being quite immovable and grave whilst the emotion and sound of laughter prevailed." [14] The quality of emotions is to be found, therefore, neither in returns from the viscera nor in returns from the innervated muscles.

POSSIBLE FUNCTION OF THE OPTIC THALAMUS

The foregoing discussion has disclosed the fact that the neural arrangements for emotional expression reside in subcortical centers, and that these centers are ready for instant and vigorous discharge when they are released from cortical restraint and are properly stimulated. Furthermore, the evidence is clear that when these centers are released the processes aroused in them become a source of vivid affective experience. That this experience is felt on only one side in hemiplegic cases is a peculiarly happy circumstance, for in the same individual the influence of the same affective stimulus can be observed under normal conditions and compared with its influence when given free rein.

The neural organization for an emotion which is suggested by the foregoing observations is as follows: An external situation stimulates receptors and the consequent excitation starts impulses towards the cortex. Arrival of the impulses in the cortex is associated with conditioned processes which determine the direction of the response. Either because the response is initiated in a certain mode or figure and the cortical neurones therefore stimulate the thalamic processes, or because on their inward course the impulses from the receptors excite thalamic processes, they are roused and ready for discharge. That the thalamic neurones act in a special combination in a given emotional expression is proved by the reaction patterns typical of the several affective states. These neurones do not require detailed innervation from above in order to be driven into action. Being *released* for action is a primary condition for their service to the body —they then discharge precipitately and intensely. Within and near the thalamus the neurones concerned in an emotional expression lie close to the relay in the sensory path from periphery to cortex. We may assume that when these neurones discharge in a particular combination, they not only innervate muscles and viscera but also excite afferent paths to the cortex by direct connection or by irradiation. The theory which naturally presents itself is that *the peculiar quality of the emotion is added to simple sensation when the thalamic processes are roused.**

---

* After describing a patient with a broken neck who lived for nearly a year completely paralyzed and completely insensitive below the level of the lesion and who yet manifested typical joy, grief, displeasure and affection, and after citing other pertinent neurological experiences, Dana (*Archives of Neurology and Psychiatry*, vi, 1921, p. 634) stated, "On the whole, I am led to the conclusion that emotion is centrally located and results from the action and interaction of the cortex and thalamus." I was unaware of this statement when I first elaborated the argument presented above.

APPLICATION OF THE THEORY TO KNOWN FACTS

The theory just suggested appears to fit all the known facts. Its service in explaining these facts may be briefly summarized.

When the thalamic discharge occurs, the bodily changes occur almost simultaneously with the emotional experience. This coincidence of disturbances in muscles and viscera with thrills, excitements or depressions was naturally misleading, for, with the rôle of the thalamus omitted from consideration, the obvious inference was that the peculiar quality of the emotion arose from the peripheral changes. Indeed, that inference is the heart of the James-Lange theory. The evidence presented in the foregoing pages shows that the inference is ill-founded; the sensations from the peripheral changes, contrary to James' view, are "pale, colorless and destitute of emotional warmth," whereas the thalamic disturbances contribute glow and color to otherwise simply cognitive states. The theory now proposed explains how James and Lange could reasonably make the suggestion which they made. The lack of factual support for their suggestion requires another account of emotional origins. This is provided by the evidence that thalamic processes can add to sensation an aura of feeling.

One of the strongest arguments advanced for the James-Lange theory is that the assumption of an attitude does in fact help to establish the emotional state which the attitude expresses. "Sit all day in a moping posture, sigh, and reply to everything with a dismal voice, and your melancholy lingers." On the contrary, "smooth the brow, brighten the eye, contract the dorsal rather than the ventral aspect of the frame, and speak in a major key, pass the genial compliment, and your heart must be frigid indeed if you do not gradually thaw!" Persons who have tried this advice have testified to its soundness, and have been convinced, therefore, of the truth of the claim that the moods have followed the assumed attitudes. Not all agree, however, that mimicking the outward appearance of an emotion results in the emotion itself. James suggested that the explanation of the discrepancy lay in variations of involvement of the viscera in the artificial expression. As already shown, however, the visceral changes offer only unreliable support for that idea. Again the processes in the thalamus offer a reasonable and simple explanation. As the cases reported by Head have shown, emotions originating from memories and imagination affect more intensely the half-thalamus that has been released from motor control than they affect the normal half. This shows that cortical processes may start thalamic processes and thus arouse an affective return from that portion of the brain. And if in addition a typical emotional attitude is assumed, the cortical inhibition of the thalamic neurones with reference to that attitude is abolished so that they have complete release. Under such circumstances the enacted emotion would have reality. On the other hand a purely cortical mimicry of emotional expression without thalamic involvement would be as cold and unaffective as some actors have declared it to be. Whether the emotion results or not, the thalamic theory of the source of feeling offers a more satisfactory explanation of the effects of assumed postures than does the James-Lange theory.

The cases of release of the thalamus from cortical control on one side, with accompanying intensification of emotional tone on the same side, present an insurmountable obstacle to the James-Lange theory. Neither the thoracic nor the abdominal viscera can function by halves, the vasomotor center is a unity, and the patients certainly do not engage in right- or left-sided laughter and weeping. The impulses sent back from the disturbed peripheral organs, therefore, must be bilaterally equal. For explanation of the unsymmetrical feeling we are driven to the organ which is functioning unsymmetrically—i. e., the thalamus. It is there that the suggested theory places the source of the emotions.

Another serious difficulty for the James-Lange theory is the evidence that the emotion increases in intensity although the expression is checked. Indeed, there are psychologists who maintain that the emotional state lasts only so long as there is inner conflict between the impulse to act and the hesitant or prudential check on that impulse. So long as the check prevails, however, the organic changes supposed to be the source of the feeling are suppressed. How then can there be felt-emotion? Two answers to this question may be found in James' argument. First he denies the objection. "Refuse to express a passion," he wrote, "and it dies." "Count ten before venting your anger, and its occasion seems ridiculous." On the other hand, he appears to admit that a pent emotion may operate disastrously. "If tears or anger are simply suppressed, whilst the object of grief or rage remains unchanged before the mind, the current which would have invaded the normal channels turns into others, for it must find some outlet of escape. It may then work different and worse effects later on. Thus vengeful brooding may replace a burst of indignation; a dry heat may consume the frame of one who fain would weep, or he may, as Dante says, turn to stone within." There is no intimation that vengeful brooding, being consumed by a dry heat, and turning to stone within are not emotional experiences. Instead of recognizing them as such, however, James stressed the importance of training for repression of emotional display. These rather equivocal and indecisive comments leave untouched the common testimony that intense fear, for example, may be felt, with a pathetic sense of helplessness, before any overt act occurs, and that scarcely does the appropriate behavior start than the inner tumult begins to subside and the bodily forces are directed vigorously and effectively to serviceable ends. The difficulties of the James-Lange theory in meeting this situation are obvious. If there is a double control of behavior, however, both the inner conflict with its keen emotional accompaniment and the later partial subsidence of feeling are readily explicable. The thalamic patterned processes are inherent in the nervous organization, they are like reflexes in being instantly ready to seize control of the motor responses, and when they do so they operate with great power. They can be controlled, however, by the processes in the cerebral cortex, by processes conditioned by all sorts of previous impressions. The cortex also can control all the peripheral machinery except the viscera. The inhibited processes in the thalamus cannot set the organism in action, except the parts not under voluntary control, but thalamic turmoil can produce emotions in the usual manner, and possibly with greater violence because of the inhibition. And when the cortical check is released, suddenly the conflict is resolved. The two controls formerly in opposition are now coöperative. The thalamic neurones, so long as they continue energetically active, provide the condition for the emotion to persist, as James claimed it does, *during* the manifestation. The new theory, therefore, not only avoids the difficulty of the James-Lange theory, but accounts satisfactorily for the poignancy of feeling in the period of paralyzed inaction.

In relation to the double control of the response there is another point that may be emphasized. McDougall [15] has objected to the James-Lange theory on the ground that it is admittedly concerned with the *sensory* aspect of emotion; it pays little or no attention to the always present and sometimes overwhelming *impulsive* aspect of the experience. The localization of the reaction patterns for emotional expression in the thalamus—in a region which, like the spinal cord, works directly by simple automatisms unless held in check—not only accounts for the sensory side, the "felt emotion," but also for the impulsive side, the tendency of the thalamic neurones to discharge. These powerful impulses originating in a region of the brain not associated with cognitive consciousness and arousing therefore in an *obscure* and *unrelated* manner the strong feelings of emotional excitement, explain the sense of being seized, possessed, of being controlled by an outside force and made to act without weighing of the consequences.

Finally, the view that thalamic processes add feeling-tone to sensation meets satisfactorily a difficulty which the James-Lange theory encountered in explaining the "subtler emotions." James had to assume indefinite and hypothetical bodily reverberations in order to account for mild feelings of pleasure and satisfaction. If a warm test tube, however, is capable of yielding keen delight on the damaged side in a case of thalamic injury, it is clear that almost any object or situation which can rouse thalamic processes can add affective quality to sensation. And just as a stimulus can become conditioned for a certain motor or glandular response, so likewise a stimulus can be conditioned for the patterns of neurone action in the thalamus. When that stimulus recurs the emotion recurs because the pattern is activated. In such man-

ner we may consider that richness and variety of our
emotional life are elaborated.

REFERENCES

1. BECHTEREV, *Virchow's Archiv für pathologische Anatomie
   und Physiologie und für klinische Medicin,* cx (1887),
   pp. 102, 322.
2. WOODWORTH and SHERRINGTON, *Journal of Physiology,* xxxi
   (1904), p. 234.
3. CANNON and BRITTON, *American Journal of Physiology,*
   lxxii (1925), p. 283.
4. BARD, *ibid.,* lxxxiv (1928), p. 490.
5. CANNON, *Feelings and Emotions: The Wittenberg Symposium* (Worcester, 1928), p. 257.
6. ROUSSY, *La Couche Optique* (Paris, 1907), p. 31.
7. KIRILZEV, *Review in Neurologisches Centralblatt,* x (1891),
   p. 310.
8. WILSON, *Journal of Neurology and Psychopathology,* iv
   (1923-24), p. 299.
9. TILNEY and MORRISON, *The Journal of Nervous and Mental
   Diseases,* xxxix (1912), p. 505.
10. BRISSAUD, *Leçons cliniques* (Paris, 1894).
11. HEAD, *Proceedings of the Royal Society of London,* Bxcii,
    (1921), p. 184.
12. HEAD and HOLMES, *Brain,* xxxiv (1911), p. 109.
13. HEAD, *Studies in Neurology* (London, 1920), II, p. 620.
14. See WILSON, *Modern Problems in Neurology* (New York,
    1929), p. 277.
15. MCDOUGALL, *Outline of Psychology* (New York, 1923), p.
    328

CHAPTER XX

ALTERNATIVE SATISFACTIONS FOR THE FIGHTING EMOTIONS

THE uniformity of visceral responses when almost any feelings grow very intense, and under such conditions the identity of these responses with those characteristically aroused in the belligerent emotion of anger or rage and its counterpart, fear, offer interesting possibilities of transformation and substitution. This is especially true in the activities of human beings. And because men have devised such terribly ingenious and destructive modes of expressing these feelings in war, an inquiry into the basis for possible substitution seems not out of place.

SUPPORT FOR THE MILITARIST ESTIMATE OF THE STRENGTH OF THE FIGHTING EMOTIONS AND INSTINCTS

The business of killing and of avoiding death has been one of the primary interests of living beings throughout their long history on the earth. It is in the highest degree natural that feelings of hostility often burn with fierce intensity, and then, with astonishing suddenness, that all the powers of the body are called into action—for the strength of the feelings and the quickness of the response measure the chances of survival in a struggle where the issue may be life or death. These are the powerful emotions and the deeply ingrained instinctive reactions which invariably precede combat. They are the emotions and instincts that sometimes seize upon individuals in groups and spread like wildfire into larger and larger aggregations of men, until entire populations are shouting and clamoring for war. To whatever extent military plans are successful in devising a vast machine for attack or defense, the energies that make the machine go are found, in the last analysis, in human beings who, when the time for action comes, are animated by these surging elemental tendencies which assume control of their conduct and send them madly into conflict.

The strength of the fighting instinct in man has been one of the main arguments used by the militarists in support of preparation for international strife. They point to the historical fact that even among highly civilized peoples scarcely a decade passes without a kindling of the martial emotions, which explode in actual warfare. Such fighting, they say, is inevitable—the manifestation of "biological law"—and, so long as human nature remains unchanged, decision by battle must be resorted to. They urge, furthermore, that in war and in the preparations for war important physical qualities—sturdiness, hardihood, and strength for valorous deeds—are given peculiarly favorable opportunities for development, and that if these opportunities are lacking, lusty youth will give place to weaklings and mollycoddles. In addition the militarists say that war benefits mankind by its moral effects. Without war nations become effete, their ideals become tarnished, the people sink into self-indulgence, their wills weaken and soften in luxury. War, on the contrary, disciplines character, it sobers men, it teaches them to be brave and patient, it renews a true order of values, and its demand for the supreme sacrifice of life brings forth in thousands an eager response that is the crowning glory of the human spirit. As the inevitable expression of a deep-rooted instinct, therefore, and as a unique means of developing desirable physical and moral qualities, war is claimed by the militarists to be a natural necessity.[1]

The militarist contention that the fighting instinct is firmly fixed in human nature receives strong confirmation in the results of our researches. Survival has been decided by the grim law of mortal conflict, and the mechanism for rendering the body more competent in conflict has been revealed in earlier chapters as extraordinarily perfect and complete. Moreover, the physiological provisions for fierce struggle are found not only in the bodies of lower animals, that must hunt and kill in order to live, but also in human beings. Since this remarkable mechanism is present, and through countless generations has served the fundamentally important purpose of giving momentous aid in the struggle for existence, the militarists might properly argue that, as with other physiological processes, bodily harmony would be promoted by its exercise. Indeed, they might account for the periodic outburst of belligerent feelings by assuming that these natural aptitudes require occasional satisfaction.*

GROWING OPPOSITION TO THE FIGHTING EMOTIONS AND INSTINCTS AS DISPLAYED IN WAR

In spite of the teachings of history that wars have not grown fewer, and in spite of the militarist argument that war is a means of purging mankind of its sordid vices, and renewing instead the noblest virtues, the conclusion that the resort to arms is unavoidable and desirable is nowadays being strongly contested. The militarists show only part of the picture. No large acquaintance with the character of warfare is necessary to prove that when elemental anger, hate and fear prevail, civilized conventions are abandoned and the most savage instincts determine conduct. Homes are looted and burned, women and children are abominably treated, and many innocents are murdered outright or starved to death. No bland argument for the preservation of the manly virtues can palliate such barbarities. Even when fighting men are held within the rules, the devices for killing and injuring are now made so perfect by devilish ingenuity that by the pulling of a trigger one man can in

---

* Graham Wallas has made the interesting suggestion (*The Great Society,* New York, 1914, p. 66) that nervous strain and restlessness due to "baulked disposition" may result from the absence of circumstances which would call the emotional responses into action. And he cites Aristotle's theory that pent passions may be released by represented tragedy and by music.

a few seconds mow down scores of his fellow-creatures and send them writhing to agony or death. War has become too horrible; it is conducted on too stupendous a scale of carnage and expenditure; it destroys too many of the treasured achievements of the race; it interferes too greatly with consecrated efforts to benefit all mankind by discovery and invention; it involves too much suffering among peoples not directly concerned in the struggle; it is too vastly at variance with the methods of fair dealing that have been established between man and man; the human family has become too closely knit to allow some of its members to bring upon themselves and all the rest poverty and distress and a long heritage of bitter hatred and resolution to seek revenge.

All these reasons for hostility to war imply a thwarting of strong desires in men—desires for family happiness, devotion to beauty and to scholarship, passion for social justice, hopes of lessening poverty and disease. As was pointed out in a previous chapter, the feeling of hostility has no definite object to awaken it. It is roused when there is opposition to what we ardently wish to get. And because war brings conditions which frustrate many kinds of eagerly sought purposes, war has roused in men a hostility against itself. There is then a war against war, a willingness to fight against monstrous carnage and destruction, that grows in intensity with every war that is waged.

THE DESIRABILITY OF PRESERVING THE MARTIAL
VIRTUES

Although there is increasing opposition to the display of the fighting emotions and instincts in war, nevertheless the admirable moral and physical qualities, claimed by the militarists to be the unique products of war, are too valuable to be lost. As McDougall [2] has indicated, when the life of ideas become richer, and the means we take to overcome obstructions to our efforts more refined and complex, the instinct to fight ceases to express itself in its crude natural manner, save when most intensely excited, and becomes rather a source of increased energy of action towards the end set by any other instinct; the energy of its impulses adds itself to and reënforces that of other impulses and so helps us to overcome our difficulties. In this lies its great value for civilized man. A man devoid of the pugnacious instinct would not only be incapable of anger, but would lack this great source of reserve energy which is called into play in most of us by any difficulty in our path.

Thus the very efficiency of a war against war, as well as struggle against other evils that beset civilized society, rests on the preservation and use of aggressive feeling and the instinct to attack. From this point of view the insistence by the militarists that we must accept human nature as we find it, and that the attempt to change it is foolish, seems a more justifiable attitude than that of the pacifists who belittle the fighting qualities and urge that changing them is a relatively simple process. We should not wish them changed. Even if in the war against war a means should be established of securing international justice, and if through coöperative action the decrees of justice were enforced, so that the occasions which would arouse belligerent emotions and instincts were much reduced, there would still remain the need of recognizing their elemental character and their possible usefulness to society. What is needed is not a suppression of these capacities to feel and act, but their diversion into other channels where they may have satisfactory expression.

MORAL SUBSTITUTES FOR WARFARE

"We must make new energies and hardihoods continue the manliness to which the military mind so faithfully clings. Martial virtues must be the enduring cement; intrepidity, contempt of softness, surrender of private interest, obedience to command, must still remain the rock upon which states are built." Thus wrote William James [3] in proposing a "moral equivalent for war." This, he suggested, should consist of such required service in the hard and difficult occupations as would take the childishness and superciliousness out of our youth and give them soberer ideas and healthier sympathies with their fellow-men. He conceived that by proper direction of its education a people should become as proud of the attainment by the nation of superiority in *any* ideal respect as it would be if the nation were victorious in war. "The martial type of character," he declared, "can be bred without war. Strenuous honor and disinterestedness abound elsewhere. Priests and medical men are in a fashion educated to it, and we should all feel some degree of it imperative if we were conscious of our work as an obligatory service to the state. We should be *owned*, as soldiers are by the army, and our pride would rise accordingly. We could be poor, then, without humiliation, as army officers now are. The only thing needed henceforth is to inflame the civic temper as past history has inflamed the military temper."

Similar ideas have been expressed by others.[4] It has been pointed out that the great war of mankind is that against pain, disease, poverty and sin; that the real heroes are not those who squander human strength and courage in fighting one another, but those who fight for man against these his eternal foes. War of man against man, in this view, becomes dissension in the ranks, permitting the common enemies to strike their most telling blows.

These moral considerations, however, are apart from the main intent of our discussion. Our earlier inquiry confirmed the belief that the fighting emotions are firmly rooted in our natures, and showed that these emotions are intimately associated with provisions for physical exertion. It is particularly in this aspect of the discussion of substitutes for war that these studies have significance.

PHYSICAL SUBSTITUTES FOR WARFARE

The idealization of the state and the devotion of service to social welfare, which have been suggested as moral substitutes for military loyalty, leave unanswered the claims of the militarists that in war and in preparations for war opportunities are offered which are peculiarly favorable to the development of important physical qualities—bodily vigor, sturdiness, and ability to withstand all manner of hardships.

In the evidence previously presented, it seems to me there was a suggestion that offers a pertinent alternative to these claims. When the body goes onto what we have called a war footing, the physiological changes that suddenly occur are all adapted to the putting forth of supreme muscular and nervous efforts. That was what primitive battle consisted of, through countless myriads of generations—a fierce physical contest of beast with beast, and of man with man. Such contests, attended as they were by the thrill of unpredictable incidents, and satisfying completely the lust of combat, are to be contrasted with the dull grind in preparation for modern war, the monotonous regularity of subservience, the substitution everywhere of mechanism for muscle, and often the attack on an enemy who lies wholly unseen.* As Wallas with nice

---

* Lord Wolseley, while commander-in-chief of the English forces, in 1897, secured sanction for not displaying the regimental colors in battle. "It would be madness and a crime," he declared, "to order any soldier to carry colors into action in the future. You might quite as well order him to be assassinated. We have had most reluctantly to abandon a practice to which we attached great im-

irony has remarked, "The gods in Valhalla would hardly choose the organization of modern lines of military communication, as they chose the play of

---

portance, and which, under past and gone conditions of fighting, was invaluable in keeping alive the regimental spirit upon which our British troops depended so much." All war has been transformed by the invention of the far-reaching and fate-dealing rifle and automatic gun, with which an enemy kills, whose face is not even seen. War is almost reduced to a mechanical interchange of volleys and salvoes, and to the intermittent fire of rifles and machine guns, with short rushes at the last, in which there is no place for the dignity and grace of the antique battle of the standard. (See *London Times,* July 31, 1897, p. 12.)

T. F. Millard, the well-known correspondent of the Russo-Japanese War, wrote as follows of the characteristics of present-day conflicts: "A large part of modern war is on too great a scale to give much opportunity for individual initiative. Soldiers can rarely tell what is going on in their immediate vicinity. They cannot always see the enemy they are firing at, and where they can see the object of their fire such an important matter as range and even direction cannot be left to them. . . . Troops are clothed so much alike nowadays that it is very difficult to distinguish friend from foe at five hundred yards, and large bodies of troops rarely get that close to each other in modern war while there is light enough to see clearly. . . . Battery officers simply see that their guns are handled according to instructions. They regulate the time, speed, objective and range as ordered. . . . The effects of the fire are observed by officers appointed to that duty, stationed at various parts of the field, often miles and miles apart, and who are in constant communication with the chief of artillery by telephone." See *Scribner's Magazine,* xxxvii, 1905, pp. 64, 66.)

The testimony of a captain of a German battery engaged against the French and English in 1914, supports the foregoing claims. He is reported as saying: "We shoot over those tree tops yonder in accordance with directions for range and distance which come from somewhere else over a field telephone, but we never see the men at whom we are firing. They fire back without seeing us, and sometimes their shells fall short or go beyond us, and sometimes they fall among us and kill and wound a few of us. Thus it goes on day after day. I have not with my own eyes seen a Frenchman or an Englishman unless he was a prisoner. It is not so much pleasure—fighting like this." (See *Saturday Evening Post,* December 26, 1914, p. 27.)

sword and spear, to be the most exquisite employment of eternity."

While it is true that physical strength can be developed by any form of hard labor, as, for example, by sawing wood or digging ditches, such labor does not stimulate quickness, alertness, and resourcefulness in bodily action. Nor does it give any occasion for use of the emotional mechanism for reënforcement. If this mechanism, like other physiological arrangements, is present in the body for use—and previous discussion leaves little doubt of that—then as a means of exercising it and, in addition, satisfying the strong instinct for competitive testing of strength and physical skill, some activity more enlivening than monotonous gymnastics and ordered marching is required.

In many respects strenuous athletic rivalries present, better than modern military service, the conditions for which the militarists argue, the conditions for which the body spontaneously prepares when the passion for fighting prevails. As explained in an earlier chapter, in competitive sports the elemental factors are retained—man is again pitted against man, and all the resources of the body are summoned in the eager struggle for victory. And because, under such circumstances, the same physiological alterations occur that occur in anticipation of mortal combat, the belligerent emotions and instincts, so far as their bodily manifestations are concerned, are thereby given complete satisfaction.

THE SIGNIFICANCE OF INTERNATIONAL ATHLETIC COMPETITIONS

For reasons offered above, I venture to lay emphasis on a suggestion which has been made before by others, that the promotion of great international athletic contests, such as the Olympic games, would do for our young men much that is now claimed as peculiar to the values of military discipline. The substitution of athletic rivalries for battle is not unknown. In the Philippine Islands, according to Worcester,[5] there was no athletics before the American occupation. The natives soon learned games from the soldiers. And when the sports reached such development that competition between towns and provinces was possible, they began to arouse the liveliest enthusiasm among the people. The physical development of the participants has been greatly stimulated, the spirit of fair play and sportsmanship, formerly lacking, has sprung into existence in every section of the Islands, and the annual meets between athletic teams from various provinces are recognized as promoting a general and friendly understanding among the different Filipino tribes. The fierce Igarots of Bontoc, once constantly at war with neighboring tribes, now show their prowess not in head-hunting, but in baseball, wrestling, and the tug-of-war.*

---

* It is reported that when these warriors first appeared at the games, each brought his spear, which he drove into the ground beside him, ready for use. As the nature of the new rivalries became known, the spears were left behind.

Is it unreasonable to expect that what has happened in the Philippine Islands might, by proper education and suggestion, happen elsewhere in the world? Certainly the interest in athletic contests is no slight and transient interest. At the time of the Great War we know that news of the games was fully as much demanded as news of the war. Already in the United States, without special stimulation, the number of young men engaged in athletic training is estimated as equal to the number in the standing army. And in England, belief in the efficacy of athletics as a means of promoting hardihood and readiness to face stern hazards has found expression in the phrase that England's battles have been won on the playing fields of Rugby and of Eton. With the further promotion of international contests the influence of competitive sports is likely to increase rather than lessen. Within national boundaries emulation is sure to stimulate extensively such games as will bring forth the best representative athletes that the country can produce. In one of the high-spirited European nations, which made a poor showing at a recent Olympic meet, thousands of young men began training for the next meet, under a director imported from the nation that had made the highest records.

Training for athletic contests is quite as likely to enure young men to physical hardship and fatigue, is quite as conducive to the development of bodily vigor, the attainment of alertness and skill and the practice of self-restraint, as is army life with its tra-

ditional associations and easy license. It may be
urged, however, that an essential element is lacking
in all this discussion—the sobering possibility that in
war the supreme surrender of life itself may be required. Death for one's country is indeed glorious.
But the argument that being killed is desirable has
little to commend it. When the strongest and sturdi-
est are constantly chosen to be fed to the engines of
annihilation, the race is more likely to lose greater
values than it gains from the spectacle of self-sacrifice,
however perfect that may be. Are there not advantages in the conditions of great athletic rivalries that
may compensate for war's most austere demand? The
race of hardy men, to secure which the militarists urge
war, is much more likely to result from the honoring
and preserving of vigorous men in their vigor than
it is from the systematic selection of such men to
be destroyed in their youth.

There are other aspects of international games
which strongly commend them as an alternative to
the pursuit of military discipline. The high standards
of honor and fairness in sport; its unfailing revelation
of excellence without distinctions of class, wealth, race
or color; the ease with which it becomes an expression
of the natural feelings of patriotism; the respect which
victory and pluckily borne defeat inspire in competi-
tors and spectators alike; the extension of acquaintance and understanding which follows from friendly
and magnanimous rivalry among strong men who come
together from the ends of the earth—each of these

admirable features of athletic contests between nations might be enlarged upon. But, as intimated before, these moral considerations must be left without further mention, as being irrelevant to the physiological processes with which we are dealing.

We are concerned with the question of exercising the fighting instinct and thus assuring the physical welfare of the race. The race must degenerate, the militarists say, if this instinct is not allowed to express itself in war. This declaration we are in a position to deny, for the evidence is perfectly clean-cut that the aggressive instincts, which through æons of racial experience have naturally and spontaneously developed vigor and resourcefulness in the body, are invited by elemental emotions, and that through these emotions energies are released which are highly useful to great physical effort. No stupid routine of drill, or any other deadening procedure, will call these energizing mechanisms into activity. War and the preparations for war nowadays have become too machine-like to serve as the best means of preserving and disciplining these forces. The exhilarating swing and tug and quick thrust of the big limb muscles have largely vanished. Pressing an electric contact or bending the trigger finger is a movement altogether too trifling. If, then, natural feelings must be expressed, if the fighting functions of the body must be exercised, how much better that these satisfactions be found in natural rather than in artificial actions, how much more reasonable that men should struggle for victory in the ancient ways, one against another, body and spirit, as in the great games.

REFERENCES

1. See ANGELL, *The Great Illusion* (New York and London, 1913), pp. 159-164.
2. McDOUGALL, *Introduction to Social Psychology* (London, 1908), p. 61.
3. JAMES, *Memories and Studies* (New York, 1911), p. 287.
4. See PERRY, *The Moral Economy* (New York, 1909), p. 32; and DRAKE, *Problems of Conduct* (Boston, 1914), p. 317.
5. WORCESTER, *The Philippines, Past and Present* (New York, 1914), ii, pp. 515, 578.

A LIST OF PUBLISHED RESEARCHES FROM THE PHYSIOLOGICAL LABORATORY IN THE MEDICAL SCHOOL OF HARVARD UNIVERSITY, ON WHICH THE PRESENT ACCOUNT IS BASED

1. "The Influence of Emotional States on the Functions of the Alimentary Canal," by W. B. Cannon. *American Journal of the Medical Sciences,* cxxxvii (1909), pp. 480-487.

2. "Emotional Stimulation of Adrenal Secretion," by W. B. Cannon and D. de la Paz. *American Journal of Physiology,* xxviii (1911), pp. 64-70.

3. "The Effects of Asphyxia, Hyperpnœa, and Sensory Stimulation on Adrenal Secretion," by W. B. Cannon and R. G. Hoskins. *Ibid.,* xxix (1911), pp. 274-279.

4. "Emotional Glycosuria," by W. B. Cannon, A. T. Shohl and W. S. Wright. *Ibid.,* xxix (1911), pp. 280-287.

5. "A Consideration of Some Biological Tests for Epinephrin," by R. G. Hoskins. *Journal of Pharmacology and Experimental Therapeutics,* iii (1911), pp. 93-99.

6. "The Sthenic Effect of Epinephrin upon the Intestine," by R. G. Hoskins. *American Journal of Physiology,* xxix (1912), pp. 363-366.

7. "An Explanation of Hunger," by W. B. Cannon and A. L. Washburn. *Ibid.,* xxix (1912), pp. 441-454.

8. "A New Colorimetric Method for the Determination of Epinephrin," by O. Folin, W. B. Cannon and W. Denis. *Journal of Biological Chemistry,* xiii (1913), pp. 477-483.

9. "The Depressor Effect of Adrenalin on Arterial Pressure," by W. B. Cannon and Henry Lyman. *American Journal of Physiology,* xxxi (1913), pp. 376-398.

10. "The Effect of Adrenal Secretion on Muscular Fatigue," by W. B. Cannon and L. B. Nice. *Ibid.,* xxxii (1913), pp. 44-60.

11. "Fatigue as Affected by Changes of Arterial Pressure," by C. M. Gruber. *Ibid.,* xxxii (1913), pp. 222-229.

12. "The Threshold Stimulus as Affected by Fatigue and Subsequent Rest," by C. M. Gruber. *Ibid.,* xxxii (1913), pp. 438-449.

13. "The Fatigue Threshold as Affected by Adrenalin and by Increased Arterial Pressure," by C. M. Gruber. *Ibid.*, xxxiii (1914), pp. 335-355.

14. "The Emergency Function of the Adrenal Medulla in Pain and the Major Emotions," by W. B. Cannon. *Ibid.*, xxxiii (1914), pp. 356-372.

15. "The Relation of Adrenalin to Curare and Fatigue in Normal and Denervated Muscles," by C. M. Gruber. *Ibid.*, xxxiv (1914), pp. 89-96.

16. "The Graphic Method of Recording Coagulation," by W. B. Cannon and W. L. Mendenhall. *Ibid.*, xxxiv (1914), pp. 225-231.

17. "The Hastening or Retarding of Coagulation by Adrenalin Injections," by W. B. Cannon and Horace Gray. *Ibid.*, xxxiv (1914), pp. 232-242.

18. "The Hastening of Coagulation by Stimulating the Splanchnic Nerves," by W. B. Cannon and W. L. Mendenhall. *Ibid.*, xxxiv (1914), pp. 243-250.

19. "The Hastening of Coagulation in Pain and Emotional Excitement," by W. B. Cannon and W. L. Mendenhall. *Ibid.*, xxxiv (1914), pp. 251-261.

20. "The Interrelations of Emotions as Suggested by Recent Physiological Researches," by W. B. Cannon. *American Journal of Psychology*, xxv (1914), pp. 256-282.

21. "The Differential Effects of Adrenin on Splanchnic and Peripheral Arteries," by F. A. Hartman. *American Journal of Physiology*, xxxviii (1915), pp. 438-455.

22. "The Effect of Adrenin on the Factors of Coagulation," by G. P. Grabfield. *Ibid.*, xlii (1916), pp. 46-55.

23. "The Physiological Basis of Thirst," by W. B. Cannon. *Proceedings of the Royal Society of London*, Bxc (1918), pp. 283-301.

24. "The Isolated Heart as an Indicator of Adrenal Secretion Induced by Pain, Asphyxia and Excitement," by W. B. Cannon. *American Journal of Physiology*, l (1919), pp. 399-432.

25. "Further Observations on the Denervated Heart in Relation to Adrenal Secretion," by W. B. Cannon and David Rapport. *Ibid.*, lviii (1921), pp. 308-337.

26. "The Reflex Center for Adrenal Secretion and its Response to Excitatory and Inhibitory Influences," by W. B. Cannon and David Rapport. *Ibid.*, lviii (1921), pp. 338-352.

27. "Further Evidence for Reflex and Asphyxial Secretion of Adrenin," by W. B. Cannon and R. Carrasco-Formiguera. *Ibid.*, lxi (1922), pp. 215-227.

28. "Reflex Hyperglycemia: A Study of the Carbohydrate Mobilization Effected by Afferent Crural, Sciatic and Vagus Stimulation," by F. R. Griffith. *Ibid.*, lxvi (1923), pp. 618-658.

29. "A Sympathetic and Adrenal Mechanism for Mobilizing Sugar in Hypoglycemia," by W. B. Cannon, M. A. McIver and S. W. Bliss. *Ibid.*, lxix (1924), pp. 46-66.

30. "The Effects of Muscle Metabolites on Adrenal Secretion," by W. B. Cannon, J. R. Linton and R. R. Linton. *Ibid.*, lxxi (1924), pp. 153-162.

31. "Pseudaffective Medulliadrenal Secretion," by W. B. Cannon and S. W. Britton. *Ibid.*, lxxii (1925), pp. 283-294.

32. "The Rôle of the Adrenal Medulla in Pseudaffective Hyperglycemia," by E. Bulatao and W. B. Cannon. *Ibid.*, lxxii (1925), pp. 295-313.

33. "A Lasting Preparation of the Denervated Heart for Detecting Internal Secretion," by W. B. Cannon, J. T. Lewis and S. W. Britton. *Ibid.*, lxxvii (1926), pp. 326-352.

34. "The Influence of Motion and Emotion on Medulliadrenal Secretion," by W. B. Cannon and S. W. Britton with the co-operation of J. T. Lewis and A. Groeneveld. *Ibid.*, lxxix (1927), pp. 433-465.

35. "The Rôle of Adrenal Secretion in the Chemical Control of Body Temperature," by W. B. Cannon, A. Querido, S. W. Britton and E. M. Bright. *Ibid.*, lxxix (1927), pp. 466-507.

36. "The Dispensability of the Sympathetic Division of the Autonomic Nervous System," by W. B. Cannon, J. T. Lewis and S. W. Britton. *Boston Medical and Surgical Journal*, cxcvii (1927), pp. 514-515.

37. "The James-Lange Theory of Emotions: A Critical Examination and an Alternative Theory," by W. B. Cannon. *American Journal of Psychology*, xxxix (1927), pp. 106-124.

38. "A Diencephalic Mechanism for the Expression of Rage, with Special Reference to the Sympathetic Nervous System," by Philip Bard. *American Journal of Physiology*, lxxxiv (1928), pp. 490-515.

39. "Emotional Polycythemia in Relation to Sympathetic and Medulliadrenal Action on the Spleen," by J. J. Izquierdo and W. B. Cannon. *Ibid.*, lxxxiv (1928), pp. 545-562.

40. "Emotional Relative Mononucleosis," by Valy Menkin. *Ibid.*, lxxxv (1928), pp. 489-497.

41. "Asphyxial Stimulation of the Denervated Adrenal Gland," by R. L. Zwemer and H. F. Newton. *Ibid.*, lxxxv (1928), pp. 507-511.

42. "Some Conditions Affecting the Duration of Muscular Work," by F. A. de M. Campos, W. B. Cannon, H. Lundin, and T. T. Walker. *Ibid.*, lxxxvii (1929), pp. 680-701.

INDEX

Adrenal extract: effect of, on muscular contraction, 80.

Adrenal glands: nerve supply of, 34; stimulated in emotion, 49-56, in struggle, 55-56, and in pain, 57-63; in relation to blood sugar, 75-78; removal of, causes muscular weakness, 80; secretion from, improves contraction of fatigued muscle, 89; variations in adrenin content of, 173; latent period of, when splanchnics stimulated, 196; stimulated by asphyxia, 213-217.

Adrenin: secreted by adrenal glands, 34; action of, identical with sympathetic impulses, 34-36, 63; secretion of, by splanchnic stimulation, 38-40; method of testing for, in blood, 43-47; secreted in emotional excitement, 49-56; secreted in pain, 57-61; effects of, when injected into the body, 64; effect of, on distribution of blood in the body, 104; quickly restores fatigued muscle to normal irritability, 116-120; specific in its restorative action, 121-125; as an antidote to muscle metabolites, 125-126; restores fatigued denervated muscle to normal irritability, 126-127; point of action of, in muscle, 128-130; antagonistic to curare, 128; induces rapid coagulation of blood, 133, 143 *ff.;* not the di-

Adrenin (*continued*)
rect cause of rapid coagulation, 151-153; fails to shorten coagulation time in absence of intestines and liver, 152-154; increases prothrombin, 154; emergency functions of, 194 *ff.;* utility of, in bettering contraction of fatigued muscle, 203-204; not a check to use of sugar in body, 205; stimulates the heart, 47, 55, 206, 207; dilates the bronchioles, 212; secretion of, increase in asphyxia, 213-217; visceral changes produced by, does not cause emotion, 355-358.

Amyl nitrite: effect of, on contraction of fatigued muscle, 124.

Anger: associated with action, 197; energizing influence of, 226.

Antagonisms: autonomic, 32; in relation to emotions, 334; between cranial and sympathetic divisions, 334-336; between sacral and sympathetic divisions, 337-339.

Appetite: compared with hunger, 269-271; presence of, after section of vagus and splanchnic nerves, 275; compared with thirst, 303.

Arteries: innervation of, 24.

Asphyxia: increases adrenal secretion, 213-217; increases blood sugar, 217.

397

Hunger (*continued*)
ance of, as time passes, 273-274; when stomach full, 275; may be absent in bodily need, 277-278; temporarily abolished by indigestible ingesta, 278; quick onset and periodicity of, 279-280; reference of, to stomach region, 280-282; not due to emptiness of the stomach, 282, nor to hydrochloric acid in empty stomach, 283, nor to turgid gastric glands, 283-285; as a result of contractions, 285-288; inhibited by swallowing, 288; method of recording gastric contractions in, 289-290; associated with gastric contractions, 290-293; function of, 295-296, 339-341.

Hydrochloric acid: not the cause of hunger sensation, 283.

Intestine: contractions of, inhibited by excitement, 14; innervation of, 25, 29; use of, as a test for adrenin in blood, 43-46; contracts when empty, 287; contractions of, may help originate hunger sensations, 294.

Instincts: relations of, to emotions, 195.

Irritability: increased in fatigued muscle by splanchnic stimulation, 98; neuromuscular, lessened by fatigue, 112-115, 118; when lowered, restored slowly by rest, 115-116, but quickly by adrenin, 116-120, 204.

James-Lange theory: statement of, 346-347; criticism of, 348-358; compared with thalamic theory of emotions, 370-375.

"Jumpers": exhibition of endurance by, 233.

Mania: endurance in, 232.

Martial virtues: claims for, by militarists, 378; importance of preserving, 382-383; preserved in competitive sports, 389-391.

Metabolites: influence of, on muscular contraction, 101-102; action of, opposed by adrenin, 125-126; increase adrenal secretion, 130.

Militarists: emphasize strength of fighting instincts, 377-379; claims of. as to value of war, 378; support for claims of, 379.

Mononucleosis, relative: induced by excitement, 191, but not if spleen removed or denervated, 191.

Mouth: dry in thirst, 304-306, 314-315, 321-324; glands of, characteristic of land animals, 318-319; dried by atropine or fear induces thirst, 325-326.

Muscle: weakness of, after removal of adrenal glands, 80; improved contraction of, after injection of adrenal extract, 81; fatigue of, 82; method of recording fatigue of, 83-85; fatigue of, lessened by splanchnic stimulation, 87-90; contraction of, when fatigued, improved by increased arterial pressure, 96-99; irritability of, when fatigued, increased by splanchnic stimulation, 98; contraction of, when fatigued, lessened by decreased arterial pressure, 100-101; explanation of effects of varied arterial pressure on fatigued, 101-103; irritability of, decreased in fatigue, 112-115, 118; decreased irritability of, slowly restored by rest, 115-116, and quickly restored by adrenin, 116-120, 204;